ADOLESCENTS

PSYCHOANALYTIC APPROACH
TO PROBLEMS AND THERAPY

ADOLESCENTS

PSYCHOANALYTIC APPROACH
TO PROBLEMS AND THERAPY

BY 19 CONTRIBUTORS

Edited by Sandor Lorand, M.D.

and Henry I. Schneer, M.D.

Foreword by David M. Engelhardt, M.D.

THIRD PRINTING 1964

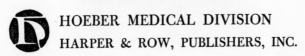

HOEBER MEDICAL DIVISION
HARPER & ROW, PUBLISHERS, INC.

ADOLESCENTS: *Psychoanalytic Approach to Problems and Therapy*

THIRD PRINTING 1964

A-O

Library of Congress catalog card number: 61-6722

Contents

Contributors

ANITA I. BELL, M.D.
>Associate Attending Psychiatrist, Lenox Hill Hospital; Psychiatric Consultant, Community Service Society, New York City

DAVID BERES, M.D.
>Faculty, New York Psychoanalytic Institute; Attending Psychiatrist, Pleasantville Cottage School of the Jewish Child Care Association of New York, New York City

PETER BLOS, PH.D.
>Consultant in Psychotherapy, Madeline Borg Child Guidance Institute, Jewish Board of Guardians, New York City

AUGUSTA BONNARD, M.B., B.S.
>Consultant Psychiatrist and Director, East London Child Guidance Clinic, London

SELMA H. FRAIBERG, M.S.
>Associate Professor of Social Work and Lecturer in Psychiatry, Tulane University; Lecturer, New Orleans Psychoanalytic Training Center, New Orleans

SIDNEY L. GREEN, M.D.
>Clinical Assistant Professor, Downstate Medical Center, State University of New York, Brooklyn; Psychiatric Consultant, Israel Strauss Pavilion for Adolescent Girls, Hillside Hospital, Glen Oaks, New York

MARJORIE HARLEY, PH.D.
>New York City

PAUL KAY, M.D.
>Assistant Professor and Consulting Psychiatrist, Division of Child and Adolescent Psychiatry, Downstate Medical Center, State University of New York, Brooklyn

SYLVAN KEISER, M.D.
>Acting Director, Psychoanalytic Division of Education, Downstate Medical Center, State University of New York, Brooklyn

JUDITH S. KESTENBERG, M.D.

Lecturer, Division of Psychoanalytic Education and Lecturer in Child Analysis, Downstate Medical Center, State University of New York, Brooklyn

SIMON KWALWASSER, M.D.

Associate Medical Director, Coordinator of Activities, and Consultant to the Israel Straus Pavilion for Adolescent Girls, Hillside Hospital, Glen Oaks, New York

RHODA L. LORAND, PH.D.

Formerly Psychoanalytic Child Therapist, Child Guidance Clinic, Beth Israel Hospital; Formerly Clinical Psychologist and Child Psychotherapist, Department of Psychiatry, Vanderbilt Clinic, Presbyterian Hospital, New York City

SANDOR LORAND, M.D.

Clinical Professor of Psychiatry, Psychoanalytic Division of Education, Downstate Medical Center, State University of New York, Brooklyn

SOLOMON MACHOVER, PH.D.

Chief Psychologist, Psychiatric Division, Kings County Hospital; Clinical Associate Professor, Downstate Medical Center, State University of New York, Brooklyn

WARNER MUENSTERBERGER, PH.D.

Clinical Assistant Professor, Division of Psychoanalytic Education, Downstate Medical Center, State University of New York, Brooklyn

HENRY I. SCHNEER, M.D.

Assistant Professor, Faculty of Psychoanalytic Division of Education; Director, Division of Child and Adolescent Psychiatry, Downstate Medical Center, State University of New York, Brooklyn

MELITTA SPERLING, M.D.

Clinical Associate Professor, Division of Psychoanalytic Education, Downstate Medical Center, State University of New York, Brooklyn

LEO A. SPIEGEL, M.D.

Clinical Associate Professor, Albert Einstein College of Medicine; Faculty, New York Psychoanalytic Institute, New York City

HYMAN SPOTNITZ, M.D., MED. SC.D.

Consulting Psychiatrist, Jewish Board of Guardians, New York City

Foreword

Viewing adolescence simply as a period of transition between childhood and adulthood tends to diminish emphasis upon those unique features which justify its identification as a separate stage of development. Adolescence is more than the emergence of earlier unresolved sexual and aggressive conflicts. Adolescence is a significant period in life, and it can and does create singular complexities. Even the re-emergence of childhood problems must be viewed in the context of adolescent strivings which are obviously different from those of the child. Oedipal wishes are intensified not only by the impact of puberty but by fears of the outside world. The fear of entering into the adult world may make the "home romance" more appealing, since it obviates competition with people outside the home.

The emphasis on adolescence as a period of great stress for the young person tends to obscure the fact that it is an equally difficult period for his parents and teachers. Castration and separation anxiety constitute a problem not only for the adolescent but for the parent as well. The parent fears and resents the potential success of the adolescent at a time when his own potency seems to be diminishing. This may result in parental efforts to coerce the youngster to remain dependent. For many parents the child's entry into adolescence marks the first time that the parent begins to see himself in competition with his children for social and sexual success. Simultaneously, the parent begins to feel the first faint signs of the still very distant but inevitable castration anxiety of the involutional period. In a sense, the parent may be as much in need of help at this time as is the adolescent.

The competition and the anxiety engendered in the parents play a major role in the development of tensions between them and their adolescent offspring. This usually results in poor communication between parents and child, which operates to obstruct further the independent strivings of the child. We begin to hear the familiar complaint that the youth of today are radically and undesirably different from their parents and that they are all potential delinquents. The degree to which these tensions impair the child-parent relationships and the adolescent's maturation will depend upon situational factors and the essential emotional security and maturity of the parents. It is clear that when a child displays a real potential for delinquent behavior, the home may be turned into hostile camps, and this hostility is then projected onto the community. It is therefore obvious that adolescence is much more than a way station to adulthood, and that, during adolescence, there emerge significant new factors in the child-parent relationship.

The teen-ager has come much closer to recognizing the unique features of his identity than has either his parent or his physician. The teen-ager has developed a subculture of his own, with specific social and sexual mores and distinctive attitudes toward society. (Witness the rash of television programs, magazines, and fashions directed exclusively to this group.) It would seem timely for the psychiatrist to concern himself in greater detail with the precise dimensions of the adolescent. This requires that much more be known about the psychodynamics of adolescence and that we recognize the fact that adolescence cannot be viewed as a variation of childhood psychodynamics. It also necessitates full recognition of the fact that parents play as important a role in the life of the adolescent as they do in the life of the child.

It is questionable whether the specialist in child behavior is qualified to treat the adolescent simply because he has been trained to deal with young people. There is no more reason to consider the adolescent as an older child than to consider him a young adult. Much more needs to be known about the norms of adolescence. Such knowledge would help us to avoid confusing the turbulence of adolescence with pathology. Moreover, pathological conflicts and adaptations would be more accurately identifiable. I believe that if adolescence were perceived as a separate state of development (just as childhood eventually came to be perceived), our knowledge of this period would grow tremendously, our ability to treat the adolescent would improve, and our understanding of childhood on the one hand and adulthood on the other would be considerably augmented. It seems to me that the period of adolescence is sufficiently different from both childhood and adulthood to justify its separation from the body of psychiatry as a subspecialty.

When one moves from the adolescent-parent relationship to the adolescent-therapist relationship, one immediately discovers the potential for some unique problems. Of particular importance is the adolescent's position of being threatened by conflicting forces which pull him toward childhood and adulthood. He may literally feel that he is torn asunder by this conflict. In terms of transference and countertransference, adolescents often present the most intense emotional reactions to be encountered in psychotherapy. There is likely to be marked confusion on the part of the adolescent as to the therapist's passive identity in terms of whether the adolescent sees himself as a child or as an adult. It takes unusual talent to handle these acute problems in such a way as to assure not only that they do not destroy the continuation of therapy but that they actually further the adolescent's maturational strivings.

The psychoanalytic orientation of the writers contributes to the value of this volume. Psychoanalysis has yielded much to our understanding of the forces at work in personality formation. At the present time these formulations seem to me to be most applicable to the understanding of the adolescent. It is worthy of note that, although the writers have a common philosophical and training background, their clinical approaches show considerable individuality.

It is most gratifying that this volume presents case records in such a fashion as to give the reader the feeling of being present throughout the full course of therapy. While not ignoring theoretical formulations, major emphasis is placed on the detailed recording of clinical observations and the therapeutic measures undertaken. This may well serve as an adolescent case-material reference book. The editors and publisher are to be congratulated on their wisdom and generosity in presenting the records completely.

David M. Englehardt, M.D.

Preface

This book is an outgrowth of a series of lectures on psychodynamics and the therapeutic applications of psychoanalytic knowledge to the handling and treatment of adolescent difficulties. Planned for residents in psychiatry by the Division of Child Psychiatry at the State University of New York, the lectures were also attended by psychiatrists, psychologists, child therapists, and social workers. The enthusiasm of this group encouraged the Editors to believe that a book based on these lectures would be of wide usefulness.

It is hoped that this comprehensive presentation of present knowledge of the psychoanalytic aspects of the adolescent period will help satisfy the pressing need for clinical studies of the problems of the adolescent. Because of its unique scope, it should appeal not only to psychiatrists and psychologists interested in the therapy of adolescents, but also to parents, educators, and social workers. The contributors have all had opportunity to study intensively the maladjustments of the adolescent and the environmental factors which, together with psychological conflicts, contributed to their patients' difficulties. The carefully selected case studies used to illustrate hypotheses and therapeutic effects and the views expressed are based on individual therapeutic experiences. The combined effect of these essays is to show clearly the extent to which early oedipal influences are involved in the problems of adolescent development.

Grateful acknowledgement is made to Dean Robert A. Moore for the funds made available by and the use of the facilities of the State University of New York College of Medicine, Downstate Medical Center, for the series of lectures. Dr. David M. Engelhardt, Acting Chairman of the Department of Psychiatry, encouraged the sponsorship of the program by the Division of Child and Adolescent Psychiatry in collaboration with the Psychoanalytic Division.

Appreciation is also expressed to the Residents and Fellows for the painstaking preparation of case reports for the lectures, the arrangement for which was under the direction of Dr. Henry I. Schneer. Mrs. Eva Dannenberg deserves credit for expediting the secretarial work. Last, but not least, is acknowledgment of our debt to the contributors who willingly converted their lecture notes into full-fledged articles for book publication.

S. L.

Lido Beach, New York

ADOLESCENTS

PSYCHOANALYTIC APPROACH
TO PROBLEMS AND THERAPY

chapter 1　Character Formation

DAVID BERES

The concept of character is not clearly defined in psychiatric or psychoanalytic writings. It is necessary, first of all, to distinguish between the descriptive aspects of characterology and its deeper psychodynamic aspects. Edward Glover,[1] in 1925, offered a useful approach in his provisional definition of character as a "set of organized behavior reactions" founded on and intended to preserve a stable equilibrium between instinctual drives and the demands of reality. The resultant of character development is a consistent pattern of adaptation to reality, whether normal or pathological. The genetic approach to character formation assumes that the fixed patterns of response which characterize the adult are foreshadowed in the early behavior and responses of the small child and pass through recognizable vicissitudes at different phases of the individual's life. The importance of adolescence in the genetic approach is that, in adolescence, the crystallization of character formation takes place. The young child deals with his conflicts by constantly varying defenses. This is the reason why we see in children such rapid shifts in clinical manifestations. It is a well-known clinical experience, in fact, that too early fixity of response in the child may presage serious psychopathology. At the same time, we recognize in the child the increasing predominance of certain defenses that indicate the direction of later character structure.

In any given instance there are a number of possible solutions to early childhood conflicts. The desirable solution is, of course, that the child develop adequate defenses with what we might call a stable, normal, character structure. (Although many unanswered questions are raised by this oversimplified statement, I cannot here discuss the meaning of "adequate defenses" or "normal character.") A second possibility is that the conflict and the defenses present themselves as a compromise formation which we recognize as some kind of symptom formation, that is, some form of neurosis. The third possibility is the development of defenses which though stable

1

and serving to keep the individual free of neurotic symptoms, present behavior patterns that clinically are recognized as pathological. We speak of these behavior patterns as abnormal or pathological character structure. In actual experience there is always an admixture of these alternatives, and in pathological states a constant interplay of symptoms and character manifestations is found.

In the ideal situation the child enters adolescence in a state of uncertainty, facing difficulty and serious conflicts, and emerging from it with stable, socially acceptable patterns of responses that we recognize as character. Adolescence, thus viewed, is the crucial transitional phase of character development. It is important to recognize that it is normal for adolescence to be a state of flux and change. It is more pathological for the adolescence to have crystallized too soon the fixed character responses than it is for an adolescent to go through what we speak of as "adolescent turmoil." It is normal for the adolescent to keep the conflicts alive in order to deal with them and test out various solutions before he fixes on any one as the most suitable.

The conflict is between the instinctual drives, which in adolescence are biologically strengthened, and the external demands that are made upon the child as he enters adolescence. Added are the demands of the superego, which has made its appearance some time before adolescence has set in, and which transforms the external conflicts of earlier childhood into an intrapsychic conflict.

In such a brief presentation only a few aspects of this problem can be discussed. I shall illustrate with a boy chosen because of the continuity of clinical knowledge of him at Kings County Hospital and at Pleasantville Cottage School. The central questions which I shall bring out are the role of defense in character structure and the significance of precocious fixity of defense patterns. I shall also make some comments on classification of character disorders and on the distinction between normal and abnormal character.

CASE REPORT

A boy, now 15½ years of age, who has been at Pleasantville Cottage School 1 year, was referred from Kings County Hospital. The presenting symptom at the time he entered the hospital was a school phobia. His parents, according to the history, attempted to deal with this by dragging him forcibly to the school. The boy responded with aggressive, destructive outbursts, the recrudescence of earlier aggressive behavior. When he refused to see a psychiatrist, the parents took him to Children's Court, and he was remanded to the hospital.

The mother is described as both overprotective and overindulgent; the father as placid, passive, dependent, and easygoing. From the time the boy was 8 months old, the father was away from home for 3 years, serving in the Armed Forces. The boy's relationship to his mother was one of conflict, a sadomasochistic one with violent physical fights and tender reconciliations. It is reported that the child slept in his mother's bedroom until he was 3½ years old, at which time he was displaced by his father. During the period that the father was away, the child lived with his mother at the grandmother's home.

The boy was bottle fed as an infant and suffered from "colic" for the first 4 months of his life, with vomiting during and after feedings. He was also subjected to frequent enemas and suppositories for constipation. It was reported that toilet training was accomplished early and easily. His early development, otherwise, appeared to be normal. Pubertal changes appeared at about 11 or 12 years of age. Masturbation was observed by the mother when the boy was about 12. Three months prior to his admission to the hospital, the mother, believing that masturbation might be a factor in his school phobia, reassured him about it. The father was never involved in the boy's sexual education. It is reported that in the past few years the boy has become prudish and will not even permit other boys to be in the room when he dresses. He has never shown any interest in girls.

A tonsillectomy was performed at the age of 7. It is reported the boy was disturbed and angry at being hospitalized and reprimanded his parents for leaving him at the hospital.

When the boy was 2 or 3 years old, he expressed fear of the dark, and at the age of 7 he had a series of nightmares. When he was sent to kindergarten, at the age of 5, he cried intensely and vomited on the way to school. He refused to join activities with other children. He subsequently did well at school, but he never took part in athletic activities and he had poor social relationships. He was very much interested in the sciences and in photography, and with another boy constructed a scientific exhibit which won a prize. He is described as moody and withdrawn. He has few friends, and those he chooses are usually boys smaller than he and interested in science as he is. With another boy, he set up an electrical workshop in his basement. His mother stated that the patient had changed in the past 2 years and had become irritable, aggressive, and hostile toward the family.

One and a half years prior to his admission to the hospital, while in his last semester in junior high school, he developed a fear of going to school. He stayed home several days at a time, explaining that he was afraid of taking examinations, although he had a fine scholastic record. At home he would sleep until 2 or 3 in the afternoon and spend the rest of his time working in his electrical workshop, watching TV, or listening to the radio. He did go to school during the week of final examinations and passed his courses. The following term, at the time of mid-term examinations, he again refused to go to school, became destructive around the house, and spattered paint on the walls. On one occasion he smashed a camera which had been a gift from his parents, and about that time he became domineering and aggressive toward his younger brother.

As is not unusual in children with school phobia, from this point on the boy succeeded in dominating the whole family. The mother waited on him hand and foot, but the situation did not improve. It was at the advice of a social agency that court action and hospitalization were carried out.

When the boy was admitted to the hospital, he was disheveled, with unkempt hair and dirty, long fingernails. His speech was guarded and evasive but spontaneous and logical; choice of language was rather compulsive, precise, and meticulous; affect was flattened and intense, with inappropriate smiling and grinning. The underlying mood was described as both suspicious and hostile. The psychological report indicated superior intellectual endowment but also marked indications of "weakened ego boundaries, decompensation of obsessive-compulsive defenses, and strong feelings of panic." According to the report, he remained generally withdrawn, depressed, and unable to participate in activities, but he was passively cooperative with the routine. The discharge diagnosis was schizoid personality with compulsive traits.

The Role of Conflict and Defense in Character Structure

If we should arbitrarily set the onset of this boy's acute illness, that is, the school phobia, at the age of 12½, we would describe him as then being in a severe and serious conflict situation. The presenting symptom of the school phobia was rationalized by the boy in terms of his not having studied for examinations and his fear of failing. But I think we must recognize, behind this school phobia, a much deeper anxiety of which some hints are present in his early history. The psychological test also gave indication of anxiety and conflicts in the psychosexual area. What we do note in his history, from earliest childhood, is a conflict around activity and passivity. The fact that this boy had no contact with his father during the first 3 years of his life must be an important element in this conflict. A further contributing factor is the different personality structures of mother and father—the mother being the dominating, aggressive parent and the father the passive, dependent, ineffectual one. It would appear that the father did not offer to the boy a model for masculine identification.

How did the boy deal with this conflict in his early life? We do not have too much information, but we are told that he had aggressive outbursts from time to time which, I believe, may be understood, in part, as an attempt to deal with his passive tendencies. Early in his life, however, certain defense patterns became evident which hinted at what might be his later character development. We are told that he would draw in an obsessive fashion and that, at a very early date, he developed mechanical interests and skills. I am anticipating when I state here that at Pleasantville this boy became quite an authority on radio and set up his own radio set, and is presently functioning as a ham radio operator. We may conjecture further, though our evidence is not too specific at this point, that this boy's basic conflict concerns his sexual identity, his masculinity, his masturbation, his passivity, and his aggression. At Pleasantville the school phobia has disappeared, and we may say that the acute psychoneurotic picture has been replaced by a constellation of defensive measures which appears, on the surface, to be protecting this boy from overt conflict. What are these defenses? We note, especially, rationalization, intellectualization, isolation, and reaction formation. Instead of the anxieties of the phobic period, the boy, at present, believes that he has no difficulties or symptoms. His behavior is egosyntonic. This is characteristic of the character problem.

The boy now at Pleasantville is very different from the boy described in the hospital records. He seems, now, to be very polite, very precise in his speech, very articulate, very well controlled, quite grown up, and very compliant. He admitted that he didn't like being placed in an institution, but he didn't put up any fight.

In every aspect of his behavior, the defenses which this boy has chosen, unconsciously, of course, to deal with his conflict, give the impression of adequate social functioning. But it is evident that this is a precarious adjustment. The conflict has been too quickly replaced by rigid defense structures.

I have spoken of adolescence as the crucial transitional phase of character development. The dynamic shifts which mark this period are part of a normal process. Two prominent characteristics of the adolescent in conflict are the tendencies toward regression and acting out. I see these not as part of the character structure but, rather, as manifestations of the adolescent flux which indicate that the individual does not have a satisfactory defense available to him and therefore regresses to defensive devices of the earlier stages of development.

The pathology of character development in this boy was a too-rapid retreat from his conflict. If we review the over-all picture, we see a boy who, in his early life, avoided serious symptomatic disturbance, probably because he was overprotected by his mother. We see in his history an occasional breakthrough of anxieties and aggressive outbursts. We also note the early appearance of obsessive-defensive patterns. His acute neurosis broke out at the age of 12½ with severe anxieties against which he protected himself with a phobic response. Instead of resolving the underlying conflict, the boy went on to a precocious character formation which may or may not protect him from a future outbreak of acute symptoms.

There are many other aspects of this case which, unfortunately, cannot be dealt with, such as the problem of masturbation which, I think, is very important in this instance. Another important problem would be the role of sublimation in such a character development as this boy has shown. I have spoken of his obsessive interest in his mechanical activities, especially his work with radio. To what extent this will serve the boy as an adequate sublimation cannot be determined at this time, and there is always the danger that a sublimated activity, so intensively invested with nonneutralized instinctual energy, may break down in a period of stress. Another point about this boy is the evident disturbance of the function of identity, both as an individual and in terms of his sexual identity. There is considerable evidence of conflict around homosexual tendencies, and at this point we cannot say with any certainty what lies ahead.

The Nosological Problem

When this boy was in the hospital, the diagnosis was schizoid personality with obsessive traits. I am not much concerned with nosological problems, but in this instance I think it is important to put in a demurrer. First of all, my reading of the record gives no convincing evidence of schizoid features such as projective defenses, denial, or disturbance of reality function; nor have any been clearly observed in our studies. Our difficulty is that the whole question of the classification of character is at present an unsettled one. I find the accepted classification not altogether satisfactory, and I believe this is an area in which much work needs to be done.

At this point we all have a right to approach the problem in our own way. We can describe character according to outward manifestations, as, for example, the criminal character or the psychopathic character, both of which I consider to be useless and confusing terms. If we seek to classify character in terms of underlying pathology, there are a number of different possibilities. We could describe character according to the different phases of development, and we might speak of oral characters, anal characters, or phallic characters. We could also define character according to certain clinical pictures which predominate, and speak of hysterical characters, depressive characters, schizoid characters, etc. A third possibility, and the one that I find most useful, is the basic and repetitive defense pattern used by the individual in conflict situations.

When applied to our boy, we can see that we are dealing with an obsessive-compulsive character structure. In terms of his defenses, this is a boy with marked reaction-formations, a compulsive attitude toward work, and an obsessive interest in a given field of activity. If the egosyntonicity of his behavior were to break down, it is likely, at this point, that the boy would develop psychoneurotic symptoms of an obsessive-compulsive nature.

I would like to point out several other types of character designated according to defense patterns. Thus there may be individuals whose basic defense is projection and who react to all situations with a paranoid response. These we may speak of as paranoid characters. There are individuals whose tendency to defend themselves is immediately to transform a conflict into action. This would be an acting-out character, perhaps a delinquent.

To return to our boy, we might speculate that one factor in his choice of specific defenses, particularly reaction-formation, is his early and intensive toilet training. He has another characteristic which is most unusual at Pleasantville, namely that he never uses obscenities. It is another indication of the reaction-formation which is the basis of his obsessive-compulsive character structure.

Distinctions Between Normal and Abnormal Character

The determination of whether a given character structure is normal or abnormal is, as I have indicated, not determined by the patient's self-evaluation but by the observations of those around him. The concept of character and its evaluation are involved to a great extent with the social attitudes, mores, and values that surround the individual. There is, at the present time, some difference of opinion as to whether we are all born with an equal instinctual endowment, but I think it is futile to argue this point, which is reminiscent of the old biological controversy of nature versus nurture. I do believe that, from our position as clinicians, the factor of social environmental forces is of predominant importance in our consideration of the problem of normal versus abnormal character structure. What becomes of the basic instinctual drives in an individual is, for the most part, determined by the life experiences of the individual and the attitudes of society toward the manifestations of the instinctual drives. These vary considerably in one or another cultural setting. From this viewpoint the goal of character development is to create optimum functioning and adaptation to the demands of the society, and there must be ample room for those deviations which allow for social change and progress. There is, in fact, no fixed distinction between normal and pathological character, but one cannot leave out the views of the social environment in making whatever distinction is to be made.

I think there will be agreement that this patient may safely be diagnosed as a character disorder, whether it is an obsessive-compulsive character, as I prefer to say, or a schizoid character, as others have designated him. Under any circumstances, the prognosis is guarded. We are not pleased with his social conformity. The precocious and rapid crystallization of character formation in this adolescent boy is brittle and fragile. He may go on to even more rigid character formations. His defenses may break down and he may again develop psychoneurotic symptoms, or, as is always a possibility with cases of this sort, he may regress and develop schizophrenic manifestations.

That I conclude on this uncertain note is a reflection of the uncertainties inherent in our subject. Both adolescence and character are problems that will engage psychoanalytic and psychiatric research for many years to come.

REFERENCE

1. GLOVER, E. The neurotic character, *Brit. J. M. Psychol.*, 1925, vol. 5, Part 4.

chapter 2   Identity and Adolescence

LEO A. SPIEGEL

One has only to remember the early work of Federn[2] on "ego feeling," of Nunberg[3] on depersonalization, and, more recently, of Hartmann[4] and Jacobson[6,7] to realize that analysis has always occupied itself with the phenomenon of identity. In recent years this topic has become of more focal interest, and it is, of course, of central importance for an understanding of adolescence.

A few clinical examples will illustrate the kind of phenomenon I have in mind. A young and extremely appersonated patient said: "I was sitting in the taxi with my mother when I suddenly realized, it dawned on me, that I am I and she is she." She was expressing a significant psychic event. For the first time in her life, she had experienced a sense of her own identity. Another patient said: "I feel liquid. . . . I feel as thin as the air in this room. If this room were double its size, I could expand and fill the whole room too, and become very thin." This feeling constituted of course, a change in her self-feeling, since one customarily has some sense of a continuing substantiality and certainly not of being thin as air. A third patient, who had a very strong aversion to intercourse with his wife and who preferred masturbation, attempted to formulate his attitude toward intercourse in the following way: "I have a feeling I would give too much. I have a feeling I would lose my personal identity." Still another patient said: "I have a mild sensation of not being me. I have to stop and think and find myself." And yet another: "Since I didn't exist alone, I was puppetlike, a part of mother—and only then complete" (that is, when with mother).*

In addition to unpleasant perturbations of self-feeling, an enthusiastic, quasi-mystical *accentuation* of the sense of identity also occurs in adolescence and appears to intimate both a loosening of structure and an encompassing of larger chunks of human experience. One young person wrote me: "I have so much inside of me that is bursting to get out. . . . I feel so rich and full; I want

* For a brief survey of the clinic of identity, see Spiegel.[8]

10

to give so much—not of material things . . . but of my feelings and my ideas. . . . It seems unfathomable to me that we are only made of carbon, oxygen, hydrogen, and a few other elements. . . . "

The emphasis that Erikson,[1] in particular, has placed on the sense of personal identity is extremely valuable for characterizing, in teleological fashion, one of the main purposes of adolescence. We can say that one of the purposes of adolescence, within the total developmental line of the individual, is the achievement of a firm sense of self.

With the advent of adolescence and the accompanying diffuse psychic dissolution, with the changes in the relations between the ego, id, and superego, with the massive shifts of cathexis, a disturbance of the sense of self occurs; the hitherto "placid" sense of identity dissolves, and an "identity tremulousness" sets in.

Toward the end of adolescence, this shifting sense of self should give way to a more constant one. This constancy must, of course, be understood as relative, since fluctuations in the sense of self continue throughout life and in some people constitute a chronic disturbance. Some patients—many of them borderline, but not all —continually chase after a constant personal identity. There are lifelong attempts to master a shifting sense of identity by varying kinds of attachments, either of a devouring or of a self-effacing kind, and by means of acting out. (For the relation of art and literature to the sense of identity, see Greenacre[3] and Wilson.[10])

Sexual intercourse for some is a means of affirming identity; for others, it is a threat. For example, a young woman found it an absolute necessity for her sexual partner to be aware of her orgasm; without that awareness, there was doubt concerning her reality. In childhood, she could not make her parents "hear" her (listen to her), with consequent severe doubts about her reality. ("If they don't listen to me, it's because I don't exist.") Later, her lover had to "hear" her orgasm; she was then "real."

But most of us, once we reach adulthood, are not troubled by a shifting sense of self. We sink into a relative solidity, or perhaps stolidity, about it.

Are the disturbances of the sense of self as universal in adolescence as I have implied, or are they limited to the "neurotic" introverted adolescent? I believe that, in fact, these disturbances exist in nearly all adolescents, but that they assume different guises among different classes and types. They are to be found in the tough delinquent as well as in the "tender-minded" neurotic. They will be found wherever the normal instability of adolescence is present. But they will not be found in the fixed structure of the severe compulsive-character–neurotic adolescent who resists the loosening effect of adolescence.

If some clinicians find difficulty in confirming this observation, it may be because the disturbance is, at times, cryptic and only to be elicited through questioning. This is true of some adult patients but is even more frequently found among adolescents. The adolescent's attitude toward any symptomatology may often be a casual one, so that what adults experience as a symptom may be more or less easily absorbed into the personality of the adolescent.

For example, from everything a 16-year-old girl said during several consultations, I felt that she must have moments of considerable anxiety. I asked her whether she had any complaints other than the ones she talked to me about. She said no. I then asked her whether she suffered from any moments of fear which came on without any cause and which puzzled her. She again emphatically said no. Finally, I asked her whether she ever had any strange feelings in her lower abdomen. In her response, she gave a perfect description of typical "butterflies." These signs of anxiety had first appeared at 14 when she had fallen passionately in love with a young man. When I asked her how she had been able to tolerate these unpleasant feelings for so long, she gave a simple answer: "I was so uncomfortable that I trained myself to ignore them." If I had not questioned her persistently, this important aspect of her disturbed state would have escaped me.

Another patient, in her early 20's, repeatedly talked about the miseries, external and internal, experienced during her early adolescence, in such a way that I was led to ask her: "But at times you must have felt unreal?" She responded by saying: "I never felt real during that entire time. I was always unreal." Yet this patient, during her analysis, never spontaneously mentioned or described her extreme state of unreality.

We are at first astonished by these lacunae. We ask ourselves how it is that the youthful patient does not complain about them. Our first thought is that the absence of complaint may be on the basis of repression or of chronic denial of symptom. But clinical facts do not support this view; neither patient had truly forgotten the symptoms, nor did either object to acknowledging their presence. Rather, the phenomenon is closer to an acceptance of the symptom, to an absorption of it into the personality. It is not experienced as ego alien or, more correctly, as nonself. The ease of absorption of the symptom appears to be a direct consequence of the looseness—one is tempted to say "sponginess"—of personality organization during adolescence. The self as a firm frame of reference has not yet been established; thus certain psychic material, which at a later date would be experienced as foreign and would be excluded, remains adherent to the self. Rather, one has the impression of global absorption, as in a lower animal; only very slowly does the detritus come to be eliminated as a more definitive self is established.

Apparently opposite to the tendency toward "symptom absorption" is the tendency of the adolescent to experience sexual tension as being alien to the self. The early adolescent, in particular, often feels sexual tension as an external force—not as part of himself. To him (and to her) the genitals possess an autonomous life; sexual sensations come and go unbidden, without apparent connection with the person. Sexuality at first appears to act *on* the individual rather than to *express* the individual. Although sexuality, to a certain extent, remains an alien force throughout life, this self-alien quality appears most marked during the first half of adolescence.

But it is also during adolescence that the gradual integration of sexuality into the self takes place. The clinical equivalent of this process is the change of id sexual tension into "I desire." The progressive transformation of the "emission discharge" into the "emission orgasm" during adolescent masturbation demonstrates the transition from sexual tension to sexual desire; from discharge, from getting rid of annoying sexual tension, to the "true" orgasm and its integration into the self.

Just as the hand is of the greatest importance during infancy in the early development of the self,[5] so it regains this nuclear role in the development of the self in adolescence through masturbation. The grasping and manipulation of the penis, the volitional production of emissions and orgasms, tend to incorporate this apparently autonomous organ into the self. More accurately stated, adolescent masturbation endows both the genitals and the associated sexual sensations with self-feeling and enlarges the self.

Although masturbation is thus of great importance in the development of the self in adolescence, I do not wish to imply that masturbation is to be viewed totally without concern. The quality, the rhythm, the frequency, and the setting are important when attempting to evaluate the significance of the masturbation. Between the two extremes of the adolescent who will not touch his genitals and the one who repeatedly seeks consolation from the trials of this world through touching them, a more moderate attitude must be sought.

It must also not be overlooked that adolescent sexual intercourse may represent an evasion of masturbation, which can appear to some adolescents as the greater danger. Especially is this true for some girls with a particularly well developed illusory penis; they wish to avoid the tactile confirmation of the psychically inferior clitoris. This can even extend to the denial of the existence of the clitoris. One such patient, during her adolescence, masturbated urethrally with a kind of flat discharge, followed by urination. Her denial of the clitoris required considerable analysis before its existence could be acknowledged and before the penis envy and illusory penis could then come into analytic focus. In another female adolescent, the clitoris was acknowledged by name but was endowed with considerable length. This patient avoided masturbation but, in periods of sexual excitement, would masturbate boys.

Identity, the self, the sense of self having only recently become a focus of psychoanalytic interest, it is understandable that, besides the inherent obscurity of the problems surrounding these phenomena, additional obscurities develop owing to a lack of conceptual differentiations. I refer here to the frequently implied equivalence of identity and identification.

Male patients with a marked feminine identification do not necessarily experience a disturbance in their feeling of self. Nor do female patients with strong penis envy and illusory penis feel like men; indeed, in some women their sense of irresistible feminine attractiveness appears linked to these very features. Although various symptoms, especially anxiety and acting out, may appear during the analysis of these identifications, such disturbances do not necessarily impinge on the sense of identity, as the following case report demonstrates.

CASE REPORT*

A 14-year-old, 7th-grade, white, Puerto Rican, Catholic girl set fire to toilet paper in the school bathroom on a dare from some

* Case prepared for presentation by Dr. Robert Palumbaum with supervision by Dr. Henry I. Schneer.

other girls. This happened around the time of a widely publicized fire which took 90 lives in a Chicago school. There was only one previous fire-setting episode: When she was 5 years old, while living with her maternal grandparents in Puerto Rico, she set fire to the grandmother's dress in the closet, using a candle from a religious arrangement.

The parents (the mother and her common-law husband who is regarded as a stepfather by the patient) complained that the girl was keeping "bad company" with "tough," aggressive girls since starting in junior high school. The mother ejected one of these girls from the home because she was smoking.

Usually, the patient was obedient and respectful to the parents. She defied a curfew hour, however, by staying out of the home till 10 P.M. instead of 8 P.M. Recently, she became more sullen and got into several fights with neighborhood girls.

The patient was born out of wedlock, when her mother was 15. The father, who was twice as old as the mother and married to someone else, never lived with the mother and has never had any contact with the patient. Paternity action was instituted against the father, but he was not adjudicated the father.

The pregnancy was uncomplicated. The mother lived with her parents throughout pregnancy until the patient was 4 years old. Delivery was at term and normal in a hospital in Puerto Rico. The birth weight was 9 pounds; neonatal period was normal.

An accurate picture of the patient's early development could not be elicited, but it seemed to be within average range. She was breast fed and on the bottle until about 3 years old. The bowel training was started at the age of 8 months and completed at 4 years. This was also the time when the mother departed for the United States, leaving the patient entirely in the care of the maternal grandmother in Puerto Rico. The patient was "trained" by the maternal grandparents, since the mother worked five days a week.

She has had the habit of head banging against the wall and floor since the age of 3. She talks in her sleep (English!).

The parents were embarrassed at the mention of her sexual development. Her menarche, however, was found to have occurred at age 12. The mother was not informed but knew of it when her own Kotex was taken. The patient's menses are usually accompanied by headache.

The patient's physical health has been good, except for many upper respiratory infections which eventuated in a tonsillectomy about a year ago.

Her school conduct was fair (described as uncooperative), and she was tardy at times. There were unexplained absences during the past term. Her grades were good except for social studies. She was religious until about 3 years ago. She doesn't attend church now.

After a separation of 3 years, the patient joined her mother in the United States. While the mother worked, the patient was placed in the care of a woman who was paid for this service. Within a few years the maternal grandparents arrived from Puerto Rico to care for the patient again. From the age of 7 to 9, the patient and her mother lived with an older man. The patient said that, although he was "all right," she was not upset when he left. Then the mother took up with a Cuban baker with whom the mother presently lives in a common-law marriage. The patient regards him as a father. He promises to marry the mother when he gets a divorce. He is 42 years old and the mother is 30. The patient considers him devoted and affectionate. She teaches him to dance. He exclaims, "She likes me too much."

A half brother was born when the patient was about 10. The parents say that she loved him and was never jealous. He and the patient get along well, with the usual fights which are sometimes precipitated when he takes her paper dolls. He is very quiet and "very nervous," in that he fidgets a lot. He goes to nursery school, and the mother says he gets along well with other children.

During the interview with the patient, she was found to be a rather childish, pretty, dark girl, relating in a hostile, demanding, and sullen manner. Beneath the façade of bravado she was found to be depressed. In further interviews she frequently cried. She had a slight Spanish accent and a southern (United States) accent, apparently an affectation. She explained this by saying she has many Negro girl friends. Her main interests were in cooking and baseball, a game in which she likes to pitch. She likes movies and TV programs about gun fights, cowboys, and detective mysteries. She likes to play with dolls and talks with them. She is extremely evasive in discussing her parents, saying that they are "nice" and she has no problems with them. She refuses to discuss her feelings about boys and is very evasive in this area too. When asked if she ever kissed a boy, she exclaimed, "No, shit!" She says she dislikes "Spanish" (Puerto Rican) children and prefers colored people, because she considers colored people to be more gentle. She feels that "Spanish people are mean." At one time she said she wanted to be a nun when she grew up. At another time she said she'd like to be a nurse because she likes to give injections. She used to give her grandmother insulin for diabetes. She denies any problems at all and does not feel that she needs any help.

DISCUSSION

The young girl presented here furnishes a case in point. This 14-year-old was born in Puerto Rico, but is now living in a North American culture. She was brought up by her mother during her earliest years; but then her mother left for the United States, and she was raised by her grandmother. Subsequently, she rejoined her mother, and a stepfather appeared on the scene. There is evidence of a marked masculine identification. Here we have abundant material for conflicting identifications, yet there are no indications of disturbance of the sense of self, either in the shape of clear-cut symptoms, such as depersonalization, or in uncertainties in her self-feeling.

A direct, one-to-one relation between identity and identification does not exist. Essentially, a disturbance in the sense of identity is a matter of constancy or nonconstancy; in contrast to an identification, it is not a qualitative phenomenon.

It is as if the ego always attempts to maintain a constancy of self-feeling, and its occasional inability to do so is experienced in one of the many ways which we label disturbance of the sense of identity. A masculine identification in a female (or a feminine one in a male) does not mean a disturbance of the sense of identity. An undermining of such an identification (even though beneficial) during analysis, however, if sufficiently sudden, may lead to a disturbance (usually transient) in the sense of identity.

Global identification in appersonated individuals can exist with a highly tentative sense of identity, but, in general, identification is a partial process. One identifies with a symptom, with a character trait, with an attitude of another person, but rarely with the total person. But the self and the sense of self are global entities. This is another reason to insist on a separation of identity and identification.

The crucial point seems to be the capacity of the ego to synthesize conflicting identifications into a stable self and sense of self.

The self and the sense of self *tend* to remain constant unless shaken by spontaneously acute cathectic shifts owing to trauma, or by similar changes under the impact of analysis, or by the massive cathectic shifts of adolescence.

REFERENCES

1. ERIKSON, E. H. The problem of ego identity. *J. Am. Psychoanalyt. Assoc.*, 4: 56, 1956.
2. FEDERN, P. *Ego Psychology and the Psychoses.* New York, Basic Books, Inc., 1952, Part I.
3. GREENACRE, P. "Impostor and Artist," in *The Psychoanalytic Study of the Child.* New York, International Universities Press, Inc., 1958, vol. 13.
4. HARTMANN, H. "Comments on the Psychoanalytic Psychology of the Ego," in *The Psychoanalytic Study of the Child.* New York, International Universities Press, Inc., 1950, vol. 5.
5. HOFFER, W. "Mouth, Hand and Ego Integration," in *The Psychoanalytic Study of the Child.* New York, International Universities Press, Inc., 1949, vols. 3, 4.
6. JACOBSON, E. "The Self and the Object World," in *The Psychoanalytic Study of the Child.* New York, International Universities Press, Inc., 1954, vol. 9.
7. JACOBSON, E. Depersonalization. *J. Am. Psychoanalyt. Assoc.* 7: 581, 1959.
8. NUNBERG, H. "States of Depersonalization in the Light of Libido Theory," in *Practice and Theory of Psychoanalysis.* New York, International Universities Press, Inc., 1955.
9. SPIEGEL, L. A. "The Self, The Sense of Self and Perception," in *The Psychoanalytic Study of the Child.* New York, International Universities Press, Inc., 1959, vol. 14.
10. WILSON, C. *The Outsider.* Boston, Houghton Mifflin Company, 1956, chap. 6.

chapter *3* Menarche

JUDITH S. KESTENBERG

Recently, Anna Freud[11] commented on how little we know from analysis of adolescents, and how little we can reconstruct, from adult analysis, about adolescence, even though the experiences of that time have not been heavily repressed.

It is therefore not surprising that the menarche, an event specific to adolescence, has been predominantly discussed in the literature within the framework of feminine development in general, and of reactions to menstruation in particular.[1,3,5,6,15,22,23,27,29] One whole issue of the *Zeitschrift für Psychoanalytische Paedagogik* (1931) was devoted to menstruation.[3,4,20,25,26,27,28,29] In this issue several authors focused on anticipation of the menarche and reactions to it. At that time the prevailing lack of preparation for the first menstrual period was especially noted by educators.

A survey of literature conveys the impression that the menarche has been considered one of the traumata within the female castration complex. The positive aspect of the menarche as a turning point in the acceptance of femininity has been greatly overshadowed by the emphasis placed on the "trauma" of the first and even subsequent menses.

Helene Deutsch,[6] as well as others, has pointed out the girl's own contribution to her lack of preparedness. Her own repressions and distortions of what she was told were felt to be important factors in the complex experience of menstruation as a trauma. The mother's role in the girl's expectation and evaluation of her menarche and subsequent menstruations was considered crucial. Some authors, principally Daly,[4] stressed the male attitude toward menstruation. Anthropological data, as well as analyses of male patients, tend to confirm the view that men are inclined to regard menstruation as a dangerous traumatic event. The role of the father and male siblings in the girl's evaluation of her menses has not been sufficiently clarified.

There is general agreement that menarche initiates a critical period in the girl's life; that she will cope with this conspicuous change in her body with a variety of reactions acquired earlier in life and now revived and intensified.

REACTIONS TO THE MENARCHE

Whether we gather our data from analyses of adult women, analyses of adolescents, or observation of adolescents, we note that there are manifold reactions to the menarche, running the gamut from the extreme of suicide and psychotic breakdown to joy over the attainment of maturity. Yet a careful review of adult and adolescent analyses of my own experience reveals a dirth of data on the effect of the first menstruation on the patients' development. I can recollect many facts elucidating particular brands of penis envy, attitudes toward siblings, and special features of the Oedipus complex as well as preoedipal relationships. I know a great deal about these patients' early and later masturbation struggles and the impact of their first sexual experiences with others. Some patients had particular difficulties in the first year of life that stand out vividly in my mind. I am quite aware of fluctuations of mood and attitude in various phases of these patients' menstrual cycles. I do not have a comparable series of data in regard to menarche. I do know that menarche initiated in these girls a personality change of which they were not aware and which did not become the focus of analysis because it constituted, in all cases, an improvement rather than a regressive development.

Three girls whom I analyzed at the time of their menarche stand out in my memory. All three young ladies were enlightened partly by their mothers, partly by their friends, and partly in their analyses. Menarche did not constitute, for them, a traumatic event. Also, in dealing casually and sporadically with a group of average girls who were being brought up by what is called progressive education, I gained the impression that the first menstruation was not considered by them a traumatic event. Apparently, their parents, teachers, nurses, and physicians had done what was recommended a quarter of a century ago for preparing girls for their first menstruations. None of them was unprepared; none was left to her own devices. Not only did the mother or the school or camp nurse help physically when menses started, but they also made sure that the previously enlightened child was still enlightened. By enlightment I do not mean that the children understood the full significance of menstruation, but they did know that the appearance of menses was normal and to be expected at a certain age, that it was part and parcel of feminine maturity and a prerequisite for having children in the future.

For example, a 12-year-old who has known about menstruation for some time has shown, in the last few months, all the signs of beginning feminine development, such as breast growth, pubic hair, and feminine hip lines, as well as the unpredictability of behavior expected of the prepubertal child. Questioned casually as to whether she still knew what menstruation was for, she replied impatiently, "Of course, I know." When I asked her to tell me what she knew, she answered quickly and with obvious scorn for my naïveté, "It's the bed for the baby that you don't need any more because you don't get the baby." She said she knew positively that she would not get her period before she was 13½ years old. When her period did arrive at the time she predicted, she did not tell her mother about it until the matter came up in connection with going swimming. In regard to time of appearance of menses, she was guided by what happened to most of her girl friends. When she later discussed the irregularity of her menses, she reassured her mother that "most girls' periods are irregular at first—this is normal." The topic has been fully discussed in school, especially its usefulness as an excuse to be absent from gym. Striking was her practical approach to the problem—an approach typical of the group to which she belonged.

In contrast to these youngsters, children brought up by old-fashioned methods of education frequently regard menstruation as a traumatic event. There is also a direct correlation between emotional disturbance and proneness to view menarche as a threat or calamity. Dr. Helen Schur, through skillful interviewing, has collected responses to questions about the prospect as well as the experience of menarche from random samples of children hospitalized in the Psychiatric Division of Kings County Hospital. From the following examples one can readily recognize the severity of these children's problems as well as their lack of carefully thought out preparation for the first menstrual period.

CASE REPORTS

Case 1

The subject is 10 years old and the diagnosis is adjustment reaction of childhood with conduct disturbance. She has not started to menstruate. Asked about it she says, "You bleed." But she does not know from where. She goes on: "It means that you grow up and get older and older. You just get it; it's normal. The first time you get it, it lasts 3 to 4 weeks. Then you get it every week, no every month. It lasts about 1 week and you have it until you die. You wear a Kotex and you have to be very careful that you don't drop it. I only want to get it when I know more about it. What puzzles me is how you get pregnant by yourself. The matron at the police said it's bad when girls fool around with each other, you know—Lesbian, they touch each other. It's worse when boys and girls get together. It always needs a female and a male, a dog and a dog, a cat and a cat so they have to be just next to each other. I don't want to wear slacks, I am not a boy."

Case 2

A 10-year-old's diagnosis is adjustment reaction with habit disorder. She has not menstruated yet. She first stated that she had never heard of menstruation, period, or monthly. But on later questioning she revealed that menstruation meant that blood came from the vagina. She was "surprised that she has not got it." She had previously thought that "period" meant vaginal examination, because her older sister goes to the doctor to get a checkup and she gets a vaginal examination. She knows about that because her sister told her, and once, when she went with her sister and mother to the doctor, the doctor sent her out. Now that she knows that "period" does not mean vaginal examination, she says, "I have nothing to worry about." She thinks that her sister has a crooked pelvis and that the doctor has told her that a baby will straighten it out. Her 11-year-old sister always goes to the bathroom to see "if she has got it." While talking, she had to go to the bathroom herself. She then wanted to know whether one can have a baby if one does not menstruate, or if the baby would die, because one of the neighbors had 8 children who all died at birth and 1 child who is crazy.

Case 3

The patient is 11 years and 9 months old. The diagnosis is schizophrenic reaction, paranoid type. She had her first period about 6 months ago. Nobody had told her about it before. She had pain in the lower abdomen. While menstruating, she also has headaches. She never knows when she will get her period but gets a headache before. The first time she noticed blood when she wiped herself. She felt scared because of the pain but did not tell anybody. She did not know where she was bleeding from. She felt too ashamed to ask. She could not explain why she felt ashamed. The bleeding was light, and she washed her underwear herself. A girl friend explained it to her spontaneously after her first period. She felt relieved that somebody else had it too. The girl friend only told her that one bleeds. She is not sure if boys get it too. She never wondered why a person gets it, and never asked for more information. In the hospital she only confided in one girl who got napkins for her. She never told the nurse. She usually restricts her activity on her own initiative, because if she gets excited she gets pain.

Case 4

A 16-year-old, diagnosis schizophrenic reaction, catatonic type, has not menstruated for the last 5 months. She thinks it has something to do with the change of climate—mountain air. She thinks she menstruated twice at the age of 14 but is not sure. Her mother had told her long before—she does not remember when—that it is natural and nothing to hide. She thinks that she saw her mother's bloody napkins, as her 2-year-old cousin does his mother's. Her aunt always sends him to the window to look for his daddy because he might get frightened (apparently on seeing the bloody napkin). She does not like the period in summer because of the sweat and odor which disturb her.

Case 5

The patient is 13 years old with a diagnosis of schizophrenic reaction, childhood type. She does not menstruate. She was embarrassed when a male doctor asked her about it previously. Her mother had told her about it when the child was 3½ years old. The mother explained to her that when she gets older she will bleed, and that's called a period. This reminded her of an accident, at the time the mother told her, in which the mother closed the lid of the piano on her fingers. She bled and needed several stitches. The patient does not know what period is. It means "that you have gotten into womanhood." She is glad that she has not gotten it because it is a big nuisance. She thinks the blood comes from the rectum. She denies wanting to know more about it but says that when she asks her friends they answer her, "It's none of your business." All during the interview she asked to be fed.

Case 6

A 15½-year-old has a diagnosis of depressive reaction. She has had her period since age 12 or 13 but does not remember exactly. Her mother had told her about it long before. She had told her what to do, "that you become a lady," and not to be afraid or ashamed. In the beginning she had no pain and seldom has it now. Would not know when she would get pain. She feels happy about it. This way she knows that she can have children and that she is healthy. But she feels moody during the period, has cramps 1 week before, sharp pains in her rectum, and often "after cramps." The period lasts 3 days. She used to get crying spells before the period and felt very tired. She does not exactly know what "period" is, although in the seventh grade the hygiene teacher explained; but she cannot remember—something about leftover and waste, but she does not know where from. During the period she also had "funny feelings" like being high up, like being very tall and looking down, which made her dizzy. She would ask for milk and wanted to be petted. She then described her emotional upset, during the period, which brought her to this hospital last year. She would "holler and scream" and tried to kill herself. She also had at those times "terrible and stupid" dreams which she could not recall. Her mother also gets cramps, as does her sister. The mother calls it "period," "monthly," or "her friend."

Case 7

A 14-year-old is diagnosed as having an inadequate personality. Menarche occurred at 12. She said she felt funny and her pants were wet. She knew that she had her period. The mother, when explaining it to her, had told her that she herself did not know when she was a girl. She had fallen down and injured herself. The patient had thought one would bleed much more; that she would have to change every hour. One friend thought it would come like a river. The patient gets pain in her back before menstruation. She does everything, although she has been told that doing certain things can stop it. She says that she is glad she got it and was scared that she might not get it, because then she would not be able to have children and she likes her niece and nephew as if they were her children. She wants to become a nurse because she can look at disgusting things, such as cuts on hands or head, or vomit. She had a vaginal examination a year ago.

Case 8

The subject is 15½ years old, with a diagnosis of adjustment reaction of adolescence with paranoid features. She menstruated for the first time for 1 day at age 10, a day after an appendectomy. She was frightened, could not imagine what it was, and thought she had been cut at the operation. The nurse explained it to her. She had her period regularly at 11. She did not worry in between because she thought that "you only get it once." She is unable to explain what menstruation is. She feels happy that she got it, because she "is a young lady." She has cramps—at times bad—and then she wishes that boys would have it too. She does not discuss it with her friends; she thinks it is disgusting that some girls talk about it.

DISCUSSION

In each of these reports one notices a mixture of information, misinformation, and fantasy. In some it is evident that instruction as to the nature of menstruation is either repressed or denied and substituted for with ideas stemming from individual problems. In some, as in Cases 5 and 6, oral regressive features stand out; in others, as in Cases 7 and 8, the problems of injury are strongly cathected. All derive a great deal of elaboration from observations of mothers and siblings. Superimposed upon the struggle inherent in the acceptance versus nonacceptance of menstruation as the girl's model of womanhood, we can see, in this disturbed group, features similar to those described in the more normal adolescent group. Here, too, menarche has its positive aspects in terms of group identity, in terms of an ego ideal of growing up and becoming a lady, and in terms of identification with one's mother.

We encounter a variety of reactions: the unprepared girls who are shocked by menarche and can only rely on fantasies to explain what is happening—the old-fashioned type; those who had been prepared but act as if they had not; those who had been prepared and seem to understand it, but retain their own fantasies along with what has been told them, with resultant confusion; and, last, those girls who give no evidence of keeping their old fantasies, having either repressed them or disposed of them.

In the more normal group many girls tend to accept menstruation as a necessary nuisance in maintaining their group identity as girls and future women and mothers. On the surface, complaints about the need to endure menstruation for the sake of feminine maturity would seem justified. The periodic bleeding, feeling of weakness, pain, and inconvenience in terms of additional bodily care and restriction of activity—all this does sound more like a sickness than a wholesome part of mature well-being. No wonder, one may argue, that the girl protests against the cruelty of nature and asks why a more pleasant way could not have been invented to get her ready for motherhood and femininity. Were we to accept such complaints at face value, we would have to ignore the normal feminine masochistic attitude toward pain and discomfort.

FEMININE MASOCHISM IN PREPUBERTY AND PUBERTY*

After Freud,[14] it was primarily H. Deutsch[6] who described the normal feminine masochism that makes women enjoy the literally bloody experiences to which they are subjected in the normal course of development (menstruation, defloration, and childbirth). On the other hand, much of feminine penis envy and resentment of men has been ascribed to the woman's lack of acceptance of a "bleeding hole" which she refuses to enjoy. The girl's discovery that she lacks a penis and the experience of her menarche are classified as *the* traumata in feminine development. Masculine identification, which goes hand in hand with denial of femininity, is used temporarily or permanently to master the traumatic situation. It is less well known that feminine masochism not only represents a specifically feminine genital-drive endowment but is also employed in the service of mastery. Pain of all shades and intensities can sharpen and define body boundaries and is used as a landmark in the process of incorporating an invisible body part into the image of one's own body.

---

* The term "prepuberty" is used throughout this chapter to define the phase in which growth of secondary sex characteristics is initiated before menarche. The term "puberty" is used to denote the phase beginning with menarche and terminating with the establishment of regular ovulatory cycles. The term "adolescence" is intended to denote the years between latency and adulthood.

Undefined, unlocalized inner sensations promote anxiety. They are the no man's land between the girl herself and the outside in which projections and introjections continuously operate, thus preventing a sharp delineation of the girl's body image, increasing the diffuseness of body boundaries. The girl, in prepuberty, experiences spurts of intense but poorly defined sensations which flow into each other.

Helene Deutsch[6] defines prepuberty as "that last stage of the latency period in which certain harbingers of future sexual drives may be discerned, but which in the main is the period of greatest freedom from infantile sexuality" (p. 4). Deutsch is aware that other authors believe prepuberty is characterized by intensified sexual needs. At times, she does concede considerable interest in sexuality in the prepubertal child: "During prepuberty her intense curiosity about sexual processes in general directs her interest towards her own body" (p. 25). Greenacre[18] and Blos[2] accept Deutsch's concept of prepuberty as the phase of greatest freedom from infantile sexuality. All three authors seem to be guided by the observable fact that girls in prepuberty show very little actual interest in the opposite sex. The girl's sexual interests at that time primarily center on her own growing body. This is a highly narcissistic state in which objects, male and female, serve as anchor points for exploration of the girl's body by comparison. The male sex is rejected because of its unsuitability for elucidation of secrets concerning the female body.

It is interesting to note the variety of definitions of prepuberty throughout the literature. (See especially Fraiberg[9] and Refs. 5 and 26.) Similarly, another transitional phase, that between anality and phallicity, has been variously assigned to either the pregenital or the phallic stages of development. In this early transitional stage[22] the child's heightened interest in her body expresses itself in a medley of pregenital and genital fantasies. The same mingling is characteristic of the transitional phase of prepuberty.

Menarche brings relief, providing the girl with fixed points of reference upon which she can now organize many of her experiences. It is important to distinguish between enjoying the discomfort of menstruation and making use of it for orientation. In prepuberty, masochistic enjoyment of unpleasure only heightens anxiety, spreads diffuseness, and counteracts organization—frustration as well as the disorganization becoming sources of masochistic pleasure.

To illustrate the difference between feminine masochistic adjustment and prepubertylike masochistic enjoyment of diffusion, I shall describe two mothers with whom I have regular contacts for research purposes, Mrs. A. and Mrs. B., each living in similar circumstances, each busy with housework and the care of several children. Each of them has an apartment to clean; each has to cook, shop for food and clothing, and perform other household necessities. Each has to take the children to the doctor and dentist. Each goes out only on rare occasions, leaving the children with an obliging relative. The children of both women are lively and quite capable of making a great deal of mess and creating general bedlam. The children fight among themselves and with other children, insist on having pets, get sick from time to time, and are naughty more often than not.

To Mrs. A., my proposed visit always appears to come at the most inconvenient time, as she has a lot of work to do, someone in the family is sick, or it is just the one day when she has a chance to go out. She lets me know that I can come anyway but that my visit will give her a lot of trouble. When I arrive, she invariably complains, in response to my queries, about one child or the other, or scolds them. They are fighting too much, she says. They do not give her a moment's peace. Her oldest daughter has been talking in school; the little one is a devil, she is so active. Her older boy has never been like this. She wishes she had another boy, instead of so many girls, because boys are so much more quiet. She may proceed to tell me about an outstanding achievement of one daughter, using it to disparage her other children by comparison. Then she may go on to tell me that they had to give the cat away because she was too much trouble. Without any transition that I can detect, she may tell me her delivery had been painful, and her cousin has not been treating her right.

Poor Mrs. A—she cannot report anything pleasurable of which she may be proud without immediately adding a negative, unpleasant, even disastrous piece of news. Her verbal productions flow into each other in a steady stream of complaints and pleasure.

Let us take a look at Mrs. B. When I phone her she is very pleased to hear from me and invites me to come at any time. Her attitude denotes her feeling that I am conferring an honor upon her. When I arrive, she interrupts her work to chat with me or to do something for one of the children who may happen to need her help at the moment. When she reports misbehavior or difficulty with one or the other child, she never puts emphasis on how much trouble it has been for her, although many times she finds herself too tired to cope with the problem that has arisen, and she lets her husband do it. She is quite eager to find out how to handle these problems, although she is not always able to carry out the advice. She is by no means a perfect wife or mother. Her children have their share of neuroses, partly because of her way of handling them.

In her everyday living Mrs. B has as many chores and as many difficulties as Mrs. A., but she does not suffer as much. She tolerates the displeasure and uses it to formulate questions and ideas as to how to make things better. Speaking of her daughter, she may report, "I never realized that she is scared of dogs until the whole trouble with the dog started that day. Then I began to wonder whether she would be less scared if I got her a pet."

Mrs. A. would have expressed it in this way: "She was so scared of this dog. My boy was never like that. We had so much trouble. She screamed and cried. It was just like that time when she got scared of the pumpkin, but I must say she is not scared to cross the street like her cousin. I watch her from the window and she is perfect. Now, my boy, he is very careless and he will get run over yet . . . " and so on and on.

Mrs. A. is confused, confusing, diffuse, unprecise. Her tough life, her feelings of frustration are a necessary by-product of her masochistic outlook. As she continuously interrupts herself, an additional interruption coming from the outside jars her and makes her feel overwhelmed by too much pressure. She is an anguished soul, forever trying to find a way out of her misery, forever hoping to finish what she had set out to do. Her complaints attempt to shift onto an outside agent her inner discontent. She seems to revel in pain, disaster, suffering, frustration, and many other shades of displeasure. One gains the impression that she finds all too brief relief in focusing on a structured experience which helps her to formulate, at times, what it is that is "too much for her." Her child is too active, which is too much for her. Or her neighbor has offended her and that was too much. Mrs. B., on the other hand, does not seem to suffer so much. She finds continuous relief in the sharpness and directness with which she acts and expresses herself. Whatever bothers her has a beginning, and there is at least an end in sight, so that she can take each new obstacle in her stride.

Mrs. A., then, is an example of a woman who cannot find lasting relief in the feminine type of enjoyment of pain but, instead, relishes the endless complaints. Her attempts to find relief are short lived and unsuccessful. Mrs. B., on the other hand, uses painful experiences to find direction and organization in her life, and she gets pleasure in so doing.

The cases of Mrs. A. and Mrs. B. have been used here to differentiate between masochistic pleasure in pain on an instinctual level and the use of pain to bring about relief through mastery on the ego level. The first one leads to disorganization of ego functions; the second promotes organization. Neutralization of energy is implicit in the transformation of uncontrolled masochistic pleasure into pleasure specifically derived from the localizing and differentiating qualities of pain.

The normal girl, who does not suffer unduly from menstrual discomfort, also attains a degree of organization which distinguishes her markedly from the disjointed child in prepuberty. Adolescents who suffer with menstruation and attach fearful fantasies to it are unable to accept or retain clear explanations. They exhibit various degrees of masochistic complaining about their discomfort. They try to combat their masochistic surrender and, like Mrs. A., they cannot succeed. Mrs. A's case represents an example of the continuation of prepubertal behavior in an adult woman. It is more usual to find that the menarche promotes some degree of organization, even in disturbances which are characterized by diffuseness of thought and masochistic tendencies.

If we survey the data collected by Dr. Schur, we find that Patients 1, 2, and 5 who had not begun to menstruate, are much like Mrs. A. in their productions. Their thoughts flow into each other. There is no clear beginning or end to what they are saying. When patients 3, 7, and 8 talk directly about menstruation, their expressions are much more clearly defined than those of the other girls. Patient 4, who suffers from amenorrhea, is vague about her menarche. Patient 6 who had been suicidal during a menstrual period, seems best organized when talking about her cramps.

All the patients are, of course, disturbed by their problems and also by the questions put to them. They all have fantasies about menstruation, and fears as well. The difference lies not so much in content as in the way they are able to talk about it. Although Patients 6, 7, and 8 tend to speak in a more diffuse fashion than other girls who have experienced menstruation, they do offer much more circumscribed data about menstruation than girls who have not had the experience. Patient 7 gets pain in her back before menstruation sets in; Patient 8 has bad cramps during it. Patients 3 and 6 can even indicate precisely where they have pain, namely in the lowest abdomen and rectum respectively. Even though they too, like Patients 7 and 8, relate a great deal of misinformation about menstruation, they are able to tell a much more coherent story than the uninitiated girls.

Patient 4 becomes more incoherent than Patient 3, but this is due more to omission than to diffusion of thought. Patient 6 feels moody during her period, has cramps 1 week before, etc. Although she has a great many sensations in connection with her period which may frighten and disturb her, she is able to describe them in a relatively organized fashion. In contrast, the three girls who have not achieved puberty tend to "talk a blue streak." Patient 1 says, "It means that you grow up and get older and older. You just get it; it's normal. The first time you get it, it lasts 3 to 4 weeks. Then you get it every week, no every month. It lasts about 1 week and you have it until you die. . . . " Whatever discomfort this girl anticipates and experiences never becomes clear cut, and it seems to go on forever. A similarly unstructured story is told by Patient 2 when she explains her confusion between vaginal examination and menstruation. Patient 5 shows diffusion and lack of organization in her story about when and how she was enlightened.

Even in this highly disturbed group of girls, those who had had the experience of menstruation exhibit some direction toward organization derived from the specificity of their physical complaints. They have a great deal of anxiety, to be sure, and many more fantasies than the prepubertal girls, but their thoughts regarding menstruation take on a concrete quality.

MENARCHE AS A TRIGGER MECHANISM FOR ORGANIZATION

The difference in organization in the patients who had achieved puberty and those who had not may not seem convincing, because many of the children whose data have been collected here exhibited various confusions owing to the disturbances which led to their hospitalization. It might be well, therefore, to turn to an example of the so-called average normal girl, for re-examination of the differences between prepubertal and pubertal behavior.

The prepubertal girl may come home from school and say to her mother, "You know what happened? This man came to school

—we giggled terribly and we had to stay after school which is very unfair because after all he did this and it was not our fault. So that's why I'm late and you don't have to get mad because everybody had to stay after class on account of this man. . . . "

By this time even the most patient mother might interrupt and ask who the man was and what was he doing in school and what made the children giggle.* I doubt, however, that she would get far in her attempt to ask these questions. The child would cut in, saying, "You're not letting me finish. You're interrupting me. I'll tell you if you listen. You never listen to me, nobody does. Remember when I had a bellyache and I tried to tell you but you wouldn't let me finish and finally I had to vomit and it was your fault because you wouldn't listen?"

Since it is obvious that we will never find out what "this man" did, let us turn to another example of typical prepubertal behavior. A girl of between 10 and 13 is getting dressed in the morning. She has absolutely nothing to wear because all the girls are going to wear brown dresses to school that day. This has been carefully established on the telephone the evening before. She has only three brown dresses and they are "no good." One is too tight and "my you know what will show and don't say the word for it, it's not decent to say out loud." The other dress is "too childish and everybody will think I'm a baby and the last one I would wear, it's okay, but you will start saying it's dirty, I know, and I only wore it for one week and I can't help it if I perspire. Every girl comes to school with some spots on her dress and no mother makes so much fuss about it. It's positively disgusting to make so much to-do about dirt."

I have selected the modes of vague, disjointed, profuse communication as examples of the over-all disorganized behavior in prepuberty, but the same is true of movements, actions, the approach to problem solving, and other aspects of functioning in prepuberty.

Mothers, exhausted, and bewildered because they feel guilty about the accusations hurled at them, come asking for advice from teachers, guidance counselors, and psychiatrists. They are able to cope with many things, but not with this avalanche of confusion.

---

* Note here the frequency of giggling attacks in prepuberty. To the adult, such behavior appears to be a never-ending exuberance of spirit for which no adequate explanation is forthcoming. Although the sexual tinge of giggling is unmistakable, no concrete sexual idea is attached to it. Any word or situation connected with sex may bring on a giggling attack in a group of prepubertal girls.

They explain that they try so hard to please their daughters. They really try to understand them. Are they failing as mothers? they ask. They have no recollection of going through a phase like this. Some add that *they* really did have nothing to wear when they were young girls, and *their mothers* really did not understand them.

One has the impression that prepubertal behavior is more contagious to mothers than to fathers. Fathers do get angry. They become upset because they feel their children are losing command of their native tongue. They try, with occasional fleeting success, to elicit clear, grammatical statements. Thus the father's attitude frequently becomes a model for attempts at organization.

Girls who have experienced menstruation may dwell on the painful physical symptoms accompanying menses and may indulge in a number of conflicting fantasies about this event, but their language is usually clear and organized. They find an outlet in the newly developed ability for clear thinking, regardless of what unpleasant experience they may discuss. They are able to start, explain, and finish what they have to say, of course within the limits of their individual personality problems, for instance they may have difficulties in finishing their work, owing to an anal type of delaying. After menarche, average so-called normal girls act very much like Mrs. B. They use various unpleasant experiences for purposes of organization. They become more settled after menarche, and increasingly more so when their cycles become regular. They do evidence the typical mood swings, often changing from one extreme to another. These may relate to their cycles or to difficult, groping, interpersonal relationships with parents, teachers, and their peers. They may be *himmelhochjauchzend zu Tode betrübt* (sky high happy—deadly depressed). Still, we can understand them much better because, in contrast to prepubertal affects, conflicting feelings are not only well defined but even grossly exaggerated in their delineation. We may not feel empathy with the intensity and the rapid fluctuations of such affects, but we know clearly the kind of affect with which we are confronted.

In re-examining the data from analyses of children who went through menarche during analysis, I wonder whether the paucity of my recollection of reactions to menarche is not due to the fact that the main change of puberty could not be classified in terms of content of material. The fantasies had not changed; they had become clearer. The conflicts had not changed; they had intensified and become more analyzable because of the sharper delineation of opposites which puberty brought about. Analyzing girls in pre-puberty is a much more difficult task than working with girls who have reached puberty.[17] One gets the same impression in going over Fraiberg's[9] examples, as many of the children she refers to belong to the prepubertal group. When analyzing both girls and boys during puberty, we must be prepared for a vehemence of resistance which may interrupt treatment. We may, as Anna Freud[10] pointed out, lose some adolescent patients in this fashion. On the other hand, we may spend weeks and months with pre-pubertal children without making headway in understanding them. Prepubertal boys often become quite uncommunicative to adults. Prepubertal girls are usually quite talkative, but it is difficult to pin them down long enough to get the material clarified or to in-terpret it to them. The exceptions in both sexes are those children in prepuberty who suffer from definite long-standing symptoms, such as phobias or inhibitions of functions, which make these chil-dren feel different from their group. The frequency with which so-called mental breakdown occurs in puberty highlights the fact that the struggles of puberty intensify conflicts. In these cases we encounter an increase of organization of symptoms rather than personality organization. Even in psychoses, one frequently gains the impression that puberty brought about exaggerated manifesta-tions of previously loosely woven trends toward psychotic regres-sion. (Compare here Eissler.[7])

The onset of menstruation makes it possible for the girl to dif-ferentiate reality from fantasy. What she knew and what she antici-pated can now be compared with how it happened to her. The sharpness of experience, the regularity of it, the well-defined way of taking care of it, the sameness of the experience as compared with her own anticipation of it and the experience of others—all these provide relief. It helps the girl to structuralize her inner and outer experiences, to regain her ability to communicate and to perceive in an organized fashion. The girl, however, is hardly ever aware of this change. She does not know that her communications were confusing, and she does not notice that she has now become clearer in her thinking.

She may now focus on the pain of menstruation to the point where it seems to us that she is enjoying it. In reality, she enjoys the sharpness of this painful experience in terms of quantity, localization, and quality of pain. I am not speaking of an intolerable pain which, by its nature, dulls the senses and brings about a state akin to loss of consciousness. I am referring to the mild cramps of uterine contractions. They are localized in the lower abdomen and have a beginning, an end, and a definite quality which makes them recognizable as menstrual cramps, in contradistinction to intestinal cramps. Some girls may have only a dull ache, less defined in quality but still relatively well localized. Although this type of pain has a less sharp beginning and ending than a cramp, it has certain time limitations, because it is usually felt on a certain day of the menstrual cycle. Girls report a regularity in the pain appearing on the first day, the second, the fourth, or the day before menstruation. They know when the pain will start and when it will go away. Or they know when their menstruation will start because the pain is a preparation for it. They seem to miss the pain when it does not come and are disturbed when it changes in quality. Their special menstruation pain is their friend rather than their "curse." Girls frequently refer to menstruation as "falling off the roof." It may be sound as if they are thinking in terms of suicide, injury, bleeding, and death. But we must not forget that they also hint at a sudden sharply delineated experience where, to be sure, one loses equilibrium but where one eventually lands on safe ground, coming from uncertain heights. It connotes a feeling that something definite has happened and is over with. Not only pain but the nature of the menstrual flow and its definite source, the regularity of the period, and the establishment of regular habits for body care at that time all add to stabilization, in contrast to previous diffuseness; to organization, in contrast to previous confusion.

Benedek[1] speaks of pain as being an integrative part of women's psychosexual experience (p. 356). She says: "It is as if menarche were a puberty rite cast upon woman by nature itself" (p. 329).

DIFFERENCES BETWEEN BOYS AND GIRLS IN PUBERTY

In contrast to girls who achieve puberty, boys who do so do not derive the same stabilizing benefit from it. Their erections as well as their ejaculations seem to them to come from nowhere, unless produced by masturbation. And even then they wonder how long the erection will last each time, how soon they will ejaculate, and how profuse the ejaculation will be. Boys give a great deal of thought to the establishment of regularity in the sexual activity of their genital organs. They are forever trying to gain control over the production of erections and ejaculations, whereas girls adapt themselves and their mode of life to what is happening regularly in their bodies. Much of the boys' preoccupation with methods of genital control becomes diverted, by crude displacement or sublimatory activity, to inventions of gadgets, push-button controls, and the creation and improvement of remote-control machines which produce a predictable quantity of material.

Boys who have not reached puberty are hampered in their experimentation and are apt to master the mystery of genital function by gross motor outlets—throwing, pushing, punching, and falling—which reproduce all variations of the mysterious activity of the penis and testicles. They don't think as much as do the boys who have reached puberty; they try out more. The road to understanding these boys lies in observation of and participation in their activities.

In puberty the gross experimentation slowly gives way to more refined methods of exploration. To some extent here too, as in menstruation in girls, ejaculation seems to structuralize the experience. A product is discharged which definitely ends the erection, either immediately or in a short time. With a certain amount of reassurance from this source, the boys in puberty have more peace of mind even though they are beset by masturbation conflicts and intense castration fears. They can grapple in thought and action with intricate problems requiring more patience than prepubertal boys can muster.

In female puberty there is less room for experimentation, less room for sublimation than we see in boys in puberty and afterward. Masturbation, with the main emphasis on exploration and experimentation, is rare in girls and frequent in boys in puberty. Similarly, intellectual curiosity wanes in girls and increases in boys at that time. In their latency years, girls pride themselves on being far better students than boys. With some variations, this state of affairs lasts through the junior-high-school years. In the last year of junior high school and in senior high school a significant change seems to take place. The once "dopey boys" now know more than the girls, can think better than the girls, and excel in mathematics and science, whereas the majority of girls are ready to acquiesce and acknowledge the boys' superiority in these subjects.

The girls may continue with their good language skills, their fine feeling for literature and poetry and for art and history. They are still conscientious about their homework. They are more settled and, despite their similar mood changes, more conservative than boys. They can use their intuition well, but they do not become adventurous experimenters. Throughout life they go on plodding along, representing the backbone of conservatism, a steadying influence, upholding the sameness of tradition, but still able to serve many masters adaptively as mothers, wives, secretaries, or teachers. They tolerate pain better than men and may even seek pain in moments of stress and uncertainty. Pain provides them with a definite relief for a surplus of varying tensions arising from fleeting and undefined stimuli for which controlled localized discharge is not always available.[22]

MENSTRUAL DISTURBANCES

To the members of the staff at Kings County Hospital who work with very neurotic and many psychotic girls having problems of delinquency and psychopathy, normal development may seem less impressive than pathological development. It may therefore be useful to focus on the irregularity in menstruation so frequently associated with emotional disturbance. This irregularity, though often the result of emotional difficulties, also contributes further to states of anxiety, depression, and disorganization of ego functions.[8]

It may be necessary to know the patient for quite some time before one becomes acquainted with her type of menstrual disturbance. Her date of menstruation may be uncertain; she may suffer from excessive pain or prolonged and profuse bleeding; she may have periods of amenorrhea. Some patients persistently ignore premenstrual and menstrual changes. They seem unable to admit the usual proneness to fatigue and the lowered resistance that come with menstruation. They may even begin to menstruate without noticing it and may not care where the blood comes from. When the denial of feminine experience, the estrangement from the happenings in their bodies, is lifted, anxiety or depression may set in. Many patients who do not suffer from menstrual irregularity have isolated the physical from the emotional experience. They are surprised to discover that their unexplained, seemingly unprovoked upsets, their tendency to get into trouble periodically, coincide either with the menstrual period itself or with the even more difficult premenstrual time.

A chart of patients' cycles reveals a high correlation between flare-ups of certain problems and hormonal changes. The irregularity of menstruation seems to be, at least in part, produced by unconscious fantasies and defensive reactions to sensations stemming from changes in the vaginal mucosa during various parts of the cycle. As noted, the irregularity, in turn, adds to anxiety, promotes fantasies, and strengthens the defensive positions. One of the signposts of improvement in a patient is the establishment of a regular and normal cycle, a regularity which foreshadows steady progress in ego organization.

The severity of pubertal problems is directly correlated to the length and extent of cycle instability so common in puberty. In turn, the menstrual irregularity is correlated to earlier development. A girl, who in earlier childhood was able to find definite, well-defined repetitive modes of discharge, invariably suffers during prepuberty from a decrease in organization of discharge modes, but, during puberty, she can recover and use the earlier patterns for reorganization on a higher level. She will have a relatively brief and easy transitional menstrual irregularity.

Conversely, the girl who, during latency, did not evidence a stable adjustment of definitely patterned repetitive modes of adaptation to inner and outer needs, in prepuberty tends to suffer from severe disorganization which sometimes continues into puberty. She may have long periods of amenorrhea, prolonged irregularity of cycle, and severe reactions to various phases of the cycle.

PHYSICAL CORRELATES TO PSYCHOLOGICAL CHANGES IN FEMININE DEVELOPMENT

Before reviewing the physical aspects of feminine development from birth to maturity, I should like to consider the paucity of data on correlation of psychological and physical phenomena prior to the attainment of a regular cycle.[1,24,30]

The genital tissues of the majority of newborn female infants manifest a transient precocity. The labia majora and minora undergo hypertrophy during the last weeks of intrauterine life and are relatively large at delivery. The vaginal epithelium is thickened and contains glycogen; a whitish discharge containing Doderlein's bacilli is present. The uterus of the newborn is congested and approximately 40 per cent heavier than that of a 1-year-old girl. There is a gradual recession of these changes over a period of 3 to 4 months.

This precocity of the infant is attributed largely to stimulations by estrogen from the mother. Prolactin, which is demonstrable in the urine of infants before and during the periods of lactation, may play a role in the frequent milk production from infants' breasts. Whether this hormone is fetal or maternal in origin is unknown. We are told that, between the third and fourth months of life until the eighth to eleventh years, sexual development is largely in abeyance. Estrogen and androgen excretions in urine are demonstrable at the age of 3, remaining more or less steady for both sexes, but with more androgen in boys and more estrogen in girls. A small increase of sex-specific hormone appears at about 7 to 8 years, and there is a gradual increase up to age 10 or 11. At this point the boys' estrogen level in the urine rises to another small peak, and then there begins a small decrease in estrogen; in girls, the estrogen level rises rapidly to a high peak, falling rapidly until age 13 to 14 and then rising abruptly again.

It is not too clear what happens in the hormonal household between 4 months and 3 years of age. It is also not known whether there is a periodic or sporadic fluctuation of hormone levels from the age of 3 on. Gonadotropin first becomes demonstrable in girls' urine at the age of 11. The menarche is associated with progressive increases in the amounts of gonadotropin and in the frequency with which it can be detected in the urine. In prepuberty the secretion of gonadotropin is sporadic, and consequently the production of estrogen is sporadic.

As the endometrium develops, it exhibits proliferative phases paralleling the ovarian estrogen cycles. Eventually, the oscillations of the estrogen levels become sufficiently pronounced to induce a vascular crisis in the endometrium, and the first menstrual period occurs. Finally, the rising peaks of estrogen production reach a level adequate to stimulate release of appreciable quantities of luteinizing hormone from the pituitary, and ovulation takes place, initiating the luteal phase of the menstrual cycle. It is believed that the release of gonadotropin in adolescence is dependent upon a neural or neurohormonal mechanism inhibited in childhood. Removal of this inhibition is thought to be dependent upon the maturation of hypothalamic centers of the nervous system, which ordinarily occurs about the turn of the first decade.

In the mature menstrual cycle, the uterus and vagina undergo definite changes which consist of a relatively long period of growth and differentiation and a short period of regression, manifested externally by menstrual bleeding. The state of the uterine mucosa is continuously changing, except for about 48 hours after menstruation has ceased. As the follicle matures, the estrogen secretion rises rapidly, and the endometrium proliferates at an increasing rate until ovulation occurs. Under the influence of progesterone, the mitotic activity ceases, and differentiation begins. The stage of premenstrual regression reflects the withdrawal of growth stimuli from the endometrium. Blood flow decreases, and the arterioles, by becoming more tortuous, accommodate themselves to the restricted space caused by the shrinking of endometrium. The stasis thus induced is held to be responsible for the necrosis of the endometrium and the weakening of the vessels, culminating in hemorrhage. Progesterone promotes a slight to moderate retention of sodium chloride and water and is, in all probability, more important than estrogen in the production of premenstrual edema. After ovulation, changes also take place in the rhythmical contractility of the uterine and tubal musculature. Not known for humans but studied in lower animals is the change in uterine motility characterized during the follicular phase by low-amplitude, high-frequency waves and a tonic type of spontaneous contraction. This rhythm alters with the changing of hormone combinations and levels.

Clinical studies by Benedek[1] established a high degree of correlation between phases of the menstrual cycle and psychological manifestations. It must be left to future research to discover what physical changes contribute to the vicissitudes of psychosexual attitudes before maturity. Whether such changes are really minimal until prepuberty and only become activated by external stimulation is difficult to ascertain, both because the available methods of testing may be too gross, and because one cannot conduct such studies without undue traumatization of the children involved. It would be feasible to explore whether the rapid differentiation in the first 4 months of life runs parallel to the decrease of phenomena of sexual precocity.

Analysis and observations of small children and reconstructive analysis of childhood experiences in adults suggest that sporadic waves of sexual excitation pervade the little girls' genitals, provoked by either inner or outer stimuli. Evidence of pleasure from genital sensations can be seen as early as the first year of life. Observable genitally derived states of excitement occur sporadically before intense genital preoccupation culminates in masturbatory experiences of the phallic and oedipal phases.

As the little girl does not have an adequate organ of discharge at her disposal, she tends to externalize her undefined primitive sensations. She seems to meet with some measure of success in the period in which she uses clitoral manipulation, producing a lightning-rod type of discharge. Although a rapid and well-defined mode of discharge offers her temporary relief, she is soon subjected again to ever-changing undefined, slow waves of excitation which seem to stem from vaginal sensations.

The little girl uses alternate ways of discharge through anal and urethral channels. The urethral pathway is chosen not only because of the proximity of the bladder to the vagina but also because changes in the vagina are associated with similar if not identical changes in the lowest part of the urethra. Deep pressure in clitoral masturbation frequently involves pressure on the distal part of the urethra. Children occasionally are able to distinguish the different sensations coming from the clitoris proper and the tissue deep underneath. The lower part of the urethra, like the lowermost portion of the vagina, is a derivative of the urogenital sinus. Both are responsive to estrogenic stimulation. In maturity the lower part of the urethra exhibits cyclic epithelial growth and cornification simultaneously with such changes occurring in the vagina. Thus this part of the urethra in itself is a source of stimulation, but it also serves as a discharge vehicle both in the pleasures of retention and elimination of urine and in the various ways of exerting pressure on the urethra through manual and pressure-of-thigh masturbation.

Many are the ways of stimulation to the vagina, and many ways of discharge are open and used simultaneously and alternately by different children and in different phases of genital needs. Direct discharge via the vaginal mucosa and musculature is rare in childhood. Seductions can enhance it. Vaginal fluor of unknown origin can act as a stimulus but may also be a method of discharge of genital sexual tension.

The multitude of stimuli of various rhythmical qualities act upon each other. Vaginal, anal, urethral, and clitoral rhythms, as well as the diverse rhythmic ministrations in physical care are added to stimuli of a kinesthetic nature which also evoke vaginal sensations. These various frequencies and intensities of stimuli sequences add to each other, combine with each other, and very frequently interrupt each other. Similarly, as the little girl uses a number of pathways for discharge both simultaneously and alternately, here, too, the discharge rhythms frequently interrupt each other. Oral, anal, urethral, clitoral, secretory, and skin discharges are used sometimes in wholesale fashion, with the resulting feeling of being flooded with stimuli and flooding the world in response. Fear of incontinence from all orifices accompanies such feelings and adds to the girl's tendency to interrupt one discharge after another.

Menarche focuses the girl's attention on one special feminine way of discharge, serving as a model for a vaginal orgastic discharge pattern. The experience of the menstrual flow enhances the synthetic function which eventually subjugates the various sources of stimuli and discharge ways to the primacy of the vagina.[12,15]

Reports of vaginal orgasm in very disturbed women, as well as mention of many vaginal orgasms following each other, seemingly contradict the foregoing thesis.[19] One wonders, however, whether such experiences are not representative of a flooding with sexual stimuli in which the vaginal sensations and partial discharges have become conscious, possibly along with conscious acknowledgment of other simultaneous or successive locations of stimulation and discharge. Psychotic women may become aware of intense sensations in the vagina, whereas neurotic women repress them. This in itself does not indicate vaginal primacy. In the rare instances when neurotic patients describe flooding with stimuli as they experience it on the analytic couch, we hear that sensations in one organ are quickly followed by sensations in another. They are retrospectively understood as waves of excitement going through the whole body, with varying wave lengths and intensities. The result is that, at some points, one organ is especially highlighted, and in the next moment there is simultaneous sensation in two or more organs. Attempts to hypercathect one organ to counteract free-flowing shifts of cathexis often produce conversion phenomena.

One such patient would become aware of vaginal sensations, then quickly wonder whether she needed to urinate or defecate, and at times oral sensations would follow. Patients with disturbances of the vaginal rhythm frequently refer to vaginal sensations as "flies, mosquitoes, birds." They seem to be describing the scattering of sensations. Their fears that, with relief, they will lose everything contained in their body betray that the stimuli have flooded the inside. In some patients only the analysis of a transitory conversion symptom leads to the understanding of the nature of their vaginal sensations. When vaginal primacy has been established, these patients are able to live through the experience of a vaginal rhythm which incorporates in one unit the various previously interfering rhythms from other organs and organ systems.

The complex adult vaginal organization presupposes a high degree of synthesis and differentiation. A preliminary basic step toward such an organization is the menarche, which paves the way for the pattern of vaginal discharge. Through frequent repetition, menstruation facilitates the specific vaginal-discharge rhythm which subordinates other rhythms to its main theme. Although a certain amount of inhibition of other excitation waves is operative in this subordination, the principal achievement of feminine genital maturity is the coordination and integration of various rhythms to a point where unity and continuity of the sexual experience are accomplished.

Not only are the various excitations from organs other than genital gathered and discharged without interrupting each other, but the simultaneous and successive excitations of different parts of the female genitals are synthesized in the same fashion. The excitability of the clitoris, urethra, labia, introitus, and the upper and lower parts of the vagina are all of a different order. During childhood, stimuli from these regions tend to jar each other rather than flow together. During successive stages of masturbatory experimentation, little girls try to focus on one or another region. If one area (most frequently the clitoris) becomes hypercathected at the expense of others for a long time, stimuli from the others undergo a lasting inhibition. At menarche this strong inhibition is suddenly disrupted, with resulting shock and disorganization. Some girls then recover the primacy of an accessory genital part and hold on to the infantile organization of dominance of the previously overcathected genital part over the vagina. This type of dominance is mainly established by inhibition.

When the childhood experiences leading to the selection of a genital part other than the vagina have been analyzed, patients go through a phase of disorganization—flooding by various stimuli accompanied by anxiety. A reorganization under vaginal dominance, which evolves during further analysis, includes the establishment of a regular menstrual cycle and the ability to adapt to changes occurring during different phases of the menstrual cycle. Still, under stress, regressive disorganization and subordination of rhythm to a pregenital level do occur.

Premenstrual edema often gives rise to such sensations as bursting, promoting anxiety, irritability, and depressive moods. The form of premenstrual reactions is determined by previous fixations; for instance, depressions are typical of women who tend to regress to the oral phase. No matter what mood changes occur premenstrually, this is the time of relative disorganization and the lowest level of adaptation in the feminine cycle. The onset of menstruation provides relief and fosters reorganization under vaginal dominance. The postmenstrual time is then used for renewed stabilization and preparation for the more intense excitations to follow in the subsequent phase of the cycle.*

Organizers of Feminine Development

Changes in adaptation during the menstrual cycle are a miniature of the happenings of the prepubertal, pubertal, and postpubertal periods. The disorganization in prepuberty is followed by a period of reorganization heralded by the menarche. The menarche acts as an organizer, as does each successive menstruation, to a lesser degree.

The turbulent pubertal phase gives the appearance of instability, as organizational attempts come in spurts and vary to the point of extremes during different parts of the adolescent menstrual cycle.[7,10] Stabilization occurs in the postadolescent stage, with the young woman consolidating her organization and preparing herself for the intense challenges of her first mature sexual experiences.

Menarche, however, is only one of the organizers in the girl's life. Another, that may even counteract the development of menarche as an organizing agent, is the girl's mother. The little girl gives up clitoral masturbation for psychological reasons, such as feminine castration fears, fears of loss of love, or deprecation of her tiny organ as compared to that of the boy. The renunciation is further facilitated by the lack of physical relief. All these factors

---

* Compare the change in uterine contractility during the follicular phase in animals mentioned on p. 40. Most likely, the rhythm of excitation in humans follows the same pattern. The excitation processes in the vagina may well be correlated to uterine contractility rhythms.

present themselves in analyses of girls, along with continual reference to the girl's mother as having encouraged one of the components over the others. Some mothers promote penis envy; others, fears of injury; still others, feelings of dissatisfaction. The influence of the mother is twofold. The mother's educational approach to the child's sexual problems is added on to the child's identification with the mother's observed attitudes toward the same sexual problems. If the mother's own solution of conflicts corresponds with the advice she offers the girl, the child is enabled to go through latency with a minimum of regressive behavior.

The girl proceeds into latency by keeping up her previously established denial of the introitus[21,22] and by reactive overcompensation of the angry feelings against her parents for not having provided a definite satisfaction for her diffuse needs. But her proneness to be quarrelsome, to have secrets, and to form cliques against one child or another betrays the continuing lack of gratification; hence the need to find a scapegoat on whom she can transfer her own feelings of inadequacy. Her successful striving for clear-cut experiences that will counteract the vagueness and diffuseness of her various needs expresses itself in her practicality, her conforming behavior, and her focusing on learning in a precise, systematic way. Here, the mother and the teacher help in the achievement of satisfaction. If guidance in terms of preciseness and definiteness is lacking, the latency girl tends to regress and has difficulties in learning.

In the prepubertal stage the young girl experiences an onrush of a greater quantity of genital excitation. She is subject to rapid changes of hormone levels, to the various internal and external stimuli stemming from the growth of different organs. Her previous latency adjustment still gives her a background of steadiness, but her new moods and her new ways of relating to others, as well as her new way of expressing herself, all betray a partial breakdown of ego organization. She tries to focus on some fad or craze (movie stars, anonymous boys, wrestling, horses, clothes, telephoning, etc.). In her great effort to find relief from tensions, she seeks pain and provokes punishment, but it fails to do the trick. At this point the mother may either promote masochistic solutions or she may help by being tolerant and encouraging structuralization of experiences.

No real intensity of affects is involved in prepubertal "crazes." The repetition and never-ending demands of the girls during such crazes mislead many parents into thinking that they are dealing with an intense experience. Furthermore, parents, especially mothers, judge the quantity of their daughters' affects by the intensity of their own disapproval of them.

Intolerance of fads facilitates masochistic solutions instead of preventing their further development. Tolerance may be used constructively. The mother who has a benevolent interest in the child's feelings for a rock-and-roll singer, for example, will help her to distinguish between his style and the features used by other types of singers. The introduction of categories thus acts as an organizer and may convert the craze into a meaningful experience in growing up.

Crazes initiated in or continued into puberty can be distinguished from prepubertal fads by the intensity of feelings and a higher integration of behavior.

When menstruation, with its relief-bringing qualities, finally arrives, the girl patterns her reactions in identification with her mother. We see the double influence of previous infantile solutions then guided by the mother and that of present maternal behavior.

The girl who has been severely traumatized by her discovery of the vaginal opening, who clings to penis envy, and maintains a homosexual libidinous position will be retraumatized by the sight of her menstruation and will tend to repeat her earlier denials of femininity. She may revert to renewed external masturbation, but more often than not she is unable to obtain relief that way because of its painful reminder that she lacks a penis.

A mother who treats menstruation as a shameful experience, a "curse," and does not, except by lip service, foster the pride of growing up and being a woman, disrupts the girl's budding efforts at feminine organization and promotes regressive behavior. Most frequently, the mother's earlier behavior is continued at the time of menarche, thus consolidating previously established fixations. A girl who, in identification with her masochistic mother, has already established a martyr complex, will exploit her menarche masochistically, magnifying and enjoying the unpleasant aspect of menstruation rather than deriving relief from the clarity of the new experience.

One type of girl, influenced by an ever-dissatisfied, nagging mother, holds onto the lack of satisfaction, to the diffuseness and fragmentation of excitation and discharge, because she identifies excitement with possession of precious goods which she is afraid to lose. She envies her mother's ability to maintain the upper hand by continuously flowing excitement. She avoids clear-cut discharge. She is forever excited, without reaching an orgasm or real achievement in other areas. She mistakes continuous excitement for aliveness and vivacity. She misuses the stimulations of the menstrual and premenstrual periods to gain and retain more excitement. Her fixation lies in the early oral-anal period of greed and hoarding where grabbing and holding onto everything dominate behavior.

Another type, given to depressions and even suicide in reaction to premenstrual and sometimes menstrual experiences, belongs to the group of oral sadistic disorders. In some of these girls premenstrual feelings of swelling evoke intense biting responses. Others react to the sight of menstrual blood with cannibalistic fantasies. (Cannibalistic tendencies are evidenced to a small extent in normal development, as remainders of an archaic reaction to the sight of blood.) Schmideberg[29] pointed out that oral sadistic impulses of the menstrual period are influenced by the girl's oral sadistic interpretations of the primal scene. In all these cases the mother's oral behavior—and here we must lay special stress not only on eating and feeding behavior but also on speech and choice of words—paves the way through identification for oral sadistic solutions. The seemingly enlightened girls who are unable to use the information given to them often report that their mothers, by their tone of voice and choice of words, have given away the fact that they themselves do not believe what they are explaining. Many mothers, by such subtle means, convey to their daughters their own fears and fantasies concerning menstruation.

Amenorrhea with conversion symptoms, amenorrhea of the anal retaining type, masochistically tinged dysmenorrhea, and menstrual irregularity produced by an omnipotent wish to gain control over the timing of physical events are but a few of the other variations in pathology. Stunting of the development of maternal feelings as well as violent wishes for pregnancy, fantasies of oral impregnation, of having a child with one of the parents—all these play a role in menstrual disturbances and difficulties in accepting the menarche. Increase of masochism in reaction to menstruation, instead of greater pain tolerance, seems not to be part of a normal feminine development but, rather, a continuation of prepubertal characteristics.

Girls who think of menstruation as a nuisance show a tendency toward tolerance of unpleasure. Those who change markedly after menarche, establish regularity soon, and become steady within the limits of their cycles, also accept their inner reproductive organs and the mode of vaginal rhythm. They adjust to changing bodily stimulations, being more energetic before ovulation, more passive after, excited premenstrually, relieved with menstruation, and quiescent for a short time thereafter.[1] This continuous readjustment to inner needs becomes a model for adapting to the changing needs of their future husbands and children of different ages and different sexes.

A discussion of the roles of defloration, pregnancy, and childbirth, as well as the role of husband and children as organizers of feminine development, is beyond the scope of this chapter. The roles of the father and siblings in early feminine development seem to be subordinated to the mother's influence. The way she reacts to the rest of the family in relation to herself and in relation to her daughter will have a lasting influence upon the child. It is important to note that successful adjustability, although governed by the models of changing inner rhythms, is possible only where a flexible mother image provides the model from outside.

SUMMARY

Menarche is presented as an organizer in feminine development. Diffuse prepubertal behavior is contrasted with the more sharply delineated pubertal organization. Feminine masochism, usually intensified after menarche, is considered normal where it leads to pain tolerance and appreciation of the relief qualities of sharp sensations. Attitudes toward menarche are described as determined by earlier infantile solutions, the identification with the mother being the guidepost in the establishment of early and present solutions. It is stressed that the mother acts throughout development as the organizer from the outside, providing models for organizing of stimuli stemming from the inside.

REFERENCES

1. BENEDEK, T. *Studies in Psychosomatic Medicine. Psychosexual Functions in Women.* New York, The Ronald Press Company, 1952.
2. BLOS, P. Preadolescent drive organization. *J. Am. Psychoanalyt. Assoc.* 6: 47, 1958.

3. CHADWICK, M. Menstruationsangst. *Ztschr. Psychoan. Paed.* 5: 184, 1931.
4. DALY, C. D. Zu meinen Arbeiten über die weiblichen Tabu-Vorschriften. *Ztschr. Psychoan. Paed.* 5: 225, 1931. (See also previous papers by same author cited there.)
5. DEUTSCH, H. *Psychoanalyse der Weiblichen Sexualfunktionen.* Internat. Psych. Verlag, 1925.
6. DEUTSCH, H. *Psychology of Women.* New York, Grune & Stratton, Inc., 1944.
7. EISSLER, K. "Notes on Problems of Technique in the Psychoanalytic Treatment of Adolescents," in *The Psychoanalytic Study of the Child.* New York, International Universities Press, Inc., 1958, vol. 13, pp. 223–253.
8. FENICHEL, O. *The Psychoanalytic Theory of Neuroses.* New York, W. W. Norton & Company, Inc., 1945.
9. FRAIBERG, S. "Some Considerations in the Introduction to Therapy in Puberty," in *The Psychoanalytic Study of the Child.* New York, International Universities Press, Inc., 1955, vol. 10, pp. 264–286.
10. FREUD, A. *The Ego and the Mechanisms of Defense.* London, Hogarth Press, Ltd., 1937.
11. FREUD, A. "Adolescence," in *The Psychoanalytic Study of the Child.* New York, International Universities Press, Inc., 1958, vol. 13, pp. 255–268.
12. FREUD, S. "Three Essays on the Theory of Sexuality," in *Standard Edition.* London, Hogarth Press, Ltd., 1953, vol. 7.
13. FREUD, S. *Das Tabu der Virginität. Gesammelte Werke.* London, Imago Publishing Co., vol. 12.
14. FREUD, S. *Das Oekonomische Problem des Masochismus. Ibid.,* 1924, vol. 5.
15. FREUD, S. "Female Sexuality," in *Collected Papers.* London, Hogarth Press, Ltd., 1950, vol. 5.
16. FREUD, S. *New Introductory Lectures on Psychoanalysis.* New York, W. W. Norton & Company, Inc., 1933.
17. GELEERD, E. "Some Aspects of Psychoanalytic Technique in Adolescents," in *The Psychoanalytic Study of the Child.* New York, International Universities Press, Inc., 1957, vol. 12, pp. 263–283.
18. GREENACRE, P. "The Prepuberty Trauma in Girls," in *Trauma, Growth and Personality.* New York, W. W. Norton & Company, Inc., 1952, pp. 204–223.
19. GREENACRE, P. "Special Problems of Early Female Sexual Development," *ibid,* pp. 237–258.
20. HORNEY, K. Die Praemenstruaellen Verstimmungen. *Ztschr. Psychoan. Paed.* 5: 161, 1931.
21. HORNEY, K. The denial of the vagina. *Internat. J. Psycho-Analysis.* 14: 57, 1933.
22. KESTENBERG, J. S. Vicissitudes of female sexuality. *J. Am. Psychoanalyt. Assoc.* 4: 453, 1956.
23. KLEIN, M. *The Psychoanalysis of Children.* London, Hogarth Press, Ltd., 1937.
24. KROGER, W. S., and FREED, S. C. *Psychosomatic Gynecology.* Philadelphia, W. B. Saunders Co., 1951.

25. LANDAUER, K. Menstruationserlebniss des Knaben. *Ztschr. Psychoan. Paed.* 5: 175, 1931.
26. MENG, H. Pubertaet und Pubertaetaufklearung. *Ibid.*, p. 167.
27. PFEFFER, E. Menstruation und Aufklearung. *Ibid.*, p. 203.
28. PIPAL, K. Wie es bei Hansi war. *Ibid.*, p. 221.
29. SCHMIDEBERG, M. Psychoanlytisches zur Menstruation. *Ibid.*, p. 190.
30. TALBOT, N., SOBEL, E., MCARTHUR, J., and CRAWFORD, J. *Functional Endocrinology.* Cambridge, Mass., Harvard University Press, 1952.

chapter 4 Masturbation Conflicts

MARJORIE HARLEY

The following remarks are in no way intended to encompass the whole of the subject of adolescent masturbation but merely reflect some random thoughts which have been stimulated by observations derived from my clinical experience and which, in large measure, tally with findings already reported by others. In general, my material has tended toward organization around problems arising from too early and intense stimulation of the genital zone and some of the implications of this for ego-libidinal development at adolescence.

Problems of masturbation* may be said to play a central role in all three of the age groups which we encounter in child analysis: prelatency, latency, and adolescence. The focus of this discussion is on adolescence, which, in one important sense, is a maturational stage, momentous and dramatic in its own right, and containing its own unique properties, many of which we do not as yet sufficiently understand. But, in another and equally important sense, adolescence bears the imprint of all that has preceded and is inevitably weighted by past experience. For this reason it would seem fitting to begin with some introductory comments pertaining to the role of masturbation in the patterning of those genetic configurations which emerge from earlier developmental levels.

The plexus of heightened bodily feelings and intricate mental contents which the term "masturbation" generally connotes is a point of intersection of much that is of consequence for the child's future psychic development. It may intensify confusions in respect to his body engram and thus further distortions in one of the most fundamental areas of his sense of identity,[16] or it may accentuate his feeling of self, as expanding genital sensations give rise to a

* Unless otherwise indicated, I have limited my use of the term "masturbation" to auto-erotic activities which involve self-manipulation of the genital zone.

51

heightened awareness of his own endogenous forces. It may contribute to his contamination of object relations through the persistence of anachronistic sexual aims and fantasies, or it may pave the way for love relationships, in adulthood, based on mature genital functioning. It may establish patterns for inhibition or other disturbances of thought processes which may severely restrict his ego functioning in work and play, or it may give impetus to his imaginative powers which, as ego maturation proceeds, may then combine and harmonize with the substance and demands of outerworld reality toward the realization of high intellectual achievement.

Auto-erotic activities during infancy and early childhood, involving the various erogenous zones, may be said to reflect the growing organism's collaboration with maturational pressures toward ego-libidinal progression as well as its attempts toward self-regulation of instinctual excitations. In this sense, auto-erotic practices are not only the child's prerogative but an essential accompaniment to his sound ego-instinctual development. On the other hand, it is commonly known that, under certain conditions and in certain forms, auto-erotism may be an indicator, if not an abettor, of fixations, regressions,* and/or other irregularities in ego and libidinal development. Whether auto-erotic activities promote or impede progression will depend on a number of interacting factors which must be assessed within the context of developmental and maturational expectancy and among which may be numbered: (1) the measure of success or failure in the child's transition from primary narcissism to object love, (2) the course of his subsequent relationships to his love objects (which obviously has an intimate bearing on the problem of narcissistic versus object-libidinal trends), (3) the ratio of stimulus intensity to capacity for satisfactory discharge, and (4) the extent to which the dominant zonal outlet within a given period coincides with the maturational sequences of phase ascendancy.

Already in infancy the genital zone is potentially a sensitive and responsive center for erogenous arousal, and awareness of genital sensations as well as some self-manipulation of the genitals more often than not occur before the advent of the phallic phase. In his

---

* By this I do not wish to imply that development moves steadily forward in a straight line and thereby to discount those instances of regression (in certain areas and at certain periods) which normally are to be expected and which actually may facilitate progression. I refer, rather, to those types of regression which outweigh progressive growth forces and which thus are detrimental to development.

Three Essays on the Theory of Sexuality,[12] which remains the cornerstone of our understanding of psychosexual development, Freud notes an initial phase of infantile masturbation during the period of oral primacy, that is, in the first year of life, when: "The anatomical situation of this [genital] region, the secretions in which it is bathed, the washing and rubbing to which it is subjected in the course of a child's toilet, as well as accidental stimulation (such as the movement of intestinal worms in the case of girls), make it inevitable that the pleasurable feeling which this part of the body is capable of producing should be noticed by children even during their earliest infancy and should give rise to a need for its repetition" (pp. 187–188). It has become a matter of fairly common observation that, by the second half of his first year, the infant has not only discovered the existence of his genital but is aware of the pleasurable sensations which it evokes, and he generally includes it in his tactile play with his own body.

Although Freud does not specifically explain what he describes as the early disappearance of this "first period of infantile masturbation," the implication is that it is largely the result of the subsequent organization of libido around the adjacent anal zone. Certainly, in the anal phase, instinctual tensions are less diffuse and achieve a greater specificity as anal excitations are brought more sharply into focus by the child's attempts toward sphincter mastery. In view of the fluidity between zonal outlets in the young child, as well as the particular susceptivity of the genital zone, it is not surprising that some genital play also may transpire during the anal phase and that, obviously, this need not be regarded as a developmental deviation. But, in the usual course of events, that is, when libidinal development is in step with maturational preparedness, during the pregenital era the genitals serve as accessory rather than principal organs for tension-discharge processes, and (allowing, of course, for the usual overlapping of libidinal phases) the main force of the libidinal current is borne first by the oral and later by the anal zones.

With the onset of the phallic phase, ego development normally has arrived at that point where object relations have attained considerable value in and of themselves. The genital zone is maturationally equipped to assume the leading erogenous role; bodily and psychic experiences acquire a new texture and enter into new organizations. Genital as well as persisting pregenital strivings are woven into the patterning of the oedipal constellation, and bodily excitations and their associated psychic contents are released through genital masturbation which now "represents the executive agency of the whole of infantile sexuality . . . " (Ref. 12, footnote, p. 189). As such, it provides the focal anchorage for the unavoidable oedipal conflicts with their concomitants of hostility, anxiety and guilt, as well as the center from which may emanate those derivative dreams of glory and fulfillment and their accompanying feelings of confidence and liberated vital energy.

Although originally Freud[12] postulated that the primacy of the genital organs was arrived at in childhood at best only very incompletely, he later revised this view, indicating his belief that infantile genital organization " . . . comes little short of that reached in maturity . . . " (p. 245),[11] since, to a large extent, component instincts already are subordinated to genital dominance. This means that the phallic-oedipal period represents that maturational phase in which the foundations of genital organization are laid down, and it has long been a truism that the degree of strength and stability of these foundations will have a determining influence on the measure of the adolescent's ability to meet and integrate the increased instinctual pressures which have their physiological basis in the growth processes of puberty.* It is just as obvious that, with the revival at puberty of infantile sexual strivings (which seems to be the necessary prelude to the final renunciation of infantile love objects and to the attainment of mature genital functioning), those psychic factors which weakened genital development in childhood will again come into play with full intensity to impede the adolescent phase of ego-libidinal progression.

The fact that it is generally between the ages of 5 and 6 that the child partially resolves and represses his Oedipus complex, and turns away from his infantile incestuous involvements, is in accord with certain maturational advances which help to equip him for this first major extension of his horizons beyond his immediate family into the society of his school and his peers. Essential body functions and the fundamentals of speech and locomotion are well mastered. The pronounced leap in cognitive development

---

* In some instances, and when these are not too severe, infantile sexual conflicts may be spontaneously resolved in the course of the structural dissolutions and reorganizations which occur at adolescence,[4] especially when this process combines with favorable reality experiences; in other instances, infantile conflicts of a relatively mild nature, which otherwise might not have impeded psychic development to any considerable extent, may provide the basis for the traumatic effect of untoward happenings at this particularly vulnerable time of life.

which now takes place contributes to the child's greater capacity and wider range for the deflection of primary instinctual strivings toward learning, acquisition of skills, and other ego-dominated activities. This is the time when we anticipate a decrease in instinctual urgencies and when we expect structural development to proceed at a fairly steady and even rate. On the one hand, it is the child's attempts toward renunciation of his oedipal wishes which mark his forward movement into this new era; on the other, his capacity to achieve this partial renunciation in one sense may be said to be commensurate with the extent to which he has been able to allow his positive oedipal development to unfold.

A successful phallic-oedipal phase of development involves processes of balance and counterbalance. More specifically, it presupposes an ego strong enough to meet and assimilate the intense biological urges which now seek genital (phallic) expression, to achieve sufficient confidence in one's own sexual identity to withstand the tension of castration anxiety and to offset negative oedipal strivings. It is primarily when his positive oedipal wishes have remained active and unrepressed for some time, when he has experienced a basically tender and affectionate relationship with his parents which mitigates his hostility and anxiety, when he has been able to tolerate the frustration of his ungratified infantile desires, and when he feels some promise that these will one day find fulfillment through substitute objects that the child is the more able to contemplate their deferment and to accept himself as a child within the society of children.

As part of the patterning of a favorable phallic-oedipal constellation such as this, the child's masturbatory activities embody those progressive forces which ultimately prevail over the regressive pulls activated by the ubiquitous anxieties of this crucial period. In its positive sense, masturbation not only provides bodily and psychic outlets for the combined tensions of genital excitations and ungratified oedipal wishes but, in addition, affirms and fortifies a fundamental awareness of the power of self and self-forces with which the child may combat his corresponding feelings of uncertainty, inferiority, and vulnerability. There is naturally something vital and impelling about whatever flows and expands, and genital sensations give rise to resilient and capacious feelings as well as to perplexities and apprehensions; to fantasy content in which object-libidinal trends predominate, and noble dreams of just attainment counteract themes of vengeful conquest and the dread of retaliation.

Following the rhythm of instinctual urges, periods of perturbation and mounting tension alternate with the rebalancing of energies; with the renewed ability to withstand the frustrations imposed by reality and to enjoy those acceptable gratifications which it offers. Thus will be avoided the dangers inherent, on the one hand, in the abrupt shutting off of appropriate bodily channels for instinctual discharge and in sudden and massive repressions, or, on the other, in the overreadiness to use masturbatory activities too much for solace and retreat from an unsatisfying and threatening reality. Instead, the child's preparedness to sacrifice his forbidden wishes and to oppose his instinctual demands for direct gratification will be the sounder because it has been attained gradually.

It is also under such conditions that the child is more likely to enter latency with the genital being the leading erogenous zone, with a sufficiently firm core of inner identity to permit the continuation of those partial identifications so essential to superego modification and enrichment, and with the nuclear image of his ego ideal based on identification with the parent of the same sex. Situated as it is between two critical epochs, that is, the oedipal phase and adolescence, and because it is a period of relative quiescence, we may tend sometimes to underestimate the significance of latency for the final outcome of psychic development. In one sense, the society of the latency child may be said to be a proving ground in that it provides a miniature culture within which he finds his place among his fellow citizens, and in which he may develop his sense of competence and intellectual powers, his self-critical faculties, and his own internal controls, thus adding dimensions to his awareness of his separate and independent identity. Although the child still maintains his basic reliance on his parents for protection and comfort, they partially lose the aggrandized aura with which he endowed them during his preschool years. Simultaneously, he selects and absorbs values of the other adults with whom he now comes into contact. These important strides in structural development, that is, ego growth and expansion through intellectual exploration and experimentation, extended object relationships and stabilization of the sense of identity; and superego additions, revisions, and further internalization form fundamental psychic equipment with which to meet the increased pressures of puberty and to implement the structural reorganizations which must follow the structural dissolutions generally taking place at this time.

It would be a mistake to assume that the instinctual life of the latency child has become completely dormant. Rather, as a result of superego demands, of decreased instinctual pressures, and of increased ego capacities, instinctual energy is used to a greater extent for purposes other than directly instinctual ones. The child now resists masturbation because it is the bearer of the instinctual gratifications and of the forbidden oedipal wishes which he is struggling to renounce; derivative masturbation fantasies undergo a greater transformation, attain further distance from their original sources, and find expression in more reality-directed daydreams, imaginative play, and creative productions. In accordance with these maturational and developmental processes, masturbation usually occurs far less frequently in latency, although its complete cessation well may be an inauspicious exception rather than the rule. In addition, it is quite possible that individual variations, based on innate sensitivities and bodily responsiveness to stimulation, should be taken into account in assessing whether the latency child's masturbatory activities exceed the amount of breakthroughs we normally would expect. Nonetheless, persistence of intense instinctual pressures in latency and a concomitant inability to free aggressive energy for ego growth are usually an indication that the phallic-oedipal phase has been unsuccessfully weathered* and that structural development, to a greater or less degree, will be impaired.

There is fairly general agreement that the genetic determinants in masturbation problems of the phallic phase often cannot be fully understood in the light of experiences encountered in the phallic-oedipal period alone. In this connection, Berta Bornstein, for example, remarks: "We should bear in mind that at the height of anal erotism, the child's ego is sufficiently developed so that he can perceive and identify with the parents' attitudes. The child will carry forward this identification into the phallic phase in an inflexible form; and he will tend to judge in later life his genital activity in terms of his parents' attitude toward his anal erotism" (p. 77).[2] Anna Freud, in turn, suggests that " . . . the possibility remains that phallic masturbation, as the latest of them [that is, auto-erotic activities], becomes invested with and 'covers' the high emotional value of all the other activities which were its equiva-

---

* This statement does not take into account specific seductions occurring during the latency period, which naturally would tend to upset the child's still-percarious ego-instinctual balance.

lents in the early phases" (p. 27).[6] Both these statements point to the importance of pregenital determinants in masturbation conflicts. They would seem, however, to refer to situations in which the usual order of phase sequence has been adhered to and, therefore, in which genital masturbation, in the main, coincides with the advent of the phallic phase.

Although Freud[12] clearly states that the order in which the libidinal phases become active seems to be phylogenetically determined, he adds that variations in temporal sequence of phases may occur, and that such variations must have a decisive influence on the final outcome of libidinal organization. Bornstein,[1] in one of her earlier papers, reports an analysis of a young child who was forced into premature genital arousal during the anal phase. She suggests that this child's excessive sexual excitations, even though arising from a genital source, normally would have been discharged through the anal zone had it not been for certain untoward events which had effected a premature anal repression. As I understand it, then, Bornstein's explanation rests not so much on the source of the instinctual excitations, or on the quantitative factor involved, as on the availability of the phase-specific zonal outlet for discharge purposes.

Taking the quantitative factor as well as the particular susceptivity of the genital zone into account, Greenacre[14,15] has drawn attention to the occurrence of too early and intense genital arousal, sometimes even long before the onset of the phallic phase, so that the immature organism is inevitably subjected to undue strain. Greenacre notes that, although this premature genital stimulation may be specific in origin, it also may result from extremely severe or repeated traumata which produce a massive stimulation, causing genital excitation in excess of the organism's maturational preparedness and leading to a precocious but perilous genital development. These traumatic stimulations may arise from severe oral stress, too early toilet training and/or the giving of enemas, early and repeated exposure to primal scenes, etc. Greenacre further observes certain effects of such premature genital arousal on future ego-libidinal development, among which are: (1) an increased narcissism due to the extreme anxiety which is evoked by the disparity between these states of excessive inner excitations and the immature ego's ability to contain them, and which prolongs the tendency toward primary rather than partial identifications; (2) the resultant heightening of bisexual strivings which not only lends an added increment to later castration problems in both sexes but which also contributes to confusions of self-identity; (3) distortions of the oedipal constellation, and hence an intensification of the oedipal problems, which tend to arise as a corollary of these earlier disturbances. It is within the context of Freud's general emphasis on the far-reaching consequences of libidinal dislocations when the usual course of maturational phase ascendancy has been interrupted, together with Greenacre's specific observations in this regard, that I shall report some of my clinical findings.

I have been impressed by these particular ways in which too early and repeated genital stimulation may tell on the character of masturbation-centered conflicts at adolescence: (1) the adverse effects of this overgreat ego-instinctual imbalance and the related oedipal anomalies on structural development during latency; (2) the intense instinctual pressures which often persist throughout latency, coupled with the sense of ungovernability and vulnerability which continues to be associated with genital arousal; and (3) the ensuing strong resistance against the maturational demands for acceptance and integration of genitality at adolescence, with frequently greater-than-average pulls toward asceticism or perversion.

My observations have been derived from the analyses of a number of children in whom the analytic evidence pointing to the occurrence within the first 2 years of life of this early and repeated genital arousal seemed convincing, although in only two cases were confirmatory reports from the parents obtainable. For the most part, the premature genital stimulation could be linked to severe oral and/or anal stress in combination with recurrent exposures to primal scenes; and in only two cases was there any indication of a possibly direct genital seduction.

Before proceeding I would underscore that, although I have singled out this one factor of premature genital stimulation for discussion, its significance lies in the ways in which it combines with other forces and conditions of experience: in the group of adolescents to be referred to, the early genital arousal was but one, albeit a major one, of several determinants which impeded ego-libidinal development. I would also add, parenthetically, that in the majority of these cases the early traumata, in so far as they could be reconstructed, seemed not to have been more severe than those encountered in other patients and which seem not to have

resulted in this genital overstimulation. This suggests the possibility that the genital precocity of these particular children may
have been due, in part, to an innate sensitivity expressible in both
bodily and psychic terms.

Perhaps one of the most far-reaching effects of premature genital
arousal may be viewed from the angle of the overload of destructive
aggression which is simultaneously mobilized and which inevitably
tends to further the organization of genitality along sadomasochistic
lines. A related factor is that, since the genital zone is activated
under conditions of *pregenital* zonal ascendancy, and often in connection with specific *pregenital* zonal stress, it initially bears a kind
of part-to-whole relationship to the oral and/or anal zones so that
the genital strivings, themselves, thus may embody much of the
primitive character of the pregenital strivings with which they are
linked both by the excessive and concurrent sensory stimulation
and by the common endeavor toward discharge.

When we take these combined factors into account—that is, on
the instinctual side, greater-than-average bisexual strivings, a
heightened readiness for genital stimulation (probably in large
measure attributable to the intense somatic manifestations of the
original stimulation*), with a surplus of primitive aggression per-
force ignited by genital arousal; on the ego side, a basic and abid-
ing sense of helplessness and uncontrollability in the face of genital
stimulation, an oscillating sense of identity, and an insufficiently
developed capacity for object relations—we can readily see how
the child will be ill equipped to meet and assimilate the new arrangements of the phallic-oedipal phase. The (positive) oedipal
attachment, although frequently clung to with a desperate intensity, is lacking in the quality of a stable *object* relationship
owing to the overreadiness to utilize primitive identification processes in the service of both instinctual strivings and defense. In
addition, the oedipal object may assume singularly dangerous proportions, serving both as a target for the child's highly erotized
aggression and as a destructive, retaliatory figure, often seeming to
be more threatening than the oedipal rival. Defensive shifts toward
the parent of the same sex will then ensue, these likewise proving
to be an inadequate solution, since they also entail these tendencies
toward primitive identification and consequent loss of the very
identity which the child is struggling to preserve. With so tenuous
an anchorage to the phallic-oedipal position, any untoward event
which the child now encounters may prove to be traumatic and

* Cf. Freud,[12] footnote, p. 242.

may weight the precarious balance on the side of regressive pulls. In extreme instances the phallic-oedipal phase may be so prematurely abandoned as to find little vital expression until puberty.

Within such a setting, masturbation obviously may encompass a variety of individual psychic patternings which form a crucial chapter in the history of genital disturbances emerging at adolescence. Among its more general characteristics is the fact that the genital sensations of the phallic phase, which these children seem to experience with particular intensity, are apt to reinstate the feelings of helplessness and uncontrollability earlier linked with genital arousal, and to lend added force to the destructive elements which tend to permeate masturbation fantasies. Another characteristic is that, frequently, the proclivity for primary identification and the related bisexual problems vitiate the affirmation of self and self-forces which, under more auspicious circumstances, constitutes one of the positive aspects of masturbation. Instead, the child may view his genital feelings not so much as arising from within himself as deriving from the other, a fantasy which he often will perpetuate in the service of his bisexual strivings and for defensive purposes because of the dangers associated with genital activity. This denial of one's own genital forces may receive an added reinforcement when the original stimulation has occurred especially early, that is, when the demarcation between self and object was still incomplete. A third characteristic is that the unsatisfactory nature of the child's object relations may result in an overreadiness to use masturbation for consolation and withdrawal, for the nursing of grievances and for the enhancement of compensatory omnipotence fantasies. But, in such instances, because of the surplus of destructive aggression which enters into the genital strivings, the anxiety and guilt components are greatly increased, and tensions are thus more perpetuated than relieved. Or, and again to cite from more extreme examples, castration anxiety may be so painfully accentuated as to cause a massive repression or denial of genital strivings and a total retreat to regressive forms of auto-erotic activities.

It is easily understandable that, when the course of the phallic-oedipal phase has been so disrupted, the basic categories of psychic structure will likewise be impaired, and the usual latency gains will be, to greater or less degree, forfeited. The prohibitive aspects of superego will be too strongly saturated with sadistic components and lacking in those nuclear elements of clemency which facilitate its increasing internalization; ego ideal will tend to consist too massively of the omnipotence values ascribed to the parental figures—frequently the parent of the opposite sex, in particular. Tendencies toward primary rather than partial identifications will impede ego-superego differentiation, with superego remaining too much a part of ego proper rather than comprising a separate psychic system. Overtly or covertly, the child still will be bound to his incestuous objects by hate and resentments and will be limited in his capacity both to form stable object relationships and to extend their range. The surplus of destructive aggression will interfere with the deflection of aggressive energy toward ego growth and expansion; ego activities will tend to be overinstinctualized and curtailed. The child probably will fail to attain that respite from instinctual urgencies which is the usual accompaniment of the latency years; and masturbation (which, in this context, often proves to be compulsive) and/or its regressive equivalents may continue in latency with little abatement and sometimes even with increased intensity. Tensions may be further discharged through provocative acting out aimed at drawing parent, parent substitute, or analyst into a sadomasochistic partnership. In other instances the child may present a relatively smooth exterior, but this picture may reflect, in a sense, the negative of acting out, in that inner pressures are held in uneasy abeyance by inhibitory and friable defenses which narrow the field of interests and hinder the full use of intellectual powers. The persistence of severe castration problems are frequently discernible in the boy's marked passive strivings and their associated anxieties, and in the girl's greater-than-average penis envy, more often than not accompanied by strenuous efforts toward the preservation of the illusory phallus.

When the latency period has been characterized by such comparatively undiminished instinctual pressures, and gains in structural development have been so limited, one might expect particularly turbulent structural upheavals to accompany the instinctual changes of puberty, so that the ego is overrun by instinctual strivings, and impulsive behavior of rather severe proportions is produced. Undoubtedly, this expectation is frequently realized. I have been, however, especially interested to observe a tendency toward the reverse process: often, constriction, constraint, and withdrawal may replace the tempestuous behavior of latency; or, in other instances, a tightening rather than loosening of the inhibiting and restricting latency defenses may occur. But, especially within the transference situation, these self-imposed restraints sooner or later are apt to break down, with sexual tensions acted out periodically through provocative, sadomasochistic behavior. That this acting out is a masturbatory equivalent is readily discernible in the rhythm of mounting tension which accompanies these states. It is equally apparent that it also frequently involves the projection of the insufficiently internalized and sadistic superego onto the analyst, with the paradoxical aims of eliciting his prohibition of the sexual excitement which is felt to be uncontrollable from within, and of inciting his participation in this very excitement. Thus the sexual gratification derived from the sadomasochistic relationship between ego and superego is now, by means of this superego externalization, sought through the analyst. On the other hand, instead of direct masturbatory activities increasing or being reinstated at adolescence, there may tend to be a decrease and sometimes even complete cessation of masturbation, with a reversion to, or an intensification of, regressive substitutes. It would seem that the pubertal child must erect especially strong barriers against the increased genital pressures, which now emerge as a maturational event, and cling tenaciously to pregenital psychic configurations and the related oedipal anomalies as a defense against the positive oedipal strivings, which are now activated, and the resultant aggravation of castration dangers. It would further seem, however, that the more fundamental and engulfing danger lies in the fact that the upsurge of genitality evokes a correlative magnification of the feelings of helplessness and uncontrollability linked to the original genital stimulation—feelings which, in turn, give added force to the dangers inherent in the more specific, sexual fantasies.

Frequently, the boy's passivity becomes more rather than less pronounced, this picture differing from the more usual one in which a thrust of active, masculine behavior eclipses rather than resolves the underlying bisexual problem, which then reappears when the intensified genital pressures of puberty subside.[5] Two of my boy patients precipitated overt passive homosexual experiences in prepuberty,* while the third, after a period in which he had repudiated all sexual strivings, barely avoided the acting out of his homosexual temptations during adolescence. A common and basic aim

---

* As with Greenacre's female patients,[14] this precipitation of a "prepuberty trauma" in one sense served as a defense against entering into the struggles evoked by the sexual demands of puberty.

contained in the homosexual fantasies of all these patients was the
redemption of the disclaimed phallic forces through identification
with the active, masculine partner.[8,21] A coexisting and dominant
masturbation theme centered around the persisting, preoedipal
image of the phallic mother, with feminine identification reflecting, therefore, not only the desire for the passive-receptive role
but for the attainment of the ultimate in strength and power. One
15-year-old boy, who had abandoned all genital activity during
the phallic phase, finally resumed masturbation in the advanced
stage of the adolescent phase of his analysis. At first, he could
carry out the masturbatory act only by means of the fantasy that
his genital sensations derived not from his own body but from
someone else: on one level, from his father, but, on a deeper level,
from his mother, who would provide him with the phallic strength
which he dared not claim in and through himself, and who also
would assume its control—a control which he felt unequipped, himself, to exert.

Under such conditions, masturbation tends to emphasize confusions of identity in that the underlying fantasies are replete with
conflicting sexual identifications in which the primary distinction
between the sexes is, itself, fluctuating and blurred. In fact it is
now, that is, at adolescence, that problems of identity which are
related to the early genital disturbances may become particularly
evident in both sexes. Ordinarily, we anticipate that the adolescent's self-image, rooted as it is in the body image, will be shaken
as body contours change, as secondary sex characters develop, and
as he experiences strange and unpredictable feelings which he can
neither fully comprehend nor regulate. With these cases, however,
the identity problems are of more fundamental and greater severity,
proceeding from the early and extreme bisexual conflicts, and
augmented by the residual drags toward primitive identifications
which are now reinforced by the heightened castration anxiety.
Personal relationships, therefore, often may be shunned not only
because of homosexual and heterosexual dangers but also because
of the threat of loss of identity which these primitive identification processes carry. On the other hand, the latter may be used as
a powerful resistance against analyzing the specificities of less
archaic centers of conflict, especially those involving castration
themes.

The nexus of uncontrollable feelings and fantasies which derive
from these early and untoward genital experiences sometimes also

may be detected in those inhibitions in learning, or interferences with learning processes, which frequently may become more acute, or for the first time discernible, at puberty, and which commonly result from the displacement of masturbation conflicts onto the intellectual sphere. Particularly because of the surplus of destructive components contained in the genital strivings, there may be an undercathexis of intellectual activities rather than their over-libidinization which so often occurs among adolescents. A 14-year-old girl, whose latency period had been marked by compulsive masturbation, accompanied by terrifying sadomasochistic fantasies connected with her severe castration complex, put it in these terms: "I'm afraid if I were to get interested in any of my school subjects I wouldn't be able to stop studying; it would control me." And, as a 15-year-old boy (see also p. 64) remarked: "If I were to really involve myself in my work, the work would become stronger than me and cause terrible disaster." This same boy, at a later point in his analysis, expressed the fantasy that, if he allowed himself full sensations in his penis, these would "sweep" him "away like a hurricane," and threaten himself and others with destruction. Also, when one's own genital forces have been disclaimed, and the fantasy that these arise from the other has been retained, any intellectual success may be regarded as undeserved, as an opportune accident, or as the result of a "borrowed" or "stolen" ability, so that, with each new intellectual task, there may be a renewed fear of failure, related both to the feeling of lack of inherent intellectual powers and to the guilt arising from the past "illegally" attained successes.

In other instances, disturbances in memory may be linked to the original traumatic experiences. For example, a 13-year-old girl was beset with the obsessional thought: "How do I know that what I remember is actually what I have read [that is, *seen*]?" This brooding (in itself obviously a masturbatory substitute) could be traced back to her uncertainty as to the reality of her early perceptions of primal scenes which she had witnessed between her nurse and a man servant. These repeated stimulating experiences had occurred during the child's second year when this same nurse (later committed to a mental institution) had subjected the child to severe toilet training, combined with teasing methods of weaning which had consisted of forcible removal of the bottle after a few token swallows.

A boy, whose compulsive masturbation during latency was accompanied by pronounced masochistic fantasies and whose puberty was marked at first by a total avoidance of masturbation, developed the fear that he would forget his history lessons—a fear which, in some measure, he managed to realize. The central theme of these masturbation fantasies had been that he was at the mercy of both men and women who would torture and disfigure him in various ways and then abandon him on a treadmill, while they became absorbed in their own conversation. Meanwhile, the speed of the treadmill would increase with his mounting genital excitement, but he "could get nowhere." The culminating scene involved the administration by one of his victimizers (generally a woman) of a particular kind of enema which would cause him to forget the terrifying aspects of his masturbation so that he would not refrain from repeating it over and over. The analysis of his fear of forgetting uncovered these latency masturbatory activities and the gratification sought through the "forgetting," as well as combined memories and fantasy contents associated with the rectal anesthesia which had accompanied a tonsillectomy in the phallic phase. At bottom, however, was the need to forget the painfully overwhelming genital feelings and the concomitant sense of abandonment to his own unmanageable genital excitations which he had experienced in repeated primal-scene exposures, dating back to the first year of life and extending into the fourth year. Although now inhibiting his genital strivings, at the same time he sought to regain his phallic sensations by the revival of these earliest experiences.

At this juncture, and before noting some observations specifically pertinent to the girls in this group of patients, it may be appropriate to make a few comments on female psychosexual development with particular reference to: (1) the question of the role of the vagina in psychosexual development prior to puberty; (2) the equating of active, masculine strivings with clitoral masturbation; and (3) Freud's assumption that the establishment of vaginal primacy at adolescence must be preceded by an interval of time during which the young woman is "anesthetic."

Although Freud gave credence to reports of early vaginal sensations, he underscored the difficulty in distinguishing these from anal sensations and implied his belief that their importance is negligible and that the actual vagina remains undiscovered until puberty. He further regarded the sexuality of the little girl and boy in the phallic phase as essentially the same: since the clitoris is homologous to the penis, clitoral masturbation, therefore, must express active, masculine strivings. The girl child thus enters into the situation of the positive Oedipus complex through the realization of the inferiority of her clitoris as contrasted with the superior organ of the boy, and the consequent abandonment of her clitoral masturbation (and thus the surrender of her active strivings). In line with this equating of clitoral with masculine sexuality, Freud concluded that a preliminary phase at puberty, in which clitoral sexuality is repressed, is requisite for the establishment of vaginal dominance. When this transfer from clitoris to vagina has taken place, the clitoris still retains a function—that of transmitting its excitations to the vaginal zone " . . . just as . . . pine shavings can be kindled in order to set a log of harder wood on fire" (p. 221).[12]

Subsequent to Freud's presentation of the psychosexual development of the girl, a presentation which he stressed was of necessity fragmentary, a number of observations have been reported on the occurrence in childhood of vaginal sensations associated with anal stimulation, as well as of vaginal masturbation, which, according to most observers, however, is limited to the introitus. Greenacre[14] has pointed to the existence of extremely early vaginal sensations which may be concurrent with or even precede clitoral sensation and which may result either from diffuse and disorganized general response to overstimulation, with discharge through many channels including the genitals, or may be more specifically and directly derived from early anal and rectal stimulation, including those instances in which oral stimulation or frustration may produce lower-bowel (and vaginal) activity.* Greenacre further notes cases in which vaginal and clitoral excitability persist simultaneously and in a mutually antagonistic way in latency, reflecting an unusual balancing of masculine and feminine identifications and resulting in a confused sense of identity; while sometimes, and under certain conditions, vaginal awareness is so accentuated as to supersede clitoral interest which, in turn, has been inhibited.

My observations support the view that, in general, the clitoris is the primary locus for organized masturbatory activities during childhood, with any manifestations of vaginal (introitus) mastur-

---

* In this connection, a mother reported her 2-year-old daughter's strenuous and excessive vaginal masturbation and vaginal discharge following a tonsillectomy.

bation more usually (although not invariably) of a transitory nature. Vaginal sensations, linked to anal-rectal stimulation, have
been frequently apparent, accompanied by confusions between
anal and vaginal zones, yet often and concurrently by some vague
awareness of distinction between the two as well. I have been particularly impressed, however, by the relative frequency with which
vaginal excitations in latency girls may be ignited by clitoral masturbation, even (though more rarely) to the point of orgasticlike
responses which seem to involve the vaginal area more than the
clitoral. Significantly, these vaginal sensations arise in connection
with clitoral rather than vaginal masturbation, and, if and when
they compel the child to extend her tactile activities to the vaginal
zone, there is often a diminution, and more occasionally an abrupt
cessation, of genital sensations, probably in large measure attributable to the complex of fears and shame associated with the vagina.

It is now rather generally conceded that the relinquishment of
clitoral masturbation as the prelude to the girl's entry into the positive oedipal relationship is by no means a universal phenomenon,
although there are, of course, instances in which this occurs. On
the contrary, the girl's masturbation may persist throughout the
oedipal period to the accompaniment of positive oedipal fantasies
as well as of those containing masculine strivings. This fact, that is,
that it is misleading to identify clitoral masturbation *exclusively*
with activity or masculinity, and vaginal masturbation *exclusively*
with passivity or femininity, has been especially emphasized by
Lampl de Groot.[20] Since anatomical, maturational, and developmental factors usually result in the clitoris remaining the more
accessible and susceptive erogenous zone during childhood, it
naturally follows that clitoral masturbation is the channel through
which both active and passive sexual aims are expressed. On the
other hand, because of the close oral-anal-vaginal affinities, it is
obvious that active, aggressive strivings, as well as their passive
counterparts, may be vested in the vaginal zone, and that these
also may be the concomitants of whatever vaginal stimulation occurs in early childhood as well as later in life. It is probably super-
fluous to add that, to a certain extent, the equating of clitoris with
masculinity is both anatomically and psychologically justified and
that the vagina is indubitably the site of feminine receptivity. The
point I wish particularly to emphasize is that clitoral sexuality
need not be incompatible with feminine strivings, and that already
in childhood it would seem that some groundwork may be laid for

the future harmonizing of clitoris with vagina toward the attainment of feminine aims.

Although it is my impression that the references in the analytic literature which deal with the girl's psychosexual development at adolescence seem to accept Freud's assumption that an initial period of clitoral repression is requisite for the establishment of vaginal primacy, my own clinical experience tends not to confirm this view. Rather, there seems more commonly to be a gradual, but occasionally more sudden, transition whereby the vaginal excitations, which the clitoral stimulation evokes, gain in strength and intensity until there is an ultimate subordination of clitoral sensations to the more compelling vaginal ones with which they now merge—a transition which, however, in general may well be dependent on the actual experience of intercourse for its completion. In fact, it has been my impression that when this clitoral repression does take place, during or following puberty, it may often reflect the persistence of stronger-than-average phallic strivings associated with clitoral arousal, so that clitoral sensations must be denied since, in these instances, they do represent an obstacle to the attainment of the simultaneously desired femininity.

Here I shall return to observations relevant to the relationship between early overstimulation and masturbation-centered conflicts in adolescent girls. As already noted, singularly acute penis-envy problems may be visible during latency, with efforts toward the maintenance of the illusory phallus often assuming a focal role. When, at adolescence, maturational pressures tend to stimulate desires for vaginal receptivity, the fear of penetration (and, as one of its frequent accompaniments, the fear of childbirth) may result in the strengthening rather than weakening of the illusory penis which, within this context, is used defensively by the girl to insulate herself against the perils of femininity and as a weapon with which to match the aggressive power of the male. It is in such instances, also, that she is especially prone to dichotomize clitoris and vagina, linking active (sadistic) strivings and the illusory phallus with clitoral sensations and clitoral masturbation, and frequently preserving strong inhibitions against tactile exploration of the vagina which signifies the masochistic perils of penetration and also the shameful "dirtiness" of the adjacent anal zone. The opposition between clitoris and vagina becomes, thus, the representation of the masculinity-femininity conflict[14] and, in one sense, serves a defensive purpose by providing specific food for alternating shifts between sadism and masochism, masculinity and femininity. Usually, however, this clitoral-vaginal dichotomy obscures an underlying kinship, in that pregenital sadistic as well as masochistic aims may be common to both clitoral and vaginal strivings, with the oral-anal sadistic elements of the vaginal fantasies often less accessible to consciousness and screened by their passive masochistic counterparts.

It would seem that the failure to effect the shift to vaginal dominance may receive an additional reinforcement when bodily experiences involving vaginal orgastic sensations, of such intensity as to threaten the physical integrity of self, have occurred in childhood. One 7-year-old girl, with a history of intense oral and anal stress in her first 2 years of life, developed an extreme fear of being struck by an atomic bomb. She was brought to treatment shortly after the onset of this symptom, and its analysis brought to light the fact that she had suddenly and unexpectedly experienced orgasticlike sensations while masturbating, which had given her the feeling that "part if not all" of her had "burst." There were indications that this orgastic response, although induced by clitoral masturbation, had encompassed rather powerful vaginal repercussions, but this could not be confirmed at the time. When, in late adolescence, this girl resumed contact with me, she revealed that for several years following the onset of puberty she had abstained from masturbation, and that only recently had she resumed clitoral masturbation. Concurrently, she strenuously repudiated all vaginal sensations—a repudiation which amounted to an almost complete denial of the existence of her vagina. She was now able to speak more specifically of her latency masturbation and to confirm the fact that her early orgastic experience had been a vaginal one.

Another adolescent girl (see also p. 65), whose latency had been marked by an increase rather than decrease in masturbation, accompanied by primal-scene fantasies in which she identified with both parental roles, and in whom the oral-vaginal and body-phallus equations were particularly pronounced, had likewise experienced, during latency, vaginal orgastic sensations of an overwhelming intensity which had given her the feeling that her whole body was being "sucked up" by her vagina. Although she had not completely abandoned her clitoral masturbation at puberty, she found it increasingly difficult, while masturbating, to experience any genital sensations—clitoral or vaginal. It became apparent that in her case, too, one of the factors which contributed to this inhibition of genital sensations was the fear of a repetition of the threatening orgastic experience. This girl frequently was aware of strong vaginal sensations (which either obscured or excluded clitoral sensations) in response to generally stimulating situations which, however, did not involve direct genital stimulation, whereas whatever genital sensations she could still evoke through masturbation were confined to the clitoris. (This tendency to experience rather clearly focused vaginal sensations in the absence of direct genital stimulation, and to limit genital sensations associated with masturbation to the clitoris, seems to be not uncommon among adolescent girls as part of a transitory stage preliminary to that of the final organization and integration of vaginal genitality.) In the case of both girls just described, the intensity of the bodily feelings had given a greater semblance of reality to fantasies involving sadomasochistic dangers and the threat of loss of identity.

Although in the examples just cited it was the force of bodily discharge which was feared, an equally great anxiety may arise, in either sex, from the threat of insufficient discharge, originally experienced in relation to the early and excessive genital excitations. In two of my patients, even faint genital stirrings tended to evoke memory traces of these former states of acute distress and to motivate attempts toward massive suppression of genital sensations. Both these patients articulated with startling clarity the fact that they somehow felt they had once, in the dim, forgotten past, experienced well-nigh unbearable genital tensions to the point of genital "pain." In this connection, Greenacre's[14] comment concerning primary masochism is relevant: "It is at least suggestive that premature erotization culminating in *genital stimulation under strain* might increase the pain component in the pleasure-pain amalgam which is the nucleus of all satisfaction, here linked with genital arousal" (pp. 295–296).

There is one more observation peculiar to girls which has impressed me and which is related to the problem of the illusory phallus. I have already alluded to the fact that when there has been a persistence of the illusory phallus throughout latency, the intensification of the bisexual conflicts at puberty may strengthen rather than weaken this fantasy. As is commonly known, when intellectual achievement is equated with phallic attainment, inhibition of intellectual functioning may occur at adolescence, not only because of the guilt and anxiety associated with the possession of phallic attributes, but also because these attributes stand in opposition to the femininity which, although now more feared, also now may be more desired. A particular problem, however, may arise when the illusory phallus coexists with, and is reinforced by, an unusual capacity for imaginative thinking. In such instances the fantasy creations, which in circular fashion arise from and give rise to especially strong clitoral excitations, may carry for the child the same sense of power as do the expanding bodily sensations themselves, to the point where the imagination may become, as it were, the psychic representation of the phallus. This was clearly illustrated by an extremely gifted prepubertal girl, whose vivid masturbation fantasies were improvised in conjunction with clitoral sensations "so big" that her clitoris, itself, "became big." During one period of her analysis, this girl implored me not to analyze these fantasies and expressed her anxiety lest by so doing I might "take away" her imagination—a possibility which, in one sense, seemed akin to a castration threat. At a later point, she confessed her frightening fantasy that were she ever to get married and assume a genuinely feminine role her imagination "would fall to pieces" and, as a consequence, she, too, "would fall to pieces." Finally, in expressing her longing for an intellectual relationship with her painter-father, which she felt would enhance her own painting ability and through which she clearly sought to partake of his phallic power, she concluded that she did not, after all, need this relationship for she had her "own imagination." It is easy to see how, with an intensification of bisexual conflicts, the imagination may then become something both precious and repudiated, illegitimately possessed and even purloined. In this way, its constructive utilization may be hindered or even totally inhibited.*

Summary

In this chapter I have noted some of the ways in which disturbances originating in the pregenital era, in connection with premature genital stimulation, may be reflected in masturbation conflicts at adolescence. Among the effects observed by Greenacre of these early and precipitate libidinal dislocations are the prolongation of the tendency toward primitive identification and the resultant intensification of bisexual strivings and confusions in the sense of identity. These impairments in ego-libidinal development

---

* After recording this observation, I noted that Greenacre had made a similar one in a recent paper.[16a]

and the consequently heightened castration anxiety may contribute to especially severe oedipal problems, including distortions of the oedipal configuration, and hence to varying degrees of failure to weather the crucial phallic-oedipal phase.[14] Since it is from the Oedipus complex itself, and its partial resolution, that structural development derives its essential categories of complex differentiation, the child thus may be limited in his capacity to achieve the usual structural advances of the latency period and to attain that relative respite from instinctual urgencies which is the usual accompaniment of the latency years. As a result of these structural deficiencies, he will be ill prepared to meet the increased instinctual pressures of puberty and will be lacking in that basic psychic equipment which facilitates the integration of genitality at adolescence. Obviously, such early ego-instinctual disturbances and their adverse effects on subsequent maturational phases may arise from a set of experiences which need not include the factor of premature genital stimulation, but the latter, when present, may well help to sway the course of psychic development into these channels.

The more particular and distinctive effects of the too early and excessive genital stimulation, however, are evidenced in the quality and patterning of the later genital strivings themselves, as well as in the corresponding feelings of uncontrollability and vulnerability which they repeatedly threaten to reawaken. It would seem that the memory traces of the extreme degree of tension caused by the disparity between the early and severe sensory stimulation and the insufficient capacity for adequate discharge tend to be revived by each successive genital arousal, with a concomitant tendency toward a perpetuation of the excess of destructive aggression linked with the original and premature genital stimulation. This surplus of aggression not only results in an increased sadomasochism which helps to shape the fantasy formations of the phallic-oedipal phase, but, by its very force, contributes to the underlying preservation of the ego's primary, as it were, sense of helplessness in the face of the intensely experienced genital pressures. Furthermore, originating as they do within the context of acute oral-anal (and probably total body) stress, the earlier genital experiences are apt to absorb and retain much of the character of pregenital strivings. It is possible that this process is augmented by what might be termed a closer and more intrinsic affinity between the genital and pregenital zones than ordinarily exists when the sequences of phase ascendancy have proceeded uninterruptedly.[14] In this sense, and under such conditions, the pregenital characteristics of genitality are not understandable solely in terms of regression and discrete pregenital fixation points, but, in addition, also must be regarded as the result of the "fixation of genitality itself to a pregenital level" —to risk a rather incongruous phrase!

With the increased genital pressures of puberty and the corresponding accentuation of the castration problems in both sexes, there is a concurrent magnification of the dangers associated with the early genital strivings. The preponderance of pregenital elements and the related oedipal anomalies is now strikingly apparent in the intensified masturbation fantasies and their attendant conflicts, and the pubertal child may desperately resist the maturational demands for acceptance and integration of genitality, frequently tending to seek refuge in perversion or sexual abstinence.

The specific manifestations of the disturbances arising from the early genital stimulation which I have noted in connection with masturbation-centered conflicts at adolescence are as follows: (1) the frequent tendency toward the decrease, and sometimes even complete cessation, of masturbation at adolescence and the resultant reversions to regressive substitutes; (2) the increased identity confusions which may accompany masturbation and which may result not only from the conflicting sexual identifications but from the fantasy that one's genital sensations derive not from oneself but from the other—a fantasy which may be strengthened by the fact that the original genital sensations occurred especially early, that is, when the differentiation between self and object was as yet incomplete; (3) the anxiety evoked by genital stirrings, which arises from the threat of insufficient discharge linked with the early situations of acute stress, and which may contribute to attempts toward massive suppression of genital sensations; (4) the additional reinforcement, in both sexes, of inhibitions or other disturbances of intellectual functioning (that is, when this has been phallicized) by: (a) an undercathexis of intellectual activities owing to the surplus of destructive components contained in the phallic strivings and to the ego's basic feelings of helplessness to control and direct these; (b) the inability to accept intellectual achievement as the result of one's own inherent ability when the fantasy that one's phallic forces derive from the other has been retained; (c) disturbances in memory traceable to uncertainties regarding the reality of the perceptions of the early traumatic situations, or to the need for their "repetition" rather than their "recollection."

In discussing the bizonal factor in the girl's psychosexual development, I have indicated that my clinical observations are not in accord with Freud's assumption that clitoral sexuality is solely "masculine" in character and that the repression of clitoral sexuality is the necessary prelude to the establishment of vaginal supremacy at adolescence. Rather, it has seemed to me that, when this repression does occur, it is frequently the result of the persistence of stronger-than-average phallic strivings associated with clitoral sensations, so that, in such instances, clitoral sexuality does represent an obstacle to the attainment of the (often simultaneously) desired femininity.

Special problems which I have observed in adolescent girls which seem to have been intensified by the factor of premature genital stimulation and which are related to the bizonal aspects of female sexuality are: (1) the enhanced need at puberty to preserve the illusory phallus as a defense against the fantasied perils which accompany the awakening desires for vaginal receptivity. It is in such cases that the girl is especially prone to dichotomize clitoris and vagina, linking active (sadistic) aims and the illusory penis with clitoral sensations, and passive, feminine (masochistic) aims with vaginal sexuality, so that this clitoral-vaginal opposition represents the masculine-feminine conflict.[14] Usually, however, this dichotomy masks an underlying kinship in that sadistic and masochistic aims, at bottom, may be common to both zones. (2) The suppression of vaginal sexuality, sometimes almost to the point of denial of the existence of the vagina, when vaginal orgastic sensations of such intensity as to threaten the integrity of self have been experienced in childhood in conjunction with clitoral masturbation.

When disturbances rooted in the pregenital era have contributed to severe and unresolved problems of the phallic-oedipal phase, and genital development has been concomitantly weakened and impaired, the indications for analysis in adolescence are especially pointed. In these situations, analysis in the latency period is undoubtedly of value in enabling maturational processes to come into fuller play as well as in facilitating the analytic work in adolescence. Frequently, however, the basic genital-oedipal problems cannot be worked through prior to puberty. Although the maturational pressures toward the establishment of genitality may now result in a defensive strengthening of the persisting pregenital configurations, the increased genital pressures simultaneously tend to bring the genital-oedipal problems into bolder relief and, in this sense, to render them more accessible. In general, I have found it helpful to interpret to the adolescent the anachronistic factor which contributes to his sense of uncontrollability in the face of genital arousal, and to relate this to that earliest time when such a reaction was unavoidable. Usually, it is not until the pregenital components of the disturbance have been analyzed that less distorted, positive oedipal strivings emerge. The subsequent analysis of the Oedipus complex poses special problems of technique and it is often at this point that the adolescent may be tempted to flee from treatment, although heretofore he may have clung to the analytic relationship with that tenacity which bears the unmistakable stamp of pregenitality. A discussion of these questions, however, is beyond the scope of this chapter.

REFERENCES

1. BORNSTEIN, B. Phobia in a two-and-a-half year old child. *Psychoanalyt. Quart. 4:* 93, 1935.
2. BORNSTEIN, B. "Masturbation in the Latency Period," in *The Psychoanalytic Study of the Child.* New York, International Universities Press, Inc., 1953, vol. 8.
3. BRUNSWICK, R. M. The preoedipal phase of libido development. *Psychoanalyt. Quart. 9:* 293, 1940.
4. EISSLER, K. R. "Notes on Problems in Technique in the Psychoanalytic Treatment of Adolescents with Some Remarks on Perversion," in *The Psychoanalytic Study of the Child.* New York, International Universities Press, Inc., 1958, Vol. 13, pp. 223–254.
5. FREUD, A. *The Ego and the Mechanisms of Defense.* New York, International Universities Press, Inc., 1946.
6. FREUD, A. "Certain Types and Stages of Social Maladjustment," in *Searchlights on Delinquency,* ed. by Eissler, K. R. New York, International Universities Press, Inc., 1949, pp. 193–204.
7. FREUD, A. "Observations on Child Development," in *The Psychoanalytic Study of the Child.* New York, International Universities Press, Inc., 1951, vol. 6.
8. FREUD, A. "Studies in Passivity." Lecture before Detroit Psychoanalytic Society at Western Reserve Medical School, Cleveland, Oct. 25, 1952 (unpublished).
9. FREUD, S. *New Introductory Lectures on Psychoanalysis.* New York, W. W. Norton & Company, Inc., 1933, chap. 5.
10. FREUD, S. "Female Sexuality," in *Collected Papers.* London, Hogarth Press, Ltd., 1950, vol. 5.

11. FREUD, S. "The Infantile Genital Organization of the Libido," in *Collected Papers*. London, Hogarth Press, Ltd., 1950, vol. 2.
12. FREUD, S. "Three Essays on the Theory of Sexuality," in *Standard Edition*. London, Hogarth Press, Ltd., 1953, vol. 7.
13. GELEERD, E. R. "Some Aspects of Psychoanalytic Technique in Adolescence," in *The Psychoanalytic Study of the Child*. New York, International Universities Press, Inc., 1957, vol. 12, pp. 263–283.
14. GREENACRE, P. *Trauma, Growth, and Personality*. New York, W. W. Norton & Company, Inc., 1952.
15. GREENACRE, P. Contributions to: "Problems of Infantile Neurosis," in *The Psychoanalytic Study of the Child*. New York, International Universities Press, Inc., 1954, vol. 9, pp. 18–24.
16. GREENACRE, P. Early physical determinants in the development of the sense of identity. *J. Am. Psychoanalyt. Assoc. 6:* 612, 1958.
16a. GREENACRE, P. Woman as artist. *Psychoanalyt. Quart. 29:* 208, 1960.
17. JONES, E. "Early Female Sexuality," in *Papers on Psychoanalysis*. London, Baillière, Tindall & Cox, 1938.
18. KRIS, E. "Some Comments and Observations on Early Autoerotic Activities," in *The Psychoanalytic Study of the Child*. New York, International Universities Press, Inc., 1951, vol. 6.
19. LAMPL DE GROOT, J. The evolution of the Oedipus complex in women. *Internat. J. Psycho-Analysis. 9:* 332, 1928.
20. LAMPL DE GROOT, J. "On Masturbation and Its Influences on General Development," in *The Psychoanalytic Study of the Child*. New York, International Universities Press, Inc., 1950, vol. 5.
21. NUNBERG, H. "Homosexuality, magic and aggression," in *Practice and Theory of Psychoanalysis*. Nervous and Mental Disease Monographs. New York, International Universities Press, 1948.
22. REICH, A. "The Discussion of 1912 on Masturbation and Our Present-Day Views," in *The Psychoanalytic Study of the Child*. New York, International Universities Press, Inc., 1951, vol. 6.

chapter 5   Homosexual Conflicts

SELMA H. FRAIBERG

In an essay dealing with the treatment of adolescents, Peter Blos[1] says: " . . . the problem of homosexuality plays in most adolescent cases a more or less significant role because the conflict of bisexuality is part and parcel of adolescence; it is indeed, the core of the intense identity struggle at this stage of maturation." In therapy we are often obliged, as Blos suggests, to postpone the analysis of the homosexual tendency and the related fantasies until the adolescent has achieved his "sex-appropriate orientation." Although Blos does not expand these remarks, I take it that he means that while the young adolescent is testing his sexual identity in the unstable and uncertain phase of early adolescence, the analysis of his homosexuality may intensify the conflict and his doubts about sexual identity and may be a hindrance to those processes in identity formation that normally are at work during this period. With these views I am generally in accord.

Some exceptions can be made, I believe, in those instances where an adolescent reveals to us that his own tendencies are not working toward the establishment of the appropriate sexual identification, and that a homosexual tendency has achieved a powerful reinforcement in puberty which threatens to become victorious. In these instances we may be obliged to deal with the homosexual conflicts, though with certain therapeutic limitations, in order to give aid to the adolescent in finding his appropriate sexual identity. While the conflict is still active, while anxiety and guilt about homosexual tendencies and homosexual activities are still present, we may have a good chance, in adolescence, of changing the direction. Even here, however, when we are obliged to deal with the homosexual tendencies in analysis, we will find that when the patient is an adolescent we may be able to deal with only certain aspects of the homosexuality. For example, we may not have great difficulty in analyzing the passive tendencies of a boy as *defense*— and it may be therapeutically very profitable to do this—but the passive *wish* and its links with incestuous objects may elude analy-

78

sis; indeed, they may never come into the treatment in a form that can be employed for the analysis.

It is not easy to assess the homosexual tendencies in adolescence and to predict for purposes of treatment whether we can expect these tendencies to subside in the course of normal development or whether their presence is a danger to development. In the exceptional cases where an adolescent has formed his identity on the basis of a reversal of sexual role, when he bears the stamp of his homosexuality, acknowledges it, and exhibits it, we have less difficulty in making a prediction. In these cases a homosexual tendency has been confirmed in the course of adolescence, a homosexual experience has brought gratification, the boy or girl has fallen in love with a homosexual partner, and the pleasure gains, along with the love of the partner, have decisively influenced the sexual orientation. We need not regard these developments as irreversible in adolescence, but clearly the difficulties are very much greater than those we encounter in cases where the adolescent has homosexual tendencies but remains uncommitted.

The adolescents we encounter normally in clinical practice are "uncommitted." The homosexual conflicts which they reveal to us will not tell us so easily what the sexual solution will be. Even in those cases where a homosexual partner has been found, we cannot make a prediction if the bisexual conflicts are still active. This is because we recognize that these conflicts are intrinsically part of the adolescent development, that homosexual practices are not uncommon in early adolescence; it is as though we are waiting for the adolescent in the borderline cases to tell us "what" he is.

I do not question at all that we cannot evaluate the homosexuality of the adolescent with those criteria that we employ with adults. There is an "allowable" homosexuality of adolescence, especially of early adolescence, which must enter into the assessment. But within this range of "allowable" homosexuality there are, I think, some deviations which can be regarded as danger signals. Later, I shall present a case of an adolescent boy which permits close scrutiny of some of the factors in adolescent homosexuality which are prognostically poor for the achievement of masculinity.

Let us, for a moment, consider the range of "allowable" homosexuality in adolescence, from the standpoint of the adolescent culture. Sex play among boys in early adolescence is not at all uncommon, as we know. Some of it occurs in the form of horseplay in the locker rooms and school lavatories or on other such occasions when boys find the sight of each other's genitals exciting. So we hear of games in which boys of this age grab at each other's genitals or games in which they exhibit erections to each other. Group masturbation is by no means rare and is not confined to delinquent or seriously disturbed boys, as directors of "nice" boys camps and schools can tell us. Fellatio, anal sexual practices, and practically the whole gamut of perverse sexual acts may be practiced furtively, and perhaps only once in this experimental period of development, and yet may not indicate pathological development in the boy and may not retard his normal progress toward heterosexuality.

We have no parallel among girls for this homosexual license in early adolescence. There is, by comparison, very little overt homosexual activity, and when it does occur it involves a pair of girls, not a group. I know of no examples of group sexual games among girls in adolescence, although I have a number of examples of such games among girls in latency and prepuberty. Some years ago, when I served as a consultant at a camp for emotionally disturbed boys and girls, I was very much impressed to see that, among the older groups (11 to 14 years), problems involving sex play among the boys were most frequently brought to my attention and problems of sex play among girls were rarely reported. In the rare instance of sex play among girls, it involved a pair relationship, never a group. It interested me that even among our impulsive and delinquent girls there was no parallel for the group sexual horseplay or sexual games of boys. From analytic observations I believe that group sex play among girls occurs mainly during latency and typically with a group fantasy of a sadomasochistic type, that such activities may extend into prepuberty and even early puberty and are then abandoned under the pressure of tremendous anxiety. Furtive homosexual games between partners are reported by an occasional girl in early adolescence. These sexual activities typically involve breast play, and more rarely include mutual masturbation. This corresponds to observations of adult female homosexuality where activity involving the breasts is usually at the center of the homosexual act. Helene Deutsch[4] has shown how "mothering and being mothered" are central to the adult female homosexual act.

These differences in the "allowable" homosexuality of boys' groups and girls' groups are, I think, very instructive. The boy in early adolescence may engage in homosexual games with some anxiety and, in fact, considerable guilt, but he flirts with these dangers and takes his risks, which suggests that the risk is not so great for him as for the girl. Among girls in puberty and early adolescence we have evidence that there are powerful prohibitions against homosexual practices. Although girls are, of course, freer in kissing or casually embracing each other than are boys, I think we should not regard this type of display as an indication of greater freedom in homosexual contact between women. These are the "innocent" forms of body contact between girls, and it will be observed that, on those occasions when the innocent kiss or embrace elicits an erotic response, the adolescent girl will normally take flight from a relationship that suddenly appears to be dangerous. Indeed, the homosexual *fantasies* of girls are the source of the greatest torments of this age. We will even find quite common among girls a morbid dread of body contact with other girls and women, and an expression of disgust and loathing toward women and women's bodies which may occur, in its most virulent form, against the mother herself. Ruth Mack Brunswick[3] speaks of "the massive repression of pre-genital impulses" required in female development, and, in the dread of homosexuality which we see so frequently in girls in adolescence, we can see how homosexuality represents for the girl a dangerous regression. Since, in the case of girls, the homosexual object is also the first love object, the greater danger lies in a regression in the ego to the stage of primal oneness with the object.

Now, if we return once more to boys in adolescence, we will find a parallel with the girls after all. There is one type of homosexual relationship that does not come under the "allowable" homosexuality of adolescent boys and is surrounded by strict taboos even among delinquent-boy groups. The experimental license among adolescent boys does not extend to sexual acts with grown men. There is a morbid dread of homosexual contact with an adult male, often accompanied by a grim fantasy: "If any guy ever tried anything like that with me, I'd kill him!" This fantasy is sometimes acted out in adolescent crime, such as "rolling a queer." (The term "rolling" a queer is not really accurate, of course.) This is a morbid game in which two or three or more boys lure a homosexual man, usually by offering one member of the group as bait. At the moment that a response is made by the older man, he is assaulted by the entire group. On some occasions, as we know, the man has been beaten to death or has been murdered outright. This shocking game is not confined to delinquents, by any means, and, in those cases where the game has had tragic consequences and has been brought to public attention, the absence of guilt on the part of the young criminals is nearly always remarked upon. We can guess how these boys can defend themselves against guilt feelings. They behave as if they were entirely justified in murdering a homosexual man who had made advances; he "deserved" to be killed. Their own provocation of the man does not enter into the picture at all as they justify their crime.

It is very important that, normally, the young adolescent boy can take the risks of homosexual games, albeit with some guilt and anxiety, in what I have called the "allowable" homosexuality of the age, and that his dread of homosexual contact, surrounded by strict taboos, comes out specifically in relation to an older man. Obviously, dread of homosexual contact does not attach itself to the games of the locker room or the occasional furtive sex games with peers, or these practices would rarely occur; the temptation would be warded off as it is in the case of girls. And the fantasy, "If any guy ever tried that with me, I'd kill him," is not directed toward peers. Two or more boys who have occasionally engaged in a sex game will often not even suffer a disturbance of their friendship. The fantasy is specifically directed toward older men.

The taboos that attach themselves to sexual contact with an older man tell us that, for the boy, a homosexual relationship with an adult male constitutes a dangerous regression to the original homosexual object, the father. In the story of Eric, this will be discussed in further detail.

The case of Eric affords an opportunity to study the impact of puberty on a boy who had exhibited passive tendencies throughout latency. Since analysis was begun in prepuberty and extended into early adolescence, we have the opportunity to study the development in some detail. Homosexual conflicts were active throughout the period of analysis, and on two occasions a relationship with a homosexual man played a significant role.

CASE REPORT

The Prepubertal Phase of the Analysis

Eric entered treatment at the age of 11. The prepubertal phase of the analysis covered roughly the period from 11 to 12½ years. At this time, definite signs of pubertal development had appeared, and puberty initiated fresh conflicts in the homosexual sphere.

At the time Eric began his treatment, he was suffering with a severe blinking tic, accompanied, occasionally, by a second tic—a twitching and wrinkling of the nose. He had a serious learning disability, with difficulty in retention, and acute and overwhelming examination anxiety. He was attending a boys' school with high scholastic standards, and there was grave question as to whether he could continue there because of his poor performance. He had ambitions for himself as an athlete, but his fear of injury and of competition in games was so strong that he could barely manage to keep up in class games.

He was a handsome, engaging child, with a good wit which he deftly employed to turn aggression away from himself and to render his own aggression harmless and inoffensive. Aggression of any kind, verbal or physical, was never manifested overtly and was so overlaid with defense that it was nearly inaccessible during the first months of analysis. Eric felt that he was closest to his mother (who showed a definite preference for Eric over the older son, Bob), that he admired his father but couldn't get close to him, and that his brother Bob was somehow connected with his most serious problems.

It is important to note that Eric's father was overseas during the first 4 years of Eric's life and that Bob, 2 years older than Eric, had played "man of the house" even as the small child that he was. Bob's jealousy of Eric was savage and destructive and, through beatings and attacks upon the younger brother, had early brought him into a sadomasochistic relationship which has great significance for Eric's character development. It is significant, too, that Bob had had repeated surgery on his eyes during his childhood and, on one occasion when Eric was an infant, had attacked the younger child with a scissors (apparently with intent to damage his eyes) and had cut Eric's lip.

Eric was an excellent patient from the beginning. He was ambitious, found his symptoms very distressing, and was deeply troubled about his cowardice and the implications of "sissiness" in his behavior. The early months of analysis dealt chiefly with his defenses against aggression—the altruism, clever jokes, denial, the passive attitudes themselves. In the transference to me we saw, almost at once, a compliant attitude coupled with fear of attack (a dream in which the analytic situation is represented as an operation) which provided the first clues to his own passivity and opened up the area of Eric's relationship to Bob. Eric described his helplessness when Bob attacked him. The superior strength of the older boy, coupled with his savagery, reduced Eric to numb surrender. It was some time before Eric was able to bring out his own rage toward Bob, and at first he could only repeat hopelessly that he really loved his brother. Again it was in transference that he first experienced anger—in an aggressive outburst toward me. When this material was analyzed, he was able at last to bring out his hostile feelings toward Bob, and, for the first time in his life, began to fight back. The tic disappeared for a time, with the analysis of the defenses against aggression—the liberation of aggressive feelings in transference and toward Bob—and finally by establishing one of the symbolic meanings of the eye tic as a fear of attack upon the eyes.

Now the analysis began to reveal extensive sex play between Eric and Bob. These, too, were aggressive games in which Bob grabbed at Eric's testicles and Eric would retaliate by grabbing Bob's. There were also wrestling games in which, for example, Bob would subdue Eric, naked after a shower, and aggressively pull his nipples. On more than one occasion Bob urinated on Eric. All this was very painful for Eric to tell me: "It makes me sick. He makes me feel like a woman!" But also there was great anxiety in connection with these games. Repeatedly, Eric mentioned his fears that his testicles could be damaged. "They could rupture," he said. He told me that his brother had had a "rupture" (a hernia) and Eric was convinced that this referred to the testicles. As the analytic material centered on the sex play and fear of damage to the testicles, the eye blinking returned full force, and, when I was able to show him how the tic appeared regularly with his discussions of possible damage to the testicles, we were able to make the essential connection: the eyes represented the testicles, in a displacement from below to above. (It was not until some time later that the nose twitching became analyzable on the same basis, for in the configuration the nose, of course, represented the penis.)

Voyeuristic activities now made their appearance in the analysis. Eric had, for many years, made occasional appearances in his parents' bedroom with complaints about inability to sleep, or a bad dream, and he had, during the early months of the analysis, reported such occurrences without providing a good opening for discussion. Now Eric organized a Private Eye Detective Agency with seven other boys at school to investigate some school locker thefts, and spying and sleuthing occupied him for weeks. When analysis revealed that the detective himself was responsible for a number of dime-store thefts in the past weeks, Eric lost interest in sleuthing, and the significance of "spying" was dramatically revealed soon afterward in a night terror in which primal-scene material made its first appearance in analysis.

The analysis of a dream of spying and the agitated tic that accompanied the telling of the dream and its associations established clearly for Eric that he had once seen something in his parents' room that assaulted his eyes, that his night wandering into the parents' room was motivated by a wish to see something again, and that the tic expressed exactly in symbolic language "to look" and "not to look" as well as denial of what had been seen. Since the night terror had taken place during a time that Eric's father was out of town, further analysis revealed his anxiety when his father was out of the house and made it possible for us to begin the exploration of his competitive feelings with his father. Fears of his father's death and fantasies of inheriting great wealth caused him great torment for a period, and very slowly, in the months that followed, we were able to pursue the analysis of oedipal wishes and Eric's fear of retaliation from his father. We were, of course, able to link this material to Eric's fear of competition in other areas and to see how fear of his aggressive and competitive feelings had led him into his characteristic patterns of denial of aggression and propitiation of his father and other men.

Castration anxiety specifically connected with the penis first presented itself in the analysis through horror of the female genitals and the persistent idea that menstruation was evidence of mutilation of the woman through intercourse. Revulsion toward the female genitals was described repeatedly, and in one example he told me that the vagina reminded him always of the time he once watched the dissection of a squirrel, as if it, too, were all "blood and guts and gore inside." He could never remember seeing a nude woman, although he claimed that his brother had once come upon their mother nude. (From the history I knew that Eric had surprised his mother on more than one occasion by coming into her bath.) The other aspects of his castration anxiety were more difficult to elicit. We recall that fear of mutilation of his own genitals was always expressed in terms of the testicles. I had reason to believe that the absence of specific material related to the penis had to do with another omission in analysis—his masturbation. Eric admitted that he handled his penis but denied that it gave him any pleasure. Since masturbation and the analysis of masturbation fantasies were excluded in one way or another from the analysis at this period, the analysis of castration anxiety in this connection was blocked and so, too, were the vital connections between masturbation and the oedipal conflicts. I was able to establish with Eric a connection between the nose twitching and anxiety about his penis as another displacement, which led to the disappearance of the nose tic but did not bring with it any conviction in Eric that he feared damage to his penis. It remained only an intellectual insight for some time.

This brings us to the close of the period I have called prepubertal, and it might be useful to summarize at this point. The symptoms were very little in evidence during the last months of this period. The eye tic had disappeared several months before the nose tic, of course. There was great improvement in Eric's ability to handle aggression and competition, and, as one unexpected bonus for such hard work in analysis, Eric achieved one of his wishes and was fast becoming a promising athlete at school. There were academic ups and downs in school, but, during the last months of this period, Eric showed definite improvement in his grades, and the examination anxiety was no longer so intense and overwhelming.

The Pubertal Phase of the Analysis

In creating this division between the prepubertal and pubertal phase of the analysis, I am not suggesting, of course, that there is actually a dividing line between these two developmental phases or a moment at which we can say of a child, "Now he is in puberty." But, along with the first signs of pubescence, the child's own recognition of bodily changes is often expressed through a dramatic incident or symbolic act which initiates the psychological onset of puberty. With Eric, for example, "psychological puberty" began in this dramatic way:

Not long after physical signs of puberty had appeared, Eric one day brought in a new discovery that awed him and produced a cocky self-assurance in him. He had gone rummaging in the attic at home and discovered his father's old Army uniforms. He had tried one on, and it fitted perfectly, he said. He was not yet 13, he boasted, and he was already growing so tall that he was bound to be taller than his father. Still under the magic of this discovery, he arrived for his next appointment with a bundle under his arm which contained the uniform coat, and Eric tried it on, carefully adjusting the shoulders, which were too big for him, and strutted around the room.

This new exultation was short lived. A few days later a chastened Eric arrived and reported a dream which he had had the night before. In the dream he was in danger of attack by a group of men and boys ("one of them looked like Dad and one I remember was a boy of 13") and he had to try by various strategems to evade them and get to the police, for he knew they were criminals. He was not aware of great anxiety in the dream but remembered calling "Help! Help!" in order to attract someone and get help in capturing the criminals. His associations led to a football game in which Eric's team was badly beaten by a group of older boys, then to trying on his father's uniform and his discovery that he was almost as big as his father. To the idea of criminals, Eric could produce no associations, and he repudiated my suggestion that he might be representing his own guilt feelings in this way. He blocked any further discussion of the dream by a long and intellectual report of his competitive feelings toward his father and how greatly improved he was these days, for he was certainly not afraid of competition with his father now the way he used to be. "Well, then, how shall we explain the dream?" I asked. Eric shrugged this off as inconsequential.

Now, for two weeks Eric brought in a series of dreams which defied analysis. In each of these dreams Eric was in danger of being discovered, or he was doing something forbidden. (In one dream, picking campaign buttons off the White House lawn was represented as the crime, and in two other dreams the theme of "buttons" was connected with danger.) Eric could produce no associations, and it was evident that something was being concealed from analysis; a conscious concealment, I thought, for this expert dream analyzer had no associations these days.

Then I received a call from Eric's mother. That morning the mother had gone to Eric's room and found in his bed a condom and a sanitary pad which had been pulled apart as if for inspection. I suggested to the mother that she tell Eric what she had found and that he take this up with me in the analysis.

In analysis, Eric tried to make light of this episode. He invented one story after another to explain the presence of the condom in his bed (although he admitted it was his father's condom, taken from his room) and did not allude to the sanitary pad at all. He

was pale with guilt, and when I drew his attention to his guilty reactions he could only say that he had, after all, stolen this condom
from his dad and that stealing was a terrible thing. He could not
bring himself in this hour to tell me what he did with the condom
but spent much of the time in self-condemnation—because he had
lied to me so often in the past. And now, as he spoke of lying, his
eye blinking returned after an absence of several months, and I
noticed, too, that he avoided looking directly into my face. This
gave the opportunity later in the hour to show Eric another
meaning of the symptom, "I can't look you straight in the eyes."

The self-reproaches about lying to me were, of course, connected
with masturbation about which he had told evasive stories in the
past. And the displacement of guilt feelings from the condom episode to "lying" clearly told us what he had done with the condom.
Actually, it was not until the next hour that Eric was able to tell
me this. In that hour the analysis of a dream detail about "petting a
dog" led into a discussion of masturbation and his admission that
he masturbates, that he gets "a thrill out of it," but that "it isn't a
good thing to do." His anxieties about the penis were identical with
those he used to describe in connection with the testicles. The penis,
he said, might "rupture." And now, with these admissions about his
masturbation and his anxieties in connection with it, he was able to
tell me what he had done with the condom.

He had "tried it on for size" (just as he had tried on his father's
uniform). This was not the first time he had done this, he admitted.
(I suspect the first time was connected with the dream about the
criminals, reported earlier, in which one of the associations was
trying on the father's uniform.) We were now able to analyze one
of the "button" dreams in which he was stealing from the White
House, and the buttons, of course, were an allusion to the rolled-up
condoms in the box in his father's bedside table. Recalling the
anxiety and fear of punishment that attended this dream and the
actual discovery by the mother of the condom in Eric's bed, Eric
was able to see how great was his fear of punishment from his
father for his competitive and aggressive wishes.

In the weeks that followed, Eric's competitive feelings and death
wishes toward his father came out dramatically in anxiety dreams.
In one, he was under suspicion of murder. He was the only person
in the house at the time the body was discovered. All evidence
pointed to him, and it appeared that he was guilty, though he was
not. This led to Eric's discovery of "why I always feel guilty

whether I am or not," that he was guilty of criminal wishes toward his father. Through the analysis of this material and his ability to acknowledge through genuine emotion the fear of the bad wishes and the fear of reprisal, Eric made good progress. For the first time he was able to take school examinations with confidence, his tics disappeared again, and in nearly every area of functioning we and his parents could see strong improvement.

This brought us to the end of June and termination for the summer, for Eric was going to camp. The whole picture looked very favorable at this time, but we should note that the episode of masturbation with the condom and sanitary napkin was incompletely analyzed. Eric had never told me about the sanitary pad (I only knew this through the mother), and since he knew that his mother had discussed this with me I had even, at one point, tried to help him out by telling him I knew about it. But he denied this completely at the time.

I think we must assume that, in the masturbation, a bisexual fantasy was enacted in which the condom played a role in the masculine fantasy and the sanitary pad the feminine, that Eric was both active male and passive and mutilated female in the masturbation. The omission of this material from the analysis had a crucial significance for the events of the summer.

Eric returned from camp after an excellent summer, from all reports. He had done well in all activities and showed outstanding skill in sports. The camp director described him as one of the most popular boys. Eric was very enthusiastic about his summer, full of self-confidence—and the tics were back! For over a month there were no clues in the analysis regarding the tics. He was back in school, performing well, enthusiastic about all subjects, and studying well. This was a puzzle, for, although all the ego gains were sustained, the symptom had returned.

In the meantime, too, I observed that Eric's relationship to his father had undergone considerable modification. I had actually begun to see changes in the relationship a few months before camp, but now the admiration of father, the cameraderie, and the active seeking of his companionship were very much present in Eric's analysis. Although it is important to note this in terms of Eric's development, from the father's point of view, too, Eric had become a more gratifying son, and his scholastic, but particularly his athletic, achievements satisfied the father's own ambitions. All traces of the oedipal rivalry which had flared up the previous spring had vanished in the home picture. Conflict, when it appeared at all at home, was mainly centered in the relationship to the mother; complaints about his mother's babying him and her excessive demands filled many hours. Criticism of the father, or overt hostility toward him, almost never appeared.

In October I began to hear a story, reluctantly told by Eric, concerning a counselor, Joe, about whom I had already heard from Eric: "A swell guy, a good coach. He really helped me to improve my baseball game." Joe had engaged in homosexual acts with Eric. It had begun with little "horseplay" acts, snapping the elastic on Eric's swim trunks, then peeking inside, and finally, while sitting on Eric's bunk at night, handling his penis. "He did it lots of times. It made me mad. And I couldn't tell anyone. He was a grown man. You can't tell anything like that. And anyway I liked him; he *was* a swell guy." And without a pause Eric continued to another theme, telling me about another counselor whom he detested, who was unfair to the kids and took advantage of them. This came out in a vitriolic outburst. It was again the same pattern we had seen in Eric's relationship to his father, admiration and affection toward father, and always there was someone else, a male teacher most typically, toward whom the fury and indignation were directed.

What was most difficult for Eric to acknowledge was his own pleasure in these acts with Joe (just as earlier he had not been able to acknowledge pleasure in masturbation). With considerable shame, in the hours that followed, he was able to see that, although he had submitted and had felt angry toward Joe afterward, he had also invited these advances and had found this homosexual play exciting.

The material centering around Joe and the homosexual conflicts stirred up in Eric now brought us into a very difficult and painful part of the analysis. Almost immediately, Eric regretted that he had told me about Joe, and in the first dream reported since he returned from camp I was represented as a dangerous foreign spy, and the idea "to betray oneself" appeared in associations to other details in the dream. Another detail, "a feeling of astonishment," produced associations to the word "astonishment" which recalled to Eric his own reaction when he read the story of Christine Jorgensen in the newspapers.

The strange case of "Christine" became one of the recurrent themes in the analysis for many weeks. "Then how could a guy be changed into a girl?" he would say. And each time he drew the inevitable conclusion, horror and revulsion overcame him. "And why would any guy want that! He must be nuts! But would those doctors really do that? Would they really cut it off?" Christine, for Eric as for other children I knew, had become almost an obsessive preoccupation.

It is significant that the "Christine" material had made its appearance through the analysis of a transference dream shortly after Eric had told me about Joe. We can see how he feared the analysis of his homosexual feelings, as if he were afraid that analysis would deprive him of his masculinity. This, in fact, was one of the motives in the resistance which we saw for a long period in the analysis.

In the midst of this period of turmoil, Eric accidentally encountered his mother in the nude when she came running out of the bath after a pipe burst. This made a strong impression on him, and in a dream that followed this event "mother had lost something valuable—jewelry, or money, or something like that" while she was swimming, and Eric was diving into the lake to retrieve it. He remembered how, in the water, he felt as if his eardrums would burst. This vividly evoked the memory of the nude mother and the feelings that accompanied it, and the detail "lose something valuable" reminded him simultaneously of Christine and of the sight of his mother's genitals. Now, for the first time in the analysis, Eric was able to see how his own castration anxiety was linked with the sight of female genitalia, and how the horror and disbelief which were his reactions to the "Christine" story were identical with the feelings evoked by the female genitals.

In the weeks that followed, there was increased resistance in analysis. Disbelief and denial, exactly those reactions which he experienced in relation to the female genitalia, now made their way into the transference. Eric repeatedly expressed disbelief at any interpretations which I gave him, including interpretations of material that had long ago been analyzed. He even denied for a while that his dreams meant anything and challenged the meaning of analysis itself. "How do you know? How can you prove it?" Since denial extended to my transference interpretations, this resistance was difficult to penetrate. He openly expressed his anger toward me, accused me of making too much of sexual problems, and expressed his contentment with the *status quo* (he was, in fact, doing very good work in school and functioning very well at home during this period), and the hostility toward me also resisted analysis when

I attempted to link it up with his feelings toward women and his fear of injury by women.

During this period of resistance I began to learn about a new attachment. Eric was now very much devoted to his school football coach, Mr. R. And Mr. R., too, was very much interested in Eric's tics and told Eric that he thought this was a nervous habit which Eric would overcome through self-control. Eric told him that he had been seeing a lady about his tic and that it had been brought under control until he went to camp this summer, but the coach was disparaging about such methods and gave Eric a number of pep talks about curing such habits through self-discipline. Eric, too, for a time was almost converted to Mr. R.'s willpower therapy but had to admit sadly that it did not work.

Nevertheless, the devotion to Mr. R. continued and, apart from the competition offered by another therapist, Mr. R. furnished another motive in the resistance, for, clearly, Eric had taken flight from the dangers of the transference to a woman at just the point where his castration anxiety was revealed in connection with the female genitals. Characteristically, his flight led him to form a new attachment to a male (another coach) and, as we should expect, he resisted the analysis of this new relationship with all his energy. In this way he was repeating his homosexual pattern in the transference, and the motive was clear, but the relationship to Mr. R. was excluded from the analysis by Eric. He also resisted even tentative suggestions from me that Mr. R. and Joe, the camp coach, might be connected in any way. The sexual episodes with Joe were over, done with, of no further consequence, and, as represented in a dream fragment of this period, "water under the bridge."

I should mention, too, at this point that Eric's relationship to his father, which had become so close since his return from camp, provided another motive in the resistance. For the figure behind the two coaches was Eric's own father, whose interest in athletics and whose coaching of Eric in football was one of the strongest bonds between them. Clearly, then, it was through identification with the masculine qualities of the father and the two coaches that Eric sought to acquire his own masculinity. Analysis of these relationships to men would result in giving up the attachments, but, in doing so, Eric would be deprived of his masculinity by identification; he would be in danger of emasculation.[7]

During this period of resistance, anxiety broke through in a number of dreams. In one of these dreams he was being pursued by an older man, and concentration-camp details in the dream led him to associations of Nazi atrocities and a story he had heard that Nazi's "would cut off a guy's penis." The associations to the old man led to the therapist and, with real conviction that it was I whom he feared, Eric brought forth a furious outburst against me. The link between his castration anxiety and the transference resistance was established for the first time.

Not long after this, Eric brought in a dream which I shall report in a little more detail. We had many occasions to refer to this dream later, and Eric, himself, gave it the name, "the change-of-states dream": "It seemed I was planning a trip to Arizona and I was studying a map. But the map was funny. I'll explain. Nevada was down where Louisiana is and seemed to be right next to Arkansas and next to it was Arizona."

These were his associations: "As if Louisiana had changed places with Nevada. Change places. I wish I could change places with Dennis. He's a whiz in mathematics. . . . " I remind him of another recent dream—the "fountain-pen dream" in which the wish to have something like somebody else's had played a part. He agrees, then is silent for a long time. Then, doggedly and tensely, he says, "Well, what comes to mind is sexual stuff. Somebody having something that someone else doesn't. Girls have breasts, boys not; boys having penises, girls not. . . . Envy. A boy at school with a very big penis. All the guys thought it was because he jacked off too much. . . . Girls. And that leads me back to Christine Jorgensen where I get stuck. Supposing he-she had never really been a guy. Maybe the army was wrong in the medical report. Because—because—would they really have cut it off, those doctors?" (I remark on his feelings—he is evidently tormented, and loathing and disgust twist his face.) Eric: "Yes, that's the problem. How did he *change his state?*" (the dream). (Does he have any other ideas?) "Yes, Look. When a flower dies, doesn't it sort of fold up again, close up. Like growing backward to what it started from?" Here, I recognize the analogy to an erection and detumescence and point it out to him. He agrees with surprise and pursues this as a fantasy: "It would shrink and shrink and shrink—" and then, half-smiling at the implication, "—until it disappears." This material linked Eric's castration anxiety with his own masturbation and, as we saw in a later discussion, it was the reversal of another masturbation fantasy in which his penis got longer and longer and longer until everyone was "amazed" at its size and envied him.

Along with the "change-places" theme of the dream, I tried at one point to suggest that Eric might wonder sometimes what it would be like to be a girl. And to this Eric said soberly, in a gentle, reasoning voice, "I'll tell you. I think you're asking me that question at the wrong time of my life. If you asked me when I was little maybe I could tell you. But right now, I mean at my age, I'm glad I'm a boy, and I can't even imagine what it would be like to be anything but a boy!"

The analysis of masturbation fantasies provided us, in the next hours, with another aspect of anxiety connected with erection. In one of these fantasies, "the penis gets longer and longer and longer and everyone is amazed, no one else has one as long." His associations: "Others will be jealous . . . they will try to . . . hurt it . . . do something to it . . . Nazi's . . . they say in concentration camps they cut it off." This brought him to speak of his great fear that if he were to be too successful, better than anybody else, he would invite envy from others and, in his fantasy, "they could do something to me, maybe kill me." He was able to see how the fantasy of the penis getting "longer and longer" was the reversal of the fantasy related earlier in which the penis would shrink and shrink and shrink. We were able to link the fantasy of "bigger and bigger" to his fear of competition with boys and men, and Eric himself was reminded of how he had told his father just the other day that he, Eric, would never wish to be a boss, that he would rather take orders. He would never wish to be President because others might be jealous of him. Thoughts of Lincoln: to be killed by a jealous man, for example.

From this material we were able to derive, in the next few weeks, some important insights into the active and passive patterns in Eric, and Eric was able to see how he defended against his active strivings by retreating to a passive position where he would be invulnerable. Material in connection with the father re-entered the analysis, and Eric saw how envy of the father and aggressive fantasies in connection with him and other males were reversed in his fears that he might be destroyed by those who envied him. Each time he made a thrust in the direction of activity and competition with males, he reversed his position out of anxiety, specifically castration anxiety, and took the passive alternative.

This period of the analysis came to a climax in a revealing anxiety dream, a dream that Eric alluded to as "the big-change dream": "My cousins and I were going to a theater. It seemed I had seen the movie before. I didn't go in. But later on I followed the crowd and went in. It was a play. The first part seemed to be about a carefree life, everything nice and pleasant. Then there was a *big change*. And I got scared. The villain, a giant, was chasing people around. Next thing I knew, we all went into a place that was like a penny arcade with little machines. Only it seemed to be a test of apprehension. I mean comprehension. I thought I saw that before, too. There was a round machine. You threw a ball in. There was sort of a hole in the machine. I was scared that if I put my finger in I might get a shock."

His associations were: *"Test of comprehension.* Like here" (analysis). "How I feel so dumb sometimes. All my life I've felt this big" (measuring an inch with his fingers). *"The big change.* Christine again. Gee we always get back to that. I heard she wasn't a woman at all after the operation. Just a man without his balls and his penis. *I had seen it before."* He is reluctant to give me his first associations, then says, "A nude woman, and my first thought was that I had never seen one before—only nude men—and I know that isn't true." I comment on denial mechanism again and the strong feelings that he suppresses in connection with nude women. To this he reluctantly agrees: "Christine again. The thought that something must have happened to the women like what happened to Christine. . . . I have seen lots of nude men. I remember the locker room at the country club." (And what comes to mind?) "Well, when I was little, how big they were to me, how big the penis was. How small I was—" (measuring, ruefully with his fingers again) "—about this big." He began to grin as he recalled how he had used the same words earlier in this hour. Again we were able to see how comparison with others, particularly men, was at the basis of his strong feelings of inferiority and his belief that he could never compete, and once again he could describe the envy aroused in him by a grown man's penis. He recalled that he used to take showers with his father.

Yet none of his associations led back to the infantile core of the dream, *the big change* that occurred when the giant entered the scene. I reminded him now of his own description of a happy care-free life in the first part of the dream and the sudden appearance of the giant which brought about a big change. I suggested to him that the dream also condensed a crucial experience in his own life, when his father came home from war and appeared as a stranger to the 4-year-old Eric. This was the giant, Eric saw immediately, and then thoughtfully said: "But why should I have been so afraid of my father when he has always been so easy on me?" Here I was able to help him see again the anxiety in relation to rivalry with his father and the disturbance created in his relationship to his mother.

The analysis of this dream brought together for Eric a number of details which we had been working on for some time in analysis, and Eric was able to see that his fear of being active and competing successfully with males centered in his relationship to his father, and how the oedipal rivalry had produced great anxiety in him which caused him to surrender his active strivings. He was able to see how this pattern had continued, and with puberty (another *big change*) the whole pattern had been repeated. As in the dream, he had seen the picture "before."

It is worth mentioning that, with this part of the analysis dealing with the active-passive patterns, the tics disappeared once more. But again it is significant that the passive longings for the father did not enter the analysis in any way that permitted their analysis.

As the time for camp came around again, Eric began to speak of Joe once more, wondering if he would be back in camp and how he should handle his relationship with him. At this time Eric brought in a dream in which his envy of Joe's athletic ability and his powerful body was represented in a dream detail, "catching a big bruiser of a fellow" (in a game of water tag). Now it was possible to show Eric another motive in his sexual relationship to Joe last summer—that in this relationship he could acquire, by identification, those masculine qualities that he admired and wanted to have for himself. Eric really understood this for the first time. I told him, too, that we could expect that as he grew more certain of his masculinity we should expect that he would not need to borrow the masculinity of others.

This brought us to June, to another summer in camp, which turned out to be entirely successful and without any repetition of homosexual attachments. (The counselor Joe did not return this summer.)

Now I must go back in this narrative about 1 month in order to interpolate a strange episode that eluded analysis at the time and which did not reveal its meaning until 6 months later. Chronologically, this episode belongs to the period just following the big-change dream and preceding by a month the material I have just reported concerning the analysis of the dream of "catching the big bruiser."

One day around the middle of May, Eric arrived for his appointment in a fury: "Boy, am I burned! Am I burned! Just let me tell you. If there's anything I hate it's grownups who take advantage of kids just because they're younger and they know they can't do anything about it!"

I waited to hear more, fully expecting a new confession, but I was baffled as Eric launched into his story.

"Yesterday, Jimmy and I took our ducks for a walk in the cemetery."

"Your what?" I asked.

"Ducks. Jimmy and I both spent our allowance on ducks last week. For pets."

"And where did you say you took the ducks for a walk?"

"In the cemetery." (Eric lived not far from one.)

He was annoyed by my interruptions and went on: "So while we were walking in the cemetery a man came up to us."

I had a chilling vision of a man materializing from the sod. For a moment I thought I had not heard right again. Or was this a dream? "Are you telling me a dream, Eric?" I said.

"No. Will you listen? So this man says that these were such nice ducks and he had a little boy who would just love to have such a duck. We thought he was poor, so Jimmy and I talked together and we decided we'd give our ducks to the man for his little boy. Then when we brought the ducks to his house yesterday afternoon we saw he wasn't poor at all. So we told the man that we each paid two dollars for our ducks and would he please pay us $4.00 please. He said no. So we didn't know what to do and we felt sorry for the little boy so we left the ducks and we went home. So we decided we had a legal right to get paid and we're going to send him a bill and a letter. I wrote this letter in school and I want you to see it."

The letter read:

Sir:
We hold your son in high regards. As kids we know the emotions of the son in this because at points of our life we have experienced this feeling. It is because of this *son we have left two ducks in your son's possession.* We don't want your son to have this demoralizing let-down though we feel we deserve money. We just as soon see other kids made happy. We hope that in the future you will regard kids as your equal.
$4.00

There was no way in which I could make sense out of this episode. When I tried to show Eric that his reactions seemed excessive, when I suggested that we should try to find out what all this meant, Eric was simply annoyed with me.

"Would you like to be cheated out of money?" he demanded. "I got a right to be mad. And anyway Jimmy and I liked those ducks. A child psychologist should understand what a pet means to kids!"

The letter was not sent. I learned in the next hour that the boys decided against their suit for payment and had kidnaped the ducks from the man's back yard. Two days later a fresh crisis occurred when the mothers of both boys insisted that they would not have the ducks around. I was prepared for a renewal of grief and outrage against mothers, but now, to my surprise, Eric described in circumstantial terms the cold-blooded schemes which Jimmy and he had worked out for disposing of the ducks. They had approached several butchers in the neighborhood who would neither buy them (at bargain prices) or accept them for nothing. A day later, these ducks, so lovingly nurtured and protected from the avarice of grownups, were taken by their owners for a long walk in the country—and lost. It occurred to me that this might, indeed, have been the original motive in taking the ducks to the cemetery that fateful afternoon.

This was all I learned about the ducks for many months. Nothing that I said or did had any effect upon Eric, whose attitude throughout was that every bit of emotion invested in these creatures and the man who did them out of a fair return that day in the cemetery was entirely justified and merited by the circumstances.

In December of this year, Eric came in for an hour in a surly mood and told me he was fed up with his coach, Mr. R. He wished that Mr. R. would not make a pet of him; he wished Mr. R. would treat him like any other student. Oh, none of this would matter, but Mr. R. had invited Eric to a football game and Eric had refused and Eric's family was "on his neck" for being so rude to Mr. R. who was, they thought, just trying to be nice to Eric.

Mr. R. had not appeared prominently in the analysis for many months. I began to raise some questions about Mr. R. as to why Eric could not accept his invitation, and Eric, with mounting irritability, began reciting his grievances. He had had as little to do with Mr. R. as possible, he said. Being a pet of Mr. R.'s at school was really a problem. Several months ago when Mr. R. was coaching Eric for the baseball season, he had become a little too chummy. Nothing very bad, not like that business with Joe at camp, but he would put his arm around Eric and several times kissed him on the forehead. It was very embarrassing, Eric said stiffly, and he began to avoid Mr. R. Then, as Eric found himself speaking of these things, his anger rose and he finished in a restrained fury. He hated the whole thing! He hated being in a position where he couldn't "tell the guy off" because Mr. R. was in a position of authority. All he could do was to avoid him. That's what was so terrible. A grownup taking advantage of a kid, and there wasn't a thing you could do!

Then I guessed when this had happened and asked Eric, "When did this take place?"

"Last spring—May or June or some time, before I left for camp."

"The time of the ducks, do you think?"

Eric said with astonishment, "That must have been it!"

"And that was why you were so furious with that man who took advantage of you in the duck business?"

"It must have been!"

"But why couldn't you tell me *then* about Mr. R.?"

Eric looked baffled and said, "I didn't even realize it bothered me so much. It happened. I handled it very well, I thought. I didn't get into anything with him like I did with Joe. Until right now, *this moment,* I didn't realize how much it meant to me. I didn't even know that it was bothering me, then!"

I have cited this episode in some detail because it illustrates so well how some of the great conflicts of adolescence can go masquerading—even in analysis—as a piece of adolescent nonsense.

The whole conflict with Mr. R., the problem of "being a pet," and "grownups who take advantage of little kids" had been acted out as if in a weird and distorted dream by way of another problem of pets (the ducks) and an encounter with a man in the cemetery who "took advantage of little kids."

All that I could be sure of in May, during the saga of the ducks, was that something had been displaced onto the man who took advantage of the boys. It sounded suspiciously like another homosexual conflict, but there was nothing in the analytic material that could pinpoint this and there was no way of discerning, in the chaos of puberty, whether this was a piece of repressed material that had broken through into consciousness under the influence of the recent analysis of the relationship to the father or whether it was a displacement from a recent experience. And while I waited for more material, the whole experience of the ducks lost its intensive emotional quality and faded away without being analyzed.

I am sure that Eric was truthful when he said that, until this moment 6 months later, he had not realized how disturbing Mr. R.'s advances had been to him. Since the intense emotional reactions were displaced and acted out by means of the duck saga, he was spared the recognition of these painful feelings in relation to Mr. R. We can also suspect that the motive in displacement arose from the erotic response which Eric needed to deny in himself.

In our discussion of the episodes with Mr. R., Eric briefly discovered in himself a longing for Mr. R. It was at the end of several hours of discussion in which Eric described his feelings: "I hated it. He made me feel—like a girl" How glad Eric was that he was good in athletics! And then, with sudden insight, he said, "Say, that must be one of the reasons it's been so important to me to be a good athlete—to prove myself a boy!" Near the end of this long outpouring, Eric said bitterly that he was afraid now to get close to anybody lest something like this could happen again.

I remarked that this was not a good solution either, and that if he could understand his own feelings better he would not, in the future, have to be afraid of such things happening.

It was then that Eric said, "It's funny. I know you didn't say it, but I thought for a moment you were saying I should go back to Mr. R."

This made it possible for us to go a little further into his ambivalent feelings and for Eric to admit that there were strong attractions as well as revulsion toward Mr. R. We learned very little more about this in analysis, but Eric, following this period of analysis, reported that he felt free and that somehow a big change had occurred in him. He no longer had to avoid Mr. R. and could accept him as a coach and take what he needed in instruction. For the first time in his life, Eric said, he felt that he was out to win a game for himself and not to please a coach, or his parents, or someone else. Soon afterward he had a triumphant dream celebrating the change he reported in himself. In the dream he returned from a football game, in which he had performed brilliantly, and found the basement of his home transformed. From an ugly storage and utility area, the whole basement had turned into a magnificent apartment, most elegantly furnished with a conspicuously luxurious double bed. He described the feeling in the dream as "a very happy and hopeful feeling," and when he woke up he associated the feeling with a change in himself. He was reminded of how much better he felt about Mr. R. and that he had acquired a new girl friend, the first girl he had ever liked much.

Although the acquisition of a girl friend was, from one point of view, a flight from homosexual dangers, it was also a healthy sign, and, in the months that followed, Eric, now 14, began to enter into the kind of boy-girl activities that were usual in his community. It does not surprise us that we learned very little more about his homosexual conflicts in these months and that Eric, symptom free, performing well at school, pleased with himself and his girl friend, had very little motive to pursue his analysis any further.

Only one other important detail pertaining to the homosexual conflicts emerged in the next months of analysis. From two dream details, "a station wagon with a kind of visor coming over the windshield" and "identifying two photographs," Eric brought in associations leading to circumcision (the visor) and the "wanted" pictures in the post office. For the first time Eric was able to speak about circumcision and could tell me that every time the subject had come up in these years of analysis he knew he had avoided it. Although he knew he had been circumcised in infancy, he had always associated it in his own mind with his tonsillectomy at 5. (Once during the "Christine" period of the analysis, he had also associated Christine's operation with his tonsillectomy.) Concerning the "wanted" pictures, Eric jokingly said, "I don't know who they wanted. Not me. They don't want me. I'm already circumcised."

From this Eric was able to see how the tonsillectomy at the age of 5, soon after his father's return from service, had seemed like the dreaded punishment for his "criminal" wishes and was fused in his mind with circumcision and with castration (Christine's operation). His joke, "They don't want me. I'm already circumcised!" provided another insight for Eric into his passive defense. The castrated Christine was "safe"; she had "nothing to lose."

The analysis was terminated when Eric was a few months past his fourteenth birthday. Eric himself felt that he had gotten from analysis what he wanted. And I felt, with some reservations, that he had probably gone as far as he could go in this period of his development. He had become a self-confident youngster; he claimed to have no special worries and much confidence in his future. His schoolwork was good; his athletic career was very promising. The tics had long been absent; the examination anxiety had diminished to something close to normal. His relationships with other boys and girls were good, and he seemed, in fact, to have somewhat less difficulty in making overtures to girls than do many boys of his age. From Eric's point of view (and from his parents', too) he was doing fine, and he could see no reason to continue in analysis.

It was in Eric's relationship to the father that I felt unease as a therapist considering termination. Here there was too little conflict for health in adolescence. Although Eric could challenge his father's opinions—and this seemed to him to be a very brave thing to do—he rarely showed any anger toward his father, nor did we see much hostility toward the father in analysis. It was almost always displaced onto a teacher or another man in authority, and always there were to Eric such excellent reasons for hating the teacher and such excellent reasons for not feeling angry at such a "good guy" as his father that only on rare occasions was I able to get behind displacement and isolation of feelings with Eric.

During the last months of analysis I drew Eric's attention again and again to some of his attitudes toward his father. I remarked on the absence of conflict, the one-sided adulation of the father, which left no room for the negative feelings which we should concede as part of any affectionate relationship. Eric was only impatient with me for what he considered to be an unwarranted interference in his relationship with his father. "I don't get you," he said on one occasion. "Here, everything is going fine and I get along great with my father and you're not satisfied because everything is going so good." In the end, I had to concede as a therapist that we had probably gone as far as we could during this period of adolescence. Behind the uncritical adulation of the father were the passive longings for father, and these had eluded analysis throughout.

Postscript

I was able to follow Eric's progress for the next years. His mother occasionally phoned me to ask my advice or just to let me know how Eric was doing. From these reports I saw that Eric sustained his gains in all areas and, in late adolescence, seemed normally busy with dating, parties, and boy-girl associations.

When Eric was 17 and in his last year of high school, he called me and asked for an appointment. Things were not going well, he told me. This semester he could not concentrate on his work, and he was just doing enough to "get by." He was discouraged. He had no idea what had happened to him this semester and couldn't imagine what might be troubling him. In the course of the hour he talked about his various activities this year and then, quite matter-of-factly, remarked that he had had his first sex experience with a woman a few months previous. His brother Bob and some of his friends had initiated him by taking him along to a house of prostitution. All he could say, he concluded nonchalantly, was that sex wasn't all it was cracked up to be. When I said, "But, how terribly disappointing this must have been to you!" tears came into his eyes, and he began to speak with genuine emotion about this experience. He was actually quite frightened throughout, he said, and all he could think of during the act was to get it over quickly and get out. And then—just as I remembered on other occasions during Eric's analysis—he said, "And then I just seemed to forget about the whole thing and until *right now* I didn't realize how much this thing was bothering me!"

Of course a first coitus under these circumstances is difficult to evaluate, and it was not until we had two more interviews and could go into Eric's relationships with girls to a greater extent that I was sure that Eric's heterosexuality remained on shaky ground. He had girl friends, but the girls seemed to be trophies in masculine competition. He did not enjoy intimacy with any of the girls, and his great fear was that if he should become attached to any girl he would become enslaved, completely subject to her control. It is interesting, too, that he had no close boy friends this year, and he himself said, "I feel afraid to get close to anyone." Under these circumstances I made no attempt to interpret this behavior to Eric, but it was very clear that both a heterosexual and a homosexual object stirred up so much conflict in him that he was avoiding close contact with either sex. It is also significant that the strong positive relationship to his father remained unchanged in the current picture.

Eric readily agreed that he needed further help. Since, in spite of his doubts about himself, he really intended to go away to school, it seemed advisable to postpone analysis until he entered college in the fall, and arrangements were made for Eric to go into analysis with a male colleague in practice near the university.

DISCUSSION

In the case of Eric we have been able to examine the influence of pubertal processes on passive tendencies which were already strongly in evidence during the latency development. The circum-

stances of an analysis which continued from the age of 11 to 14
permit a detailed study of the homosexual conflicts in the prepubertal and pubertal phases.

I found it instructive to see how, in the prepubertal phase of the
analysis, the analysis of the defenses against aggression produced
personality changes which superficially resembled a shift from
feminine to masculine attitudes. The timid boy became assertive,
the passive partner in the brothers' sadomasochistic relationship
became aggressive, the homosexual games were relinquished, the
cowardly ballplayer became a confident and aggressive player, the
student who feared the competition of learning began to achieve
scholastically, and the tics temporarily disappeared. In short, the
whole picture was seemingly altered in favor of active and masculine attitudes. Although I do not wish to diminish these achievements—and the greater stability of the ego must be counted a
gain under any circumstances—I think it is of the utmost importance to see how the passive tendencies persisted and, in the end,
exerted a decisive influence upon the attainment of heterosexuality.
I find myself speculating: If we had ended the analysis at the
close of this period, we might not have been able to judge through
superficial observation that these new evidences of masculinity
were in part a defense against the passive strivings. All of which
suggests that we need to assess carefully such therapeutic results
in prepuberty, and, although there may be circumstances in therapy with boys of this age that require us to be satisfied with even
this much achievement, we should probably take a cautious and
reserved attitude toward the prognosis in such cases.

We are reminded of Anna Freud's comments[6] on the spontaneous
changes which puberty may bring forth in a passive boy, a shift
in passive to active that is promoted by the strong currents of the
drives in puberty. She warns us that, after the powerful impetus of
the drives diminishes in later adolescence, we may find that the
passive attitudes have reinstated themselves. In Eric's case the
dramatic shift which we observed after the first year of the analysis
was a result of therapy, but a therapy that had powerful reinforcement from the drives themselves in the prepubertal development.

The pubertal phase of the analysis permits a close examination
of the structure of Eric's homosexuality. We saw how oedipal
fantasies briefly, yet forcefully, emerged into consciousness and
were acted out in the pathetic and ill-fated drama that began with
the trying on of the father's coat and ended in the discovery of his

masturbation with the father's condom and the mother's sanitary pad. Now, of course, in every boy's puberty such fantasies will emerge into consciousness, more or less disguised, and for every boy there will be anxiety, shame, and some form of flight from the dangerous wishes. Typically, the masturbation itself, as the vehicle for the forbidden wishes, becomes the area of conflict, and the temptations appear to the pubertal boy as emerging from the masturbation itself. Here we see the familiar picture of the boy alternately submitting to masturbation and heroically resisting it, tormented by fears of genital damage, defending himself against the temptations arising within and the fantasied dangers through magical devices, or neurotic symptoms, or sometimes through flight and acting out. Normally, in early puberty the boy retains his masturbation, the incestuous fantasies are buried under elaborate disguises, and we begin to see fantasies centering around a girl whose real presence and nearness would cause the pubertal boy to die of agony, but whose imaginary presence becomes indispensable to his erotic fantasies. In this way he makes the displacement from incestuous object to nonincestuous love object by way of the imagination and in preparation for the real shift in object choice that may not take place for a while.[2]

In what ways, then, does Eric's pubertal development deviate? We saw that the second edition of the Oedipus complex was brief, that rivalry with the father was quickly abandoned, and that he fell back upon the infantile solution and took the rival as his love object. I think it is impressive that the analysis actively dealt with the castration anxiety aroused by the envy and rivalry with the father during this period; that analysis diminished the anxiety and temporarily dissolved the symptoms. Yet analysis did not prevent the regression or the acting out of homosexual wishes in the summer episode with the counselor. This tells us that the passive wishes were really the decisive factors in this regression and, of course, it was just these that Eric had excluded from the analysis.

At what point in this development does homosexuality present itself as a danger? The passive solution to the oedipal rivalry with the father does not, in itself, predict homosexuality. At this point all we can say is that, without therapeutic intervention, we can predict failure or at least severe disability in the achievement of masculine goals in later life. The bisexual masturbation fantasies do not, in themselves, permit a prediction in favor of homosexuality, since they are more or less characteristic of puberty. The long history of homosexual games with the older brother have some predictive value for passivity, but we cannot make inferences from them for a homosexual choice in later life.

Among all the decisions and solutions along the way in Eric's bisexual conflicts, I think only one might have dangerously tipped the scale in favor of homosexuality. My impression is that Eric's deviation must be seriously appraised at the point where he offered himself to an adult male as a sexual partner. I have said that the "allowable" homosexuality of male puberty does not include sexual contact with an adult and is, in fact, walled off by rigid taboos in the boy culture. From this we can conclude that, for the boy, a homosexual relationship with an adult male constitutes the dangerous regression to the original homosexual object, the father.

In Eric's case the choice of an adult male sexual object tells us that he had taken the dangerous regressive step. The infantile sexual aims toward the father were revived and sought an object in the transparent father figure, the coach. In this relationship both nonsexual and sexual attitudes toward the father were united. There were admiration, envy, and overestimation of the coach as well as passive sexual longing. In normal adolescent development the attachment to an adult male which has the quality of hero worship is based on the nonsexual attitudes toward the father which are readily displaceable in this period of development and may play an important role in the boy's emancipation from his father. But the infantile sexual wishes for the father are not revived, and their repression is strictly maintained. The diffuse homosexuality of puberty shows us that there is a partial breakthrough of the infantile homosexuality (this is true for latency, too), but these homosexual wishes do not center again in the father and are not transferred to other adult males.

It is undoubtedly very significant that, following the first homosexual contact with a man, Eric's relationship with his father gained in positive strength with a resurgence of infantile overestimation, and that this relationship remained unshakably firm and unambivalent for the period of adolescence. We are reminded again of Anna Freud's observations that the absence of conflict between the adolescent and his original love objects can be an ominous sign.[6,8]

Although I have proposed that Eric's homosexual experience with a man was a crucial point in his development, a dangerous regression that may easily lead to a homosexual position in adolescence, I am fully aware that a case illustration from analytic practice does not prove the point. We cannot demonstrate that, without therapeutic intervention, Eric might have become a homosexual, although our therapeutic experience with adult homosexuals frequently focuses our attention upon adolescence as the time of decision. Erikson[5] draws our attention to the delicate balance that may throw decisions of identity in one direction or another during the crisis of puberty, so that the adolescent who doesn't know yet "what" he is may take the identity tag that is given him by his community. The uncommitted delinquent or the wavering homosexual awaits our judgment and the name we give him. In this respect the child who is in psychotherapy at the time he engages in a homosexual act has the advantage of our therapeutic attitude in addition to anything else that we bring him in the way of insight. We do not promote a homosexual identity through our behavior or our own attitudes. At the same time, another factor enters into the homosexual identity in adolescence. When the rare adolescent boy or girl says, "I wasn't sure, but now I know I'm a homosexual," it is not only that he has been "tagged" but that he has acquired his identity through inner knowledge. He means that he has found a homosexual partner to whom he is bound through love. He has found the sexual experience exciting and satisfying, and he commits himself, through love. In the occasional frank autobiographical statements that come to us—I think of Gide[9] offhand—it is this falling in love that crystallizes the homosexual identity: "Now I *know.*"

Then, if we return to our patient once again, we see that he has taken the dangerous regressive step in a homosexual relationship with an adult man, but he is not yet committed! He has not fallen in love with the counselor; he has probably not achieved enough sexual satisfaction in these acts to bind him to the partner. He undoubtedly found it exciting—he reluctantly admitted this much in his discussion—but guilt and anxiety probably inhibited response, for, if he had achieved satisfaction, we would have seen this in a bond to the partner that would have resisted analysis, at least for a time, and we would have encountered either the wish to repeat the pleasurable experience with another partner or a repetition of the homosexual experience with another partner. Anxiety deterred the erotic response. In the second encounter with a homosexual man—the coach at school—Eric withdrew in alarm after the first sexual overtures.

After the homosexual experience with Joe, we see the repressive forces take over again. In the analysis Eric exhibited all the defenses against homosexual strivings that we are accustomed to see in boys of his age. For the analysis this meant that we were unable to analyze the passive wishes, but for Eric's development it was necessary for him to rebuild his defenses against them.

It is impressive to see how much of the analysis dealt with envy of males, of male competition, fear of castration by males, the acquisition of masculinity by identification with males, and, in every instance, how the figure of the father emerged into the foreground of these conflicts, yet the bond to the father remained undisturbed. This is not difficult to understand. For the passive longings for the father, the feminine attitudes resisted analysis throughout. We saw how difficult it was to deal with this material even in a tentative and cautious way. It was possible to show Eric how passivity served as a defense against activity and how activity became, at times, a defense against passivity, and this much he could accept and employ profitably. But the identification with women, the erotic longings for the homosexual objects, never entered the analysis in a way that promoted our objectives. They were excluded by Eric from analysis as in the denial of the use of the sanitary napkin in masturbation, and the two homosexual attachments to men were reported in analysis at such a safe distance from the time of their occurrence that they were robbed of a large measure of their original emotional significance. During our exploration of one of the Christine dreams ("to change places") I had asked the obvious question if Eric himself had sometimes wondered what it would be like to be a woman, and he had responded gravely, "You ask me that at the wrong time of my life."

He was quite right, in a way. We know how difficult it is to analyze the feminine attitudes of boys and men at any age. In puberty the feminine wishes must be warded off with all the energy at the child's disposal. The integrity of the ego is imperiled if such wishes emerge into consciousness. We can also understand why Christine became such a terrible symbol to Eric. For to admit a feminine wish would be equivalent to asking for castration, like Christine. The great fear in Eric was that analysis would reveal the feminine wish, and behind the monstrous symbol of the operation on Christine ("Would the doctors *really* do that?") was the fear that analysis might reverse his sexual role. It is worth mentioning that one of the first transference dreams represented analysis as an operation and one of the last transference dreams equated analysis with an operation (circumcision).

From the analytic material we see that the predisposing factors in Eric's passive development lay in the early, prolonged, and unambivalent attachment to the mother during the father's 4-year absence in service, the sadomasochistic relationship to the older brother who used him sexually as a girl, and the belated appearance of the father in the young boy's life, an event that deserves to be called traumatic. As in the big-change dream, the father, who was a stranger, appeared suddenly to assume his prerogatives as a husband and a father, and before this figure of the giant the little boy felt tiny and insignificant. Such phallic masculinity as we can grant a little boy shrank to near nothingness by contrast with that of the father. The return of the father was symbolically a castration. We see little evidence of an active conflict with the father during this period. The attenuated struggle that we normally see during the oedipal phase cannot take place even in telescoped form when a little boy confronts his rival under these extraordinary circumstances. And although a little boy normally is aided in resolution by the well-established and durable positive ties to the father, there was no previous relationship between father and son to shelter the child in the brief storm of this conflict. If we dare risk an inference from the pubertal edition of the oedipal conflict, the infantile conflict must have been brief and overwhelming, and the struggle ended in the child's partial surrender of masculine aims. (As in the screen memory of a circumcision at the age of 5, Eric sacrificed part of his masculinity in order to retain part.)

In the infantile solution Eric gave up the sexual aims in relation to the mother in favor of identification with her, and he abolished the competition between his father and himself by offering himself as a love object to the father. The erotic relationship with the older brother was employed throughout latency for the acting out of the feminine identification and the passive wishes in relation to the father. The father's role in latency was shadowy. Although there was little intimacy between Eric and his father, there was awe and a kind of adulation that colored the relationship from that point on.

To all of this we must add another important motive in the abandonment of masculine strivings. A voyeuristic component, which was manifest in the characteristic symptom of the eye tic in latency, derived its most powerful impetus from observations of the female genitalia in the preoedipal period and later received reinforcement from primal-scene observations. From transference observations particularly, we must attribute to this horror of the female genitalia a strong motive in the flight to homosexual objects in puberty. The female genitalia confronted him with the "evidence" of castration that could not be denied. In choosing male objects, his denial could be sustained, and castration anxiety could be kept in abeyance. We also see that he protected himself against castration by men by surrendering competitive aims and offering himself as a passive partner. Passivity became the only alternative between two dangers.

We were able to see, too, how the relationships with men also served to recover his lost masculinity, for while he was passive he acquired masculinity through identification with certain qualities of the male partners. As in the cases of male homosexuality cited by Anna Freud,[7] the passive partner acquired his own lost masculinity through identification with the male partner. And as in Anna Freud's cases, Eric's identification was a partial one. It was the athletic prowess and the powerful body of Joe that attracted Eric. He must have had many opportunities to see his counselor's penis, too, and we can guess that the man's penis must have exerted a strong attraction for Eric as a masculine symbol. It was clearly not the man himself but the attributes of the man that excited the boy, and it was through such partial and primitive identifications that Eric attempted to acquire masculinity. For all these insights we are very greatly in the debt of Anna Freud.

I must also cite Anna Freud for another most valuable insight into male passivity. She discovered, in her analytic work, that fear of being deprived of the homosexual partner was one of the greatest dangers of analysis as seen by her patients. For these patients the loss of the partner was equivalent to castration, for it was through the partner that the patient acquired his masculinity. It was through employing these insights analytically that Anna Freud was able to restore her passive patients to active masculinity.

Eric was able to give up his homosexual relationship to Joe. The relationship to Mr. R., the school coach, was more ambiguous, since Eric himself abandoned the relationship after the first sexual overtures were made by the teacher. Thereafter, he did not become involved in further homosexual relationships, but neither did he free himself from the tie to his father.

How shall we assess the analytic work with Eric? It was incomplete—as it often must be in puberty and early adolescence. Castration anxiety was analyzed in terms of the rivalry with the father and other males and as a reaction to the female genitalia. The identification with males in order to "borrow" masculinity was dealt with. Activity and passivity, as defense, were extensively dealt with in the analysis. The feminine wishes were not available to analysis at all. The analysis produced certain changes from passive to active, with greater freedom in aggressive competition with males; it removed the inhibitions in learning that had so severely restricted him; it dissolved the symptoms, the eye and nose tics, and brought about greatly improved ego functioning in all areas. At the time therapy was terminated, Eric had achieved an equilibrium that could sustain him very well for this phase of adolescence. His homosexual conflicts had subsided, his masculinity could stand up well by the criteria of the young adolescent—that is to say, he could be aggressive, he could put up a good fight when necessary, he was an outgoing athlete in school, and he could conduct himself well on dates with girls. He had no need yet to prove his potency.

It was in later adolescence, following his first sexual experience with a prostitute, that his masculinity suffered a severe blow. We recall, too, that it was his brother who initiated him, and the homosexual coloring of his first sex experience must be weighed in the consequences also. This time the failure of his masculinity did not cause him to take refuge in a homosexual relationship. He did not regress; he did not develop a neurosis. Instead, we saw an inhibition in relationship with both sexes, exactly characterizing his dilemma, for he could move in neither direction now. The blow to his masculinity resulted in self-depreciation and a temporary loss of ambition. In the absence of firm goals for himself, his schoolwork began to suffer. It was at this point that Eric returned for further help.

REFERENCES

1. BLOS, P. "The Treatment of Adolescents," in *Psychoanalysis and Social Work*, ed. by M. Heiman. New York, International Universities Press, Inc., 1953.
2. BLOS, P. Pre-adolescent drive organization. *J. Am. Psychoanalyt. Assoc.* 6: 47, 1958.
3. BRUNSWICK, R. "The Pre-oedipal Phase of Libido Development," in *Psychoanalytic Reader*, ed. by R. Fliess, New York, International Universities Press, Inc., 1948.
4. DEUTSCH, H. "On Female Homosexuality," in *Psychoanalytic Reader*, ed. by R. Fliess, New York, International Universities Press, Inc., 1948.

5. ERIKSON, E. The problem of ego identity. *J. Am. Psychoanalyt. Assoc. 4:* 56, 1956.
6. FREUD, A. *The Psycho-analytical Treatment of Children.* London, Imago Publishing Company, 1946.
7. FREUD, A. "Studies in Passivity." Lecture before Detroit Psychoanalytic Society at Western Reserve Medical School, Cleveland, Oct. 25, 1952 (unpublished).
8. FREUD, A. "Adolescence," in *The Psychoanalytic Study of the Child.* New York, International Universities Press, Inc., 1958, vol. 13.
9. GIDE, A. *If It Die (Si le grain ne meurt).* London, Martin Secker & Warburg, Ltd., 1951.

chapter 6 The Adolescent Exhibitionist

SYLVAN KEISER

The problem of genital exhibitionism presents many unsolved phenomena, whether it is manifested by an adult or an adolescent. As is well known, it is a normal developmental phase and frequently appears in dreams as a wish to return to the innocence of childhood. A multiplicity of meanings can be attributed to it, for the child as well as the adult. Among the many purposes that exhibitionism serves, a few might be mentioned. On one level we see the child seeking love and admiration for his beloved possession with all its narcissistic endowment. For the child as well as the adult, it gives reassurance against the fear of castration. Of course it always expresses the reversal of the wish to look at the genitals of others. In the author's experience, adults recalling the freedom of childhood also recollect the rage and humiliation suffered by them because of the adults' indifference to their genitals. In adolescence the exhibitionistic desires are ordinarily repressed, and the reaction-formation of shyness takes over with the development of pubic hair. The exhibitionism usually is in the homosexual setting of group activities with other boys. When public display of the genitals does occur, it seems likely that a major disturbance in the ego-superego relationship has occurred also. The patient usually regards himself as a hopelessly ill and degenerate person. This is one reason why genital exhibitionists do not seek analysis, and, as a consequence, analysts have not had much opportunity to investigate the problem with the psychoanalytic method. More often, it has been an incidental symptom uncovered during an analysis for other complaints; or it came under observation through the same circumstances, as in the instance of the case report below, that is, legal incarceration. But analysts have the opportunity to study dreams and fantasies which express exhibitionistic wishes. Christoffel's[1] article is probably the best analytic discussion of the subject. The expression "genital exhibitionism" is used to emphasize its specific and circumscribed

113

nature which must be distinguished from exhibitionism in general. Furthermore, it is intended to emphasize the fact that the patient's problem is not simply an uninhibited expression of the exhibitionism normal in childhood.

CASE REPORT*

Physical Examination

The patient is a short (5 feet, 3½ inches), thick-set, moderately obese (170 pounds), 15-year-old, blond white boy, with some acne lesions on his face. His blood pressure, on admission, was 150/82; later, it read 120/80. There were apical murmurs, without transmission. No cardiac enlargement was detected by either X ray or percussion. The rest of the examination, including the electroencephalogram, produced normal findings.

Present Difficulty

About 4 years ago, the mother became aware for the first time that the patient was "exposing and playing with himself" in public. A neighbor told her about it. She was shocked and enraged, but she kept it from the patient's father, who has a bad temper. During the months following her first knowledge of his acts, she got similar complaints from different people. Finally, this was brought to the father's attention. He also became angry, but he limited his punishment to a severe verbal lashing, "because if I laid a hand on him, I would have killed him."

A friend suggested psychiatric help, and the mother took the boy to the Parent-Child and Adult Guidance Center. For the past 3 years he has been seeing a psychologist at the center, once a week for about 50 minutes. His deviant behavior became less frequent, ranging from about one to three times a month, during the first year of treatment, to once every 3 months during the second year and only once during the last year, this last occasion leading to his hospitalization.

Two days before admission, when he was in his English class—the last period of the day—the teacher called him. He was scribbling his initials in his notebook and failed to hear the teacher, who then punished him by taking the notebook away. She refused to give it back to him, even when the class was over and the patient

* Prepared under the supervision of Dr. Henry I. Schneer.

asked for it. He was very angry but said nothing. Instead, he walked around "trying to cool off." He went to a nearby college library because he "had no place to go," and he started to feel the urge to expose his penis. He wandered over to the men's toilet and had a desire to peep, but he saw no one.

He then went to a phone and called his mother to let her know, as he always does, that he wasn't going home right away. His mother told him to come home as his aunt was visiting and had pictures of his baby cousin which he might want to see.

He did not go home but went, instead, to a side entrance of the college, exposed his penis, and started to masturbate. A girl saw him but walked past him. Two minutes later, the matron came with a detective who apprehended him.

Family History

The patient's mother was born and raised in a small mining town, the second to the youngest of six living children. Five other children died in infancy and early childhood. She was told that one sister had died from burns caused by toy sparklers and another from burns received when she fell into a washtub filled with boiling water.

The patient's maternal grandfather was a miner. He died 8 years ago of a heart condition. The maternal grandmother died of a blood clot when the patient's mother was 17. The grandfather was strict, the grandmother outgoing and generous. After the latter's death, the patient's mother came to New York City where she worked and lived with a family as a baby sitter. She married her present husband after knowing him 3 years. After marriage she never worked, and, even though her husband has recently told her to go out and get a job to help pay expenses, she refused, saying that her children needed her at home.

The patient's father, 41 years of age, is an iron welder. His work involves climbing high scaffolds. A month prior to the patient's admission, the father was in an accident at work, sustaining a small laceration of the left lower cheek. Recently, he bought a car which he needs in his work, and, as a result, the family finances are strained. He has berated the patient for the expense of treatment, without enough results.

Relations between the parents are strained because of finances and of the patient's problems. When arguing, they often use foul language. The mother resents the father's drinking, but she gives excuses for it to the children, saying that he works hard, lives dangerously, and that his boss wants the boys to have a drink or two after work.

Sibling

The patient's brother, 12 years old, is in the seventh grade. He seems attached to his mother, who worries about his poor eating habits. During his first year of life, he had an abdominal hernia which caused his mother to be worrisome and overly gentle with him. He also uses foul language and has frequent tantrums, especially about food.

The family lives in a three-room apartment. The boys sleep in separate beds in the bedroom, and the parents occupy a sofa bed in the living room. The patient slept in a crib in the parents' room until the age of 3½ years. For a time, both the patient and his brother occupied cribs in the parental bedroom.

Developmental History

Pregnancy occurred during the first year of the parents' marriage. Although not planned, the mother was happy about it, but the father "had to get used to the idea." In retrospect, the mother feels that she might have been better off without children, because "I care too much."

The period of gestation was "not too bad," the mother experiencing no vomiting or undue discomfort. Birth came spontaneously, at full term, after an easy labor. The baby was healthy and weighed 6 pounds, 6 ounces.

The mother reported that she "dried up in a few days" and could not breast feed the baby. He was bottle fed for 1½ years. There were no feeding and weaning problems—"he weaned himself." At 2 years of age he had diarrhea for a week. His appetite was always good, and he was chubby from his first year. About 5 or 6 years ago, he started gaining weight rapidly.

He was "a wonderful, good-natured baby with an angelic smile." He was babied a great deal by his mother and the aunts who visited frequently. He sat up at 8 months and walked at about 1 year of age. The mother cannot recall details of his teeth growth, but she remembers that the only slow part of his development was talking. He spoke words and short phrases until he was 4 (after the sibling's birth), when he was able to say complete sentences.

The patient was bowel trained, with difficulty, at 3½ years of age. "He was unpredictable, and I spanked him for it," said the mother. He was bladder trained, by day, at 3½ years. From that time to the present, he has been enuretic about two to three times a week, except when he has been away from home. He has been spanked by his mother for this also.

There has been no thumb sucking, but he bites his nails constantly. The mother reported no teeth grinding or head banging, and she said that at the age of 10 to 14 months he rocked himself to sleep.

On two or three occasions, the patient says, he has dreamed of "a big hairy thing—a monster coming at me," which makes him feel trapped. He is afraid of heights. He hates school and is sometimes truant.

Sexual Development

When the patient was 11, the mother discovered him masturbating and told him that it was sinful. The father also discovered it and yelled at him for this "filthy habit." Throughout the next year the mother found him with his hands on his genitals, but she has learned not to be too upset by this.

He is very modest. During hot summer days, when the mother wears shorts, "he has a fit," insisting that she is only half dressed and should put on more clothes. In spite of this, he himself walks around in his underwear, and his mother tells him to wear pants or regular shorts. He has pictures of nude or half-nude women under his pillow or in his dresser drawers, but he says he hates women. Lately, he mentioned that when he was 10 a man took his pants off and felt him, and the patient wonders if this is how he "got started."

Health History

At 1 year of age and again at 11, the patient had measles. He had scarlet fever at 9. There were no complications. His tonsils and adenoids were removed when he was 2, and his mother reports that he was not unduly upset by the 1-day hospitalization. At age 7, he came home crying, saying that a playmate had poured nail polish in his ear, but there were no complications. At 4 years of age he fell two steps downstairs to a cement walk and received a small lacerated wound on the left temple. He was somewhat dazed but not unconscious. His appetite is very good. As for sleep habits, he likes to stay up late.

School History

The patient is in his fifth term at high school. He was about to enroll in a trade school, but his application came late. His mother feels that he was never good "with his head" but is much better "with his hands." A report from his high school shows truancy and poor scholarship. He is interested in electricity and mechanics.

Social History

This boy is very close to his mother, is at times openly affectionate, and tells her that he loves her. She has been greatly troubled by his deviant behavior and, in anger, has told him, "Go get killed," or "Go out and get run over by a bus," etc. She keeps close watch on his activities, even checking the comics that he reads in the bathroom. She feels that she has babied him too much but that she has "smacked him plenty," too.

The father drinks and is often irritable, and the patient complains that the father spends too little time with him. The father likes to "yell and holler," especially in regard to cleanliness, about which he is very strict. He also uses foul language, which upsets the patient. He has seldom meted out physical punishment except for slapping the patient once when he discovered the boy handling his genitals.

The patient resents the attention given to his sibling, who is sickly and gets a lot of the mother's special consideration. The patient gives his brother a "crack" or a slap sometimes, and the mother steps in and says, "Leave him alone. Should I beat him up just to make you happy?"

The patient has few friends and seems ill at ease in the company of other people. He likes to tease girls. He lies, but the mother detects this easily, and he confesses. He steals small change from her. She scolds him for this, but she keeps the fact from his father, who might be in a bad mood and lose his temper. The boy seldom has temper tantrums; he simply yells and slams doors when very angry. He has stolen comics, knives, and cigarette lighters from stores, but he never has been caught.

Present Personality Make-up (as Described by Mother)

He is a gentle, friendly boy, always smiling. He does not mix very well. He dislikes sports, except swimming. He loves animals and had a dog, 2 years ago, to which he was greatly attached. For lack of room, it had to be given away, and he was heartbroken. He hates drinking and the use of foul language. He often says that he can't do things and learn things as well as other boys. He hates being ordered around. His one great ambition is to join the Army, to be the top sergeant and give orders. He hates fighting and walks away from it. He is rather untidy and disorderly about his clothes and belongings. The mother has not noticed any excessive daydreaming.

Religion

The family belongs to the Protestant Lutheran faith, but, because of a paternal uncle who is deeply involved in Jehovah's Witnesses, they now incline toward that religion. The mother insists that the patient read the Bible frequently and drills into him "the fear of hell and the avoidance of the devil."

Mental Status

The patient is very ill at ease at each interview. He fidgets, picks at his face, and smiles very often, at times in an embarrassed fashion and at other times also inappropriately. His manner is friendly, he is somewhat meek, and he talks softly. His speech is often circumstantial and rambling, at times irrelevant, but always coherent. His anxiety often interferes with his productivity. He becomes evasive or he blocks. There is some loosening of associations. Following is a sample of his speech:

"What do you enjoy doing?"

"I like to tease girls—pull out their kerchiefs, play football with their shoes. I like to see them get mad. Then they chase me."

"Anyone hurt?"

"Not really. A little scraped up perhaps—" (pause) "—I like skin diving—used to go skin diving. A few girls would come along. You can really get scraped up there."

"How?"

"The barnacles on the rocks."

The patient's affect is, for the most part, appropriate, except for his constant smiling. His mood is neutral. It was hard for him to talk about the circumstances that led to his admission. In later interviews he discussed it to some extent, stating that he is very much ashamed when talking about it, especially in front of a woman.

He exposes himself when he is upset or angry. It is most difficult to make him reveal the fantasies he has while masturbating or when exposing his genitals. One of his first statements, after a few minutes of blocking, was that he missed his dog very much; he used to take it on walks and would often talk to it. At another time he said that, while masturbating, he gets very frightened and thinks of an incident that happened when he was 12 years old. While walking with two boys near the railroad tracks, two of them accidentally held a live wire. One boy was electrocuted, and the other had to have his hands amputated. (The mother substantiates this incident, but she can hardly recall the details.)

The patient also says that he sometimes stands in front of a mirror and examines himself. Then, in a very anxious and embarrassed manner, he whispered, "I wonder if women do the same thing."

He would like to be smooth and charming to girls, but he ends up being awkward and teasing them. He describes himself as a "very teasable guy." Sometimes he feels that other boys don't like him. They call him names and adjectives alluding to his being obese. Once in a while he hears a voice calling his name. He turns around but sees no one. He has no idea who it is but says it sounds like a man's voice. He forgets easily, but, with help, he can readily recall events.

Once he went with his classmates on a half-hour visit to a Ford automobile plant. He watched the hoods and seats being lifted up and into the cars. The next day, he could not recall anything at all about the trip until the psychologist, by giving hints, helped him to remember.

He mentions occasional *déjà vu* phenomena. His sensorium and memory are clear. His intelligence appears to be below average. Proverbs are concretized and personalized. His insight and judgment are poor.

At a guidance center, where he was in therapy with a psychologist for the past 3 years, the aim of treatment was to improve his reality testing and to provide him with an adequate male with whom to identify. He never missed sessions. He would come early to chat with a middle-aged secretary. He liked to be helpful. He talked of being a "big shot" and wondered whether drinking would make him one. Before stealing or exposing himself, he would prepare an excuse in case he should be caught. The parents refused to be involved in the treatment.

On the hospital ward he was friendly to patients and ingratiating to personnel. He became upset when he was in the adolescent ward.

After a few days he was discovered in the bathroom "playing with another adolescent's penis."

Psychological Report

He functions at the level of a mild mental defective, although he is capable of better performance. His verbal I.Q. is 74; performance, 67; full scale, 67. His thinking is autistic and bizarre. Projective tests reveal feelings of having sustained physical injury and of experiencing tremendous uncontrollable hostility which he cannot manage. People, animals, and objects are blown apart, caving in, oozing blood. His Bender-Gestalt responses are primitive. Machover figure drawings show a tendency to dissociate: the tipped-over stance of figures; weak, helpless arms and legs; empty, unseeing eyes; and battered, phallic nose suggest a passive, dependent person. His defenses lie in obsessiveness and denial.

DISCUSSION

In considering a patient's history, it is important to realize that a discussant, *post hoc*, can readily detect imperfections in the information elicited during history taking. The questions I pose in the following material should not be construed as criticisms; rather, they underline the difficulties we meet in fully understanding any patient confronting us. As a prototype for this kind of omission is our ignorance of the timing of the mother's severe punishment for this boy's masturbation. Did it precede his genital exhibitionism, since both are said to have occurred when he was 11 years of age? It could be a significant factor in reinforcing his castration anxiety and his consequent feelings of rage toward his mother. An incident of that sort, at that age, would not be etiologic, but it could serve as a trigger mechanism for the outbreak of his perversion. In all likelihood, it can be assumed that his pathological behavior antedated the first time he was detected at age 11. Actually, this type of patient often has not had a true latency period but has indulged in sexual play with other children during those years. But, in this instance, we do not know. If true, this reflects a defect in the normal development of those reaction-formations which help eventually to sublimate infantile sexuality.

Concerning the episode that led to his arrest, did he believe that the teacher had unjustifiably punished him and had "stolen" his book? The salient question is, did he feel castrated at that moment, enraged, and have the need to reassure himself and to take revenge via the genital exhibitionism? Inordinate hostility is always acted out in the perverted act, which also always serves as a reassurance against castration.

Another question is, "How openly did he present his penis?" Did he ejaculate? Could he have deluded himself into believing that he was simply outdoors and was not interested in the girls or inviting detection?

My interest in this question derives from an adult patient who, during adolescence, would go outdoors to his father's car or to a deserted street to expose his penis and masturbate. But he was never detected. Not until he stated the simple fact that it was "exciting to be outdoors" were the usual associations elicited from him. To be outdoors meant escape from his bedroom and bathroom—his usual retreat for masturbation. To be outdoors meant to be bold, defiant, courageous, and, interestingly enough, an apparent denial of the incestuous fantasies. It also meant that he could indulge in his voyeuristic fantasies more easily when outdoors. Not until then could he report his wish to expose himself in front of women and the concomitant associations.

The history of an uneventful weaning following bottle feeding for 18 months must be regarded with some skepticism. If for no other reason, 18 months on the bottle is bound to develop in the infant a reluctance to yield it up. The more we get, the more we want. This fact acquires importance when it is realized that regression to the oral sadistic level occupies a prominent place in the pathology of the genital exhibitionist.

Whether the dreams accompanying his enuresis are of an incestuous nature or are dominated by hostility toward his mother could also give us some enlightenment. One of the significant findings reported for genital exhibitionists is the need to believe that he has a breast for his own use. Thus he equates his own penis with a breast, and then he may deny the need for an object for love. His own penis is his source of love and may symbolize the mother.

The lack of associations to the dream of the hairy thing coming at him does not permit positive interpretation. To take the license of probabilities, however, we can assume that it represents a terror of the vagina as a devouring mouth which will destroy him. This, too, is an expression of an oral sadistic fixation which has been projected onto the woman. This fear of the woman rationalizes the avoidance of sexual relations and the fact that orgastic relief is obtained only by exhibitionism. It is characteristic for these patients to have no real object relationships but to stand off and secretly look but never actually to seduce the woman. To come close to a woman is to be exposed to the threatened danger of being devoured as well as being castrated. The purpose of the exhibitionism is not to seduce, since they must turn away from women. Nor do they wish to see the totally nude woman, but only the partially undressed, or glimpses of parts of the female figure which are usually covered by outer clothing. For one patient, a girl dressed in underwear was exciting, whereas her nude body destroyed all sexual desire. In a more dramatic fashion, another patient would have erections on the street while noticing attractive women, but he was completely impotent with a nude female. He was also preoccupied with the fantasies of exhibiting his penis before women, in public, but he was most modest in front of a girl! For him, it not only permitted the fantasy that a woman had a penis but also that the sight of his penis would overwhelm the woman with passion. He could then indulge in a variety of sadistic abuses on the woman.

The male genital exhibitionist enjoys the terror and fear engendered in the spectator. Not infrequently, the exhibitionist has difficulty concealing his pleasurable feeling when recalling a victim's reaction. At other times, he considers his arrest most unjust. Such patients will innocently proclaim that the women had nothing to fear, since the patients had no intention of doing them harm. Ultimately, they confess to impotence with women, but they also have scorn and hatred for them.

In the patient under discussion, we have the juxtaposition of shyness with people and the genital exhibitionism. Thus it is possible to recognize shyness as a defensive reaction against unconscious exhibitionism. This is also emphasized by his anxiety when his mother walks about in shorts, which, we may suspect, were really *brief* shorts. He may fear that he will react and that his erection will be observed by her, for which he will be punished. At the same time there is concern lest he really excite his mother by his exhibitionism, that she might expose herself, and that he would be subject to seduction by her. Paradoxically, he regresses to the pseudo innocence of childhood and appears before her inadequately clothed, as if to say, "I am just a little boy. My exposure is of no consequence." Obviously, a male child cannot be happy with such a solution, particularly if his mother actually behaves as though his penis is insignificant—as though it is of no interest to her. This he interprets as ridicule of himself as a man. Exhibitionism enhances his narcissism, and he succeeds in having his penis noticed.

The next point to be considered concerns his mother's hostile injunctions: "Go out and be run over by a bus," and "Go out and get killed." Although both the boy and his mother would protest that these are merely figures of speech, we must consider them as true expressions of the mother's hostility, and we must realize that the child takes them literally. Such a complete lack of sympathy for the boy's problem undoubtedly expresses the existence of unconscious motivations for this reaction to the boy's behavior. Why? We can speculate that her own exhibitionistic wishes and guilt over her incestuous fantasies must have created guilt and this murderous attitude toward the boy as a reaction of denial. Her own penis envy and her guilt for having deprived this boy of normal maternal love must also contribute to her hostility. One must wonder if she does not feel guilty for not gratifying her son after exciting him.

Exhibitionistic mothers behave as though they believe their sons have no sexual excitability, but during their own analysis they reveal guilt that they have not satisfied the desire which they have stimulated. In the case of such a perversion, both the child and the mother believe on one level that the untoward behavior would have been averted if the sexual urge had been gratified by the mother. Unfortunately, perverted behavior is not simply a substitute for adult genital relations, which can satisfy only a healthy desire. The perverse act derives from infantile needs which are symbolized in the symptomatic act.

Of concern to the analyst is the patient's interest in the girls' kerchiefs. As is well known, this can well be representative of a transitional object of childhood and can ultimately represent the breast for the baby. Since the genital exhibitionist has enormous oral sadism and primary oral fixation, the correlation becomes obvious. In like fashion the shoes of the girls undoubtedly became phallic breast symbols for him, as well as symbols of the vagina.

The history of self-examination before the mirror makes me wonder if the patient did not hide his penis between his legs. This serves the purpose of the voyeuristic need to see the female figure, but with the reassurance that the penis is really there! In this act, both voyeuristic needs and reassurance against castration are combined. It also beautifully demonstrates the interrelationship between voyeurism and genital exhibitionism, and between the perverse and narcissistic gratifications sought after. The denial of the need for an object is supported by his narcissistic love for the fantasied object that he sees in the mirror—himself. The wish to look at the other person's genitals at the price of exposing one's own organs is also documented by this bit of history.

It is rather remarkable that this brief history has demonstrated so many of the basic problems manifested by the genital exhibitionist—the denial of castration, hostility toward the female spectator, oral sadism, fear of being devoured, fear of object relationships, narcissistic needs, and a close resemblance toward the homosexual perversion and the root of the symptom of shyness in the repressed exhibitionistic wish.

There are certain observations about adolescents, however, which have not been elucidated up to this point. We should remember that the adolescent is struggling with biological processes kindled by hormonal maturity. Accompanying this is an intense preoccupation with bodily development and adult sexual needs. To retreat to exhibitionism avoids coitus. But exposure of the penis also means an inability to displace the genital wishes onto the body as a substitute. For instance, the body-building exercises, the absorbing interest in athletics or any competitive exercise, including the intellectual, during adolescence may serve for displacement of the wish for admiration of the penis. One must keep in mind that adolescence is a period of intense preoccupation with the body. The dramatic physiologic changes evoke enormous anxiety about the transformation from a sterile to a fertile male with the potential for expulsive, ejaculatory orgasm. This brings him an entirely new experience which is pleasurable but also frightening. The action itself provides a source of fear—that it may cause injury. Nonetheless, he is driven to repeat the experience.

Concurrently, the adolescent has an almost schizoid concern about his body build. He is plagued with doubts about epitomizing masculinity or whether he is becoming feminine in appearance. If any slight deviation from the theoretical norm is detected, he becomes concerned that it reflects femininity. With the growth of axillary and pubic hair, he again develops uncertainty about its significance. In his past, the remote past as well, he has developed the association that hair means the female. But now he must shift his belief to the fact that it signifies masculinity. Probably this is why hair on the chest becomes such a characteristic male boast.

Simultaneously, the young male begins to preen and exhibit more openly before the female. This, however, is done with an oscillation from contempt for the female and a total disregard of her to the other extreme of meticulous attention to details of his dress for a date. The loitering on street corners and similar acts are all attempts to attract attention from the girls walking past, but vehement denials of this wish are usually made when a boy is confronted with such an accusation. He will insist that he simply wants to be with the boys.

This brings us to another major problem of the adolescent. To pursue a girl with affection is to be considered effeminate by his contemporaries, yet to use a girl for sexual purposes alone profanes his oedipal feelings and evokes fear. Thus he frequently is obliged to vacillate between his heterosexual push and homosexual friendships. Of course I am referring to latent homosexual satisfactions, though overt behavior is much more frequent than is commonly supposed. His wish to peep in the men's toilet and his behavior on the hospital ward is symptomatic of his homosexuality.

A complication ensuing from this need is an urge to be exhibitionistic with his male companions. He seeks not only admiration but reassurance about his genital development. The same need enhances his voyeuristic impulse under the guise of a wish to compare genitals for reassurance. Our patient was blocked in using these potential sources of gratification and reassurance.

By endowment, our patient is a person with few avenues for self-expression. To this the burden of his traumatic personal history has produced a boy with intense feelings of inferiority, a craving for love and affection, unexpressed aggression, and an unresolved oedipal complex. Their concentration seems to have produced his present dilemma.

In the genital exhibitionist who has not had a true latency period with its reaction-formations and repression, ego development is impaired. Rather direct gratification has been the rule. This is characteristic of the urge for gratification of need and without cathexis of the object.[2] In other words, we might say that ego functions were not being developed for the satisfaction of id impulses which would conform to the superego and to the external world. But it would be unrealistic to suggest that the patient does not have a harsh superego. On the contrary, he appeared somewhat depressed during my brief meeting with him, and we have heard him described as shy, fearful, and remorseful. It more probably might be considered as closer to an archaic superego which will exact direct punishment for any transgressions. Interestingly enough,

Christoffel[1] reports that the exhibitionist will subtly attract the attention of the police to other exhibitionists. On one occasion the culprit was a police inspector known to be especially harsh on exhibitionists.

Police vice squads reportedly use policemen who expose their penises to trap homosexuals and voyeurs frequenting public places. This is officially denied, but many victims give the same account of their arrests, including people who have had no previous contact with the courts. The close connection to the unconscious sense of guilt is demonstrated by a prisoner charged with exhibitionism for the first time. He had been a recidivist who had spent many years in jail. After marriage to a woman 10 years older than himself, he had avoided conflict with the law for about 15 years before being arrested for indecent exposure. Did his former criminal life reflect a need for punishment, and were its roots an unconscious wish for genital exhibitionism?

The voyeuristic element in the psyche of one patient, who never courted arrest and who had sought treatment for anxiety and potency disturbances, is exemplified by the following symptom: To enjoy potency, he had to visualize himself having intercourse. As soon as the image left his mind, potency collapsed and was reasserted only when he could again conjure up the picture of observing intercourse. Obviously, this represented his observation of the primal scene. This was complicated by seductive behavior by his mother and excessive stimulation by her. Analysis revealed not only reassurance against castration anxiety but also the fantasy that "looking" could go on to eternity, whereas actual intercourse must end. For this man, eternal feeding signified no separation from mother. It also negated his destructive impulses toward his mother, since she is never destroyed but is always able to feed him. The same fantasies were associated with his partial voyeuristic activity —he could spend all day at looking, and this he did with his hobby of photography.

One should also note that there is a feminine identification in these patients. In their fantasies they see women becoming sexually excited at the sight of their bodies or their penises, as men ordinarily react to women's breasts, etc. On the conscious level they will present the idea that their supermasculinity is what they are displaying, but it is done with a passive feminine orientation, to be looked at, to be admired, and to be sought after. They think not in terms of achievement or personality but only from the viewpoint of physical appeal. Their identification is with the narcissistic, exhibitionistic female who uses her body for a phallic denial of her feelings of castration.[3]

Though the analyst does not have many opportunities to analyze the exhibitionist, he does hear a good deal about patients' reactions to the exhibitionist. It is amazing what a large percentage of my female patients have had such an experience in their childhood or adult life. It becomes quickly apparent that the exhibitionist appeals to the voyeuristic needs of his spectator. After the initial shock and amnesia, the patients claim that they cannot recall any details about the genitals. Invariably, after analysis progressed, it became clear that minute particulars had registered on their minds —the degree of erection, its size, its color, and whether manual manipulation was going on. Finally, some disappointment that they did not see more was conceded; that is, a wish to see all of the genitals, which connected to early childhood wishes, was finally acknowledged. Some of the patients would fantasy that their extraordinary attractiveness had provoked the perverted act. In others, a certain awe and envy would be aroused, not only of the penis but for the "courage" of the exhibitionist in daring to display his genitals. There is a wish to do the same. Of course, fears of an insane man's rapist desires activate fantasies of being raped. It seems likely that the exhibitionist depends on all of these reactions which thus create guilt in his victim. The two are participants in the voyeuristic-exhibitionistic act and are thus equally guilty. This is confirmed, to a certain extent, by the relatively infrequent times the exhibitionist is arrested. Not one of my adult patients ever reported the man to any authority—whether it happened in a movie, the subway, the street, or in a museum, in any of which places it would have been an easy matter to report the exhibitionist to some police official. The percentage of arrests must be infinitesimal in comparison with the number of such incidents that take place. The arrests that do occur must be a direct result of the exhibitionist's need for punishment. It seems that he can usually choose his "victims" with a good degree of safety, until the guilt has mounted sufficiently for him to provoke arrest and punishment.

It is also necessary to compare the typical voyeur's need to peep from a secret hiding place and the exhibitionist's apparent boldness. The voyeur would also hope to have a sharper view of the scene. The exhibitionist is taking the role of the observed parent, coming out into a public place so that he may be seen. But he too must retain the surreptitious quality of the act. In effect, he is saying, "I will allow you to look, as I was not permitted to do. This is what can be seen—a penis only. Everybody has a penis." Of course the exhibitionist who ejaculates is also saying that he has no need of the woman. By exposing his genitals to a strange woman, he is denying any need for a specific woman. In that way, he negates any incestuous patterns and actually reveals the avoidance of a real object. The attitude that anybody will do permits a denial of the incestuous problem which is rooted in an oral fixation on the mother, plus an identification with her on an archaic level. This last contributes to his denial of the reality of the penislessness of the woman. This is also true for the homosexual to whom the exhibitionist is very close.

Just as the voyeur incorporates, devours, takes in with his eyes, but from a distance, so too the exhibitionist indulges in the wish to be eaten, to be devoured, to become identified with the onlooker, but, again, from a distance. This may be paraphrased as follows: "I identify with her by taking her into me," or, "I will be taken in by her and thus be like her." It seems that the exhibitionist has the latter goal in mind.

It is necessary to indicate again that we have been discussing a genital exhibitionist. How does he differ from the usual exhibitionist, particularly the stage performer who has sublimated his exhibitionistic desires? Our patient could not make the displacement from his penis to his body and then derive pleasure from bodily exhibitionism. In addition, genital exhibitionism is not a mere continuation of the "innocent" exhibitionism of the young child which frequently is important in the psychology of the performer.

Incidentally, it may be mentioned that the performer who is tense on stage evokes displeasures in the audience. The person in the audience is both a voyeur and, in fantasy, the exhibitionist on the stage. The star performer projects the impression of complete acceptance of his role as an exhibitionist, of enjoyment that he is being looked at, and so he assuages the guilt of the audience.

To return to our adolescent patient, it would be tempting to believe that his seduction by a man at the age of 10 was an important factor in his pathological behavior. Unfortunately for this simple rationalization, the victims of such seductions already have a personality which predisposes them to becoming victims of the perverts. In the author's experience, the child frequently plays an active role in seducing the adult. In other words, the young man's pathological sexual difficulty most likely had begun before the age of 10 years.

The role of the alcoholic father also warrants some speculation. It has been noted that alcoholic fathers frequently are genitally exhibitionistic with their children. Although I have more often found this complaint in female patients, I have seen it in the male. The drunken father is helpless, must be undressed, neglects the fly of his trousers, wets his pants, etc. As a further complication, such parents have frank sexual play or thinly disguised activity in front of their child. We don't know if this actually happened in this case, but the inhibited mother parading in brief shorts could be a likely partner for her husband. (Incidentally, the apparent prude who is fundamentally seductive poses an almost insurmountable problem for her young son. She binds him with her sexual seductiveness yet creates enormous guilt by her mock modesty. He must deny her role in exciting his sexual fantasies and, ultimately, any sexual awareness of his mother. Afterward, he can only look and be aroused at a distance—a symbol of the separation that never took place.)

It must be apparent by now that the early regressive mechanism of denial is an important one in the exhibitionist. He denies the female's penislessness, his fear of castration, and the fact that he has sexual desires for a woman. He denies that he enjoys his exhibitionism and insists that it is a compulsive act—which it is, to a certain extent. He denies that he wants to have the breast of the mother by identifying his penis with a breast (and thus he does not need hers), but in so doing he denies his orally determined need. With his shyness and childlike dependence on a woman (often they are married to older women), he denies his gross hostility to women.

Of significance is the avoidance of courtship of a woman. Courtship requires patience on the male's part. The exhibitionist frequently is an impatient person who does not have the capacity for slow, tedious work for an eventual reward. He must reach his goal quickly.

SUMMARY

We have dealt with a case of an adolescent with a defective ego, with a passive feminine personality structure, but who is struggling for recognition of his masculinity. In addition, he requires reassurance against castration anxiety and is fearful of object relations. A deficit in narcissistic supply drives him to seek admiration for his bodily parts—the genitals. In the competition with the father, he feels himself a hopeless failure. His rage is vented against strange girls who reassure him that he is a male. This rage is displaced first from his mother and secondarily from his father. The difficulty in proper identification with his parents left him with his inadequate ego which could not develop either a sublimated activity or a symbolic expression for his need. Instead, the primitive urge was forced into overt expression—exhibitionism.

REFERENCES

1. CHRISTOFFEL, H. *Male Genital Exhibitionism in Perversions, Psycho- dynamics and Therapy,* ed. by Lorand, S., and Balint, M. New York, Random House, 1956.
2. FLIESS, R. *Erogeneity and Libido.* New York, International Universities Press, Inc., 1956.
3. RANGELL, L. The nature of conversion. *Am. J. Psychiat.* 7: 4, 1959.

chapter 7   Delinquency

PETER BLOS

On the front page of the *New York Times* book review of May 22, 1959, appeared in heavy letters the sensational title: "The Artist as a Young Delinquent." What followed was an article on the Irish writer Brendon Behan. This incident gives us an idea how loosely the word "delinquent" is used. Behan was an Irish freedom fighter; since his activity was unlawful, he was put into prison at the age of 16. Consequently, the writer of the review called him a delinquent.

This is the legal definition of delinquency: "The act of being in conflict with the law before adulthood." In addition to the legal approach, the sociological approach dominated the picture of delinquency research for some time by an attempt statistically to discern environmental factors which account for delinquent behavior. Clifford Shaw, of the Chicago Institute for Juvenile Research, was a pioneer in this approach. Few data could be significantly correlated between environmental factors and delinquency. One factor which *is* significantly correlated is the broken home. This, by now, has become a cliché which explains nothing. Statistically, we also know that delinquency makes its appearance usually between the ages of 8 and 11. That does not mean that at this age it is always brought to the attention of the law. In taking histories of delinquents, we find that delinquency was already manifest at this early age. We are interested here in the third approach to delinquency, namely, the psychological approach. The fact that a different word is used for a child offender and for an adult offender—"delinquent" and "criminal"—tells us that we are dealing here with a pathological maturational process. We speak of a delinquent when the personality has not attained adult status. Consequently, in the discussion of delinquency, we are concerned with maturational problems; those of adolescence are the most significant ones.

Delinquency, or antisocial behavior, is not a diagnostic entity. It

132

is a clinical fact. It does not clarify the pathological condition. It is a phenomenological term and not an explanatory one as, for instance, the term "phobia" is and consequently tells us a great deal about the condition, its dynamics and structure. The term "delinquency" tells us nothing of the sort. Ruling out organicity and mental defectiveness, there are delinquent manifestations in connection with all kinds of psychopathology—be it psychoneurosis, psychosis, character disorder, psychopathy, immature personality, addiction, perversion, etc. In order to understand delinquent behavior, it becomes necessary to reinstate it into a dynamic interaction system between the individual and his environment. In addition, it needs to be related genetically to antecedents in earlier stages of development, such as fixation, trauma, ego deformation, and similar pathogenic malformations. It is worth noting that delinquency is not restricted to those labeled as delinquents. We know from our work with children, adolescents, and adults that each individual has a certain share in delinquent fantasies, with the difference that they are never acted out. Furthermore, many adolescents have transient delinquent manifestations which never consolidate into delinquency. Probably the majority of people have committed acts in their youthful years which, if detected, would have been considered proof of delinquency. But we did not become delinquents.

Delinquent fantasies always appear, somehow, somewhere, in the analysis of adults, and very often strong defenses such as appear, for example, in agoraphobia are built up against such delinquent propensities. On investigation we often find that it is the fear of committing delinquent or criminal acts (usually of a sexual nature) which restricts the individual to a certain place. There are isolated delinquent areas in all of us which, for instance, are noticeable in the borrowing of books. People who would never forget to repay a borrowed penny have no compunctions about keeping a borrowed book. This is one of those innocent areas of delinquency among the civilized. It is not delinquent fantasies that are surprising, because we all have them, but the fact that the delinquent has no inhibition in carrying delinquent thoughts, intentions, and impulses into action. In this sense there is only a quantitative difference between unconscious delinquency, against which a normal person has established workable defenses, and manifest delinquency.

There is also a qualitative difference of no minor order, because the lack of action, inhibition, that is typical for the delinquent puts him into a class by himself. The absence of a clear delineation of fantasy and reality is, of course, an ego problem. There is an ego defect in the delinquent. Such an ego defect stems from an early pathological ego development; you might call it an ego deformation. By this I mean not that the total ego is immature but, rather, that its development is uneven, marred by precocities and retardations. In fact, many delinquents are superior in certain ego functions, such as the faculty to evaluate the tensions, weaknesses, and personalities of the people they meet. Such highly developed skill we might call a hypertrophic ego development[3] which, in itself, represents a pathological phenomenon.

On the other hand, we have the ego aspects of serious retardation usually referred to as immaturity. If we look for the ego defect we meet in delinquents, we have to concentrate on the problem of mastery of the environment. The ego's mastery of the environment belongs to the early phase of ego development which follows the gradual individuation; separation from the mother and identification with her promote a gradual ability to master the environment independently of her help. The development of motility helps to articulate this ability. The point of pathological deformity lies in this phase where a rupture in progressive development occurred. The mastery of the environment depends on the earliest experience of the child and has its roots in what Benedek[2] calls "confidence" and Erikson[4] calls "basic trust." Trust and confidence assure the child that tension will be relieved; that there is a benign object in the outside world who can be counted on to be there at the moment of despair. The reliability of the outside world is introjected and molds a positive attitude toward the environment. If we go into the history of delinquent adolescents, we find that this phase of early trust or confidence has never reliably existed and that, early in life, a sadomasochistic bond developed between mother and child. We find in the histories a battle of wills, a battle for power, and an absence of any reliable, dependable object relationship which is the prerequisite for the development of a stable self. Through the control rather than the mastery of the environment, the child averts tension and avoids pain which, in a sadomasochistic relationship, represents a constant threat. In order to keep in control of the environment, the child maintains a position of omnipotence. This constellation is prototypical for the delinquent. He has established a position of omnipotence and there is no way of reasoning with him. He must constantly prove that the environment has no power over him. This position masks strong dependency needs and walls off an awareness of the feeling of helplessness. These are primitive security operations which express a very primitive need, namely, to get and to have; to be given and to be done to as wanted; to be in control of the object; in short, to be omnipotent. The adolescent continues this dependency, which could be described in Mahler's terms as a dependency on the illusion of symbiotic omnipotence.[7] The case under discussion will illustrate this rule; we also shall see the enormous hostile dependency on the mother.

The problem of action is a nuclear problem in delinquency. No internal conflict is felt, nor is the delinquent able to create one. Inner conflict is circumvented by establishing instead a conflict with the outside world. The need constantly to manipulate the environment is an alloplastic adaptation. To say it more correctly, it is a "negative alloplastic adaptation"[3] which fails to mediate successfully between the need system and reality. It contains elements of magical thinking. The negative alloplastic adaptation creates situations which will eventually destroy any secure enjoyment or any lasting and enduring achievement in reality. Owing to these conditions which I have described and which precede manifest delinquency, we can speak of a predisposition to delinquency. Aichhorn[1] spoke in the 20's of what he termed "latent delinquency." This is a very useful concept, because it refers to the fact that, before manifest delinquency becomes apparent, there exists a period of latent delinquency which prepares the stage for delinquent action. For the sake of prevention, we would like to know all about the predelinquent period in order to forestall the outbreak of delinquency. This two-phasic structure of delinquency has, in some cases, been quite conclusively demonstrated.

With reference to delinquent behavior, we have to make certain distinctions; here I shall follow some suggestions by Glover.[6] He has described the "functional delinquent" in which he recognized a discharge phenomenon. Such delinquency "blows over." It is the kind of delinquency most of us went through in our adolescence. We could refer to it as a situational neurosis or, to use the literal translation of Freud's term, "actual neurosis."[5] Another type of delinquent Glover calls the "facultative delinquent." The facultative delinquent is one for whom delinquency is optional. If some situation presents itself—if the facultative delinquent gets into a certain crowd—he might join them and also smash windows. There is no delinquent character present; there is no substratum of delinquency; there is no latent delinquency. We can rule out the facultative delinquent as a pathological phenomenon. Glover reserves the term "pathological delinquent" for a special group, namely, those in whom there exists the precondition of latent delinquency. Pathological delinquency, then, must have a latent stage and is identical with psychoneurotic delinquency, where action is directed against the environment and where symptom formation is circumvented.

This brings us to another interesting aspect of delinquency. The delinquent does not form a symptom, and we should not call the delinquent act a symptom. Glover[6] calls it a "symptom equivalent," which is a much more correct designation. When we speak of a symptom we infer that the symptom is a compromise formation, and this is precisely what the delinquent is unable to accomplish. Therefore, the term "psychoneurotic delinquent" is really a contradiction, but we can use it as long as we know what we mean by it. Delinquent acting out is, of course, always egosyntonic, which renders the delinquent inaccessible to insight. In fact, the delinquent resorts to any means to avoid exposure to displeasure (anxiety). Perhaps the delinquent's need to avoid unpleasure is greater than to seek pleasure. When the delinquent finally enters the stage where he gives up his delinquency, we usually find, behind the "action screen," a depressed and bewildered person who, when exposed to tension and unpleasure, reverts to most infantile dependency expressions in relation to the therapist or other meaningful persons in his environment. In the etiology we try to establish a sequence of unconscious predisposing factors leading to latent delinquency; the latent stage is brought to an end by socalled precipitating factors. Within this scheme we shall always keep in mind what we usually refer to as constitutional factors, or anlage. The precipitating factors are often of a biological nature, such as the onset of puberty, or they constitute environmental influences, such as hyperstimulation by exposure to violent aggression or sexual stimulation with which the young person is unable to cope in terms of his defensive organization.

We can, furthermore, make a distinction in the evaluation of delinquency between those delinquents who have traversed the latency period and those who have never established a latency period. The latter enter puberty without the mental acquisitions of the latency period, jumping directly from early childhood into pubescence and sexual maturity with the heightened influx of tensions and internal stimulations. I think that the prognosis in these two categories is different: where we have an outbreak of adolescent delinquency with an established latency period preceding it, the prognosis for treatment is more favorable. The whole technique of treating the delinquent consists—to put Aichhorn's idea[1] in a nutshell—in turning delinquency into a neurotic symptom. One can treat a neurotic conflict, but one cannot treat delinquency per se. This transformation requires skill and resourcefulness and constant mindfulness of the fact that delinquency is not treatable by a frontal attack. In order to lend a foundation to this concept, I introduced the preceding theoretical considerations. Otherwise, we do not really know what we mean when we talk about delinquency.

CASE REPORT*

When the patient was 13 years and 2 months of age, a school request was made for contact with the Kings County Hospital clinic because the patient was failing the seventh grade, was lying to his mother, and was stealing money. He took $60 from his mother's purse at the beauty parlor where she works, and was at a loss to explain how he had spent the money. Recently, at his mother's friend's home, he stole $36. This was recovered in time and was returned. The church he attends suspected him of taking religious articles. He went to some stores borrowing money on some pretext (that is, that he had lost his keys and couldn't get into his house to get his own money), and his mother had to make restitution. He also took to lying. His mother said, "When I know that he has dropped something and point out that he did this, he will deny doing it. What I can't understand is that he has no guilty conscience about lying or stealing. Recently, he has become more sexed up. I found sex books with pictures of nude people in them under the rug and around the house. Before this he was not ashamed of me and would take a bath in front of me, but the past year he seems to have become ashamed. He has taken to soiling by day—never by night. It must have something to do with the food he eats by day. He says that he does not have enough time to get to the bathroom when he feels that he has to go." (He had been soiling for the last few years.)

* Case prepared by Drs. Henry Rosner and Moisy Shopper under the supervision of Dr. Henry I. Schneer.

The mother feels that he is too developed sexually for his age, and she notes that he "plays with himself often." She tries to divert him with a chore, but he becomes annoyed and ignores her.

The patient indicated that the start of his illness was 2 years ago when his mother increased the number of her working hours at the beauty parlor. This left him alone in their six-room house. He felt lonely, was afraid of the dark, began to steal, and made up stories. At times he would explain to friends of the family that his father was a pilot in the Air Force and that his mother came from an unusual background, all of which these people knew to be untrue. In the past year he has begun to soil himself by day while he is on his way to the beauty shop. There is no history of similar difficulties in his early childhood.

His mother pointed out that he is a dull, awkward boy who frequently falls over and at times complains of headaches or other bodily symptoms. In recent months there has been a succession of medical problems: two broken arms, a head injury with concussion, and an infected ear. "He's always sick with something." At night he sometimes gets up and moves about, apparently unaware that he is up. During the past month the mother kept the patient at the beauty parlor whenever he was out of school, but her employer found this objectionable. It was decided to admit the patient to the hospital for observation with regard to recommending a residential treatment center.

Family Constellation and Living Arrangements

The family consists of the patient, his mother, and an older brother who entered the Air Force 4 years ago. For the past few years they have been living in Brooklyn, in a six-room apartment for which they pay $41 per month rent. There are provisions for hot water and heat, and the patient and his mother have separate bedrooms. The neighborhood appears to be a good one. There is no problem with gangs, and there are pleasant children with whom to play within a reasonable distance.

The parents were married in October, 1932. The father was a house painter and a chronic alcoholic, always accusing his wife of infidelity. He seldom brought money into the house, and his wife had to take a job as house superintendent in order to be sure that her rent was paid and to have money for food.

The patient hardly knew his father because, from the time the boy was 3, the father had been essentially separated from the mother. The patient is said to have always gotten along well with his mother, although he has always been babied by her. The mother says that she indulged him insofar as she was able. He got along well with his older brother, also. They used to have their fights, but they were friendly. He always liked to wrestle with his brother and ended up the winner.

The patient's father is the oldest of five siblings whose father, in turn, was an alcoholic and was said to be "mean and grouchy." The patient's father explained to his wife that he mistrusts all women because, when his own father went away from home one night, he found his mother in bed with another man. The patient's father was never a steady worker, drank mostly beer, made two suicide attempts by taking gas, and had episodes of aggressive outbursts when drunk, during which he would destroy the house furniture. He is described as having been very well educated, having read many books, spoken several languages, and finished high school.

The patient's mother, 47 years old, was born in Latvia, the second of three siblings. Her sister is currently in Germany, and she has not been able to locate her brother since the end of the war. She was vague about her childhood but explained that her father died when she was 11½ years old and her mother died about half a year later. Following this, she said, "I was orphaned and pushed from one house to another. That is why I'm so sorry for him and give him anything he wants. My parents were wealthy and very affectionate." She was sent to live with a "rich" grandmother, but she felt that she was abused there. From there she was sent to live with a "poor" aunt where she was more comfortable.

She was sent out and taught to be a beautician. In 1928 she came to the United States, working her way as a ship's beautician. She had a relative in the United States. She met her husband through an introduction. He courted her for 7 months. For the past 10 years she has been working at the same beauty parlor.

The patient's brother is married and has recently been honorably discharged from the United States Air Force after 4 years of service. When the brother was 13 years old, he had trouble "taking things." Among the things he stole, he recalls, was a shotgun. His stealing, however, stopped after adolescence. He has been married for 1½ years.

Developmental History

The patient was born in September, 1942. Both parents are Russian Orthodox, but the patient was baptized a Protestant. The patient was unwanted by both parents, and the mother did not know that she was pregnant and learned of it only in her last trimester. Previously, she had had six miscarriages.

Prenatally, the mother suffered episodes of hemoptysis. She was told that she had gallstones, but the actual etiology of the hemorrhages the mother does not completely understand. She knows that she had no infections during pregnancy and thinks that there was no blood-group incompatibility.

Her husband had venereal disease after the patient's birth. The children were blood tested and found to have negative Wassermanns.

Feeding History and Early Development

The patient's birth weight, following a vertex delivery, was 6 pounds and 12 ounces. No gas anesthesia was used. The mother received sedation by injection. The baby was breast fed during the first 3 months. He fed well and had no problems with diarrhea, colic, or constipation. He had to be immediately withdrawn from the breast because the mother was taken to the hospital with cholecystitis and pneumonia. While the mother was in the hospital being operated on and recuperating, the baby was sent to a nursing home where he remained until he was 6½ months old. At 3 months he weighed 16 pounds. When he was taken out of the nursing home by the mother, he had to be taken to Cumberland Hospital because it was noted that he had a high fever. He was lifeless and dull and could not sit up. He was noted to have his first tooth at that time. When he was taken home from the hospital, he seemed to be normally active and fed well. It was some time around the age of 18 months when he was weaned from the bottle. Apparently, he wanted to imitate his brother drinking from a glass. He sat up at 9 months, stood up at 11 months, walked at 13 months, started talking at 9 months, and seemed to be a good speaker.

Toilet Training

The mother contended that her child was never punished in the course of toilet training. He merely followed his brother's example and trained himself for bladder control. Enuresis or day wetting was never a problem. The mother would put him on the toilet seat to stimulate bowel training.

Habit Disturbances, Fears, and Phobias

The patient had a habit of making holes in things with his finger. He was afraid of water and of riding on the merry-go-round. The mother said that he overcame his fear of water when she took him on a ferryboat and told him, after the ferry left the pier, that he was riding on the water. She showed this to him, and he was no longer afraid.

School History

Before 3 years of age, the patient was sent to a day nursery when the mother went to work following her separation from the husband. At that time, it was noted that the boy preferred to play in the girls' section of the nursery. The mother was told by the nursery personnel that it is all right if a boy likes to play with dolls and if a girl likes to play with guns.

He was a good boy. He always did what he was told, and he never had to be punished. He never played much with the other children but would play with his older brother, who was described as entirely different from the patient. The brother was a friendly child, always on the go. If the patient played with other children, they were usually younger than he. He did not want to go to public school but was brought there by his mother, and he remained there. After a while he got to like school. He was never a behavior problem in his early schooling. He was a "good student." He read early, enjoyed geography, and seemed fair in arithmetic. He seemed to do better with men teachers than with women teachers.

In 1950 the family moved to Brooklyn, and he attended public school there. At school in 1953, he had his first difficulty when he opened a fire-alarm box. The principal did not take any action because there had been no previous history of a behavior problem in school. At the time, it was noted that he seemed to enjoy lighting matches, but recently he stopped doing that.

Throughout life he has not found it easy to make friends, and this has been particularly true in the last few years. He never brings friends home, and most of the people he knows are members of his church. In the summer of 1955, he went to camp. He seemed happy, and his behavior improved while he was there.

Physical Examination

The patient is in no distress and has no complaints. His weight is 170 pounds; his height 5 feet, 10 inches. The results of his physical examination were within normal limits. Urine, Kolmer test, electroencephalogram, and chest and skull X rays were negative. The examination revealed the spinal tap traumatic with normal pressure, normal chemistries, and negative colloidal gold.

*Psychological Report**

The patient was extremely affable during testing, his manner being extraordinarily effeminate. Only very sketchy testing was done, since the patient was ill up to an hour prior to the conference. The principal purpose of testing was to rule out organicity. The Bender and Block Design tests gave no hint of organic pathology. What is evident from the Bender is a good deal of tension over controlling aggression, and the indications are that this tension mounts as he continues to work at a task (there was increasing pressure and attempts to confine himself to limits in making dots).

The few Rorschach cards show tendencies toward arbitrary combinations of concepts (two people leaning on a head, Card III), much bodily preoccupation, oral preoccupation (gophers eating a tree), feminine identification (figures on Card III seen as women), and a contemptuous self-image (ants rather than more formidable animals are first seen on Card VIII). The drawings, with their bearded outline, enormous ears, overalert eyes, and tremendous oral emphasis strongly suggest the possibility of self-referent delusions under what appears to be a decompensating, obsessive-compulsive front.

To summarize, it tends to describe a female-identified boy with ingratiating psychopathic defense, masking an incipient paranoid break against which existing controls may well prove inadequate.

Mental Status

The patient is noted to be a tall, mildly chubby, well-developed young man who has effeminate mannerisms and ways of speaking. He enters the interview with the idea that we know he has been stealing, and he is at a loss to explain his stealing and his soiling as well. Still, he cooperates with questioning, remaining coherent and relevant throughout. He shows a certain amount of talkativeness in making "small talk," but he does not seem to have a real appreciation of his current situation. The seriousness of it he denies. He shows average psychomotor activity and an ability to modulate his affect appropriately. Still, his basic mood is of the depressive variety, with a considerable repressed hostility.

He is grossly oriented to time, place, and situation. No hallucinations, delusions, or thinking disorders were elicited. He associates to the stealing the idea that his mother increased the number of

* Prepared by R. Hausman, psychologist.

her evening working hours. Under this circumstance, he explains, "It's almost as though she's dead." Incidentally, he went on to explain that because of her work he must visit her and stay with her in the beauty parlor where she works, and staying with her in the beauty parlor is "murder." He makes numerous statements of low self-estimation and, indeed, derogation: "I'm such a monster." He does not like other children and feels that he is not liked by them. He keeps away from fights and has a passive approach to relating to people. Indeed, he prefers older people to his peers. His insight and judgment are poor.

Progress on the Ward

On the ward the patient was aloof from his peers but friendly toward attendants and the nurse (older people). His soiling never appeared in the hospital. He has remained cooperative during his stay.

A residential treatment center was recommended, but placement could not be effected. The patient remained at home with his mother, and within a year he had to be readmitted to the hospital.

In the interim he wrote to his nurse on his former ward, fabricating his being away from home. He was not promoted at school, but apparently he was not bothered by this. He went to a Y.M.C.A. camp during the summer and told the camp nurse that he was of a rich family. In the fall he had an appendectomy. Subsequently, he played truant and had lengthy telephone conversations which the mother discovered by the increasing telephone bills. He stole money again. He took a Novocain pack from his dentist.

He has been intermittently preoccupied with religion, alternating his desire to be Jewish, Catholic, or Protestant. He expressed the belief that Catholicism was the true religion, and he carried a Bible around with him. Recently, a friend of the mother's saw him on a train, making speeches and collecting funds for a Jewish organization.

Shortly before readmission, the patient obtained a job in the Coney Island "Fun House," where he made sexual advances to a 6-year-old girl and was subsequently apprehended by the police. He had obtained employment against his mother's advice. The second day on the job, while leading the customers through a dark tunnel, he suddenly picked up a 6-year-old girl and put his hand under her dress. She ran away and told her mother, and he was arrested the next day.

The patient's mother says that he has received telephone calls from girls; he seems to like older girls and ladies and often says that he is older (17 or 18) than he actually is. His conduct in school has been "C," and he is failing in most of his subjects. He has fixed the telephone wires and doorbell and taken cards out of the mail box in order to prevent the school or victimized individuals from contacting his parent. The mother feels that her son is sick and requires placement in an institution where he can obtain psychiatric aid. She feels unable to manage him at the present time.

The readmission mental status found him to be effeminate, verbose, and ingratiating. The mood, however, was depressed. The patient was unable to explain why he fondled a 6-year-old girl. He was not sure why he steals but says possibly it is because he wants to get even with his mother whom he hates and with whom he cannot get along. He denied ever feeling that he was being watched or that people were talking about him. He thinks that he does not do well in school because he is lazy. He wants to be a doctor when he grows up, but he cannot state why. He denies any drug intake. The money he steals, he spends on "trifles." No evidence of a thought disorder was noted. Delusional or hallucinatory experiences were not elicited. Suicidal or homicidal trends were denied. Insight is slight. While on the ward he has been openly affectionate toward the nurses. He called a nurse his "second mother" and frequently attempted to kiss the nurses. He says he "hates" his mother and thinks up things to do that will hurt her.

He was discharged to Children's Court and sent to Youth House. He was sent home from there, pending placement which never materialized.

While at home, he graduated from junior high school. He no longer berated his mother for his not having a father. His probation officer for the incident of sexual delinquency wanted him placed, despite his improvement. His mother considered him improved and no longer desired placement. It was learned that he frequently visited the charge nurse of Kings County Hospital ward and told her of his improvement. His grade adviser considered him improved in regard to his studies but felt that he tended to tell "fantastic stories."

Outpatient therapy was recommended in May, 1958, in connection with his probationary situation with the court. It became possible to have him treated. Shortly thereafter, the court dropped his probationary status, which removed the aspect of enforced therapy. It was soon apparent that the therapy problem was in dealing with disordered characterology involving regressive tendencies bordering on a psychosis.

In the course of therapy, he spoke of a conflict over religion. "Why does not my mother want me to be a Russian Orthodox member?" His habit was more like that of a minister than of an adolescent. Without his mother knowing it, he was baptized a Russian Orthodox the summer before starting therapy. He recognized the religion as "difficult" but the only one he wanted. He talked of his "family tree" and a relationship to Russian royalty. If the monarchy were re-established, he would have an important position, he said. Although he longed for the church and referred to himself as a "Sunday school teacher," he did not attend church just prior to Christmas, because he "was tired." It may have been that he did not want to attend confession, the first since his baptism. He spoke of becoming a priest "because of all the bad things I've done." He also spoke of becoming a nurse, possibly modeling himself after the male nurse on the ward.

As to his occupational activities, he usually assists his mother on Saturdays at the beauty parlor. He rinses hair. Saturday nights he does not have dates. He denies masturbation or interest in the opposite sex. If he goes to a party, it is after a church affair with older boys and girls, with no petting or exploration. In his first year of high school, he speaks of his classmates with scorn. He regards himself as a "dictator" with his peers. He is definitely failing in mathematics, but he is passing in history. He arranged to have coffee with his English teacher after school, and once, when he "cut" school for two weeks and the principal was to punish him, he said that he stayed out of school to mark papers for the English Department, for which he said he had sanction. He uses an elevator pass illegally at school. In the clinic he befriended a 12½-year-old girl patient of another doctor. He assumed the role of teaching her English and described himself to her as having been in Dachau concentration camp. There were no reports of petting or kissing. He came to the clinic even when a therapy hour was canceled. For a time, it was a question as to whether he was coming to the clinic to walk the girl home. It was also a question of whether he was enacting, unconsciously, a fantasy of defying the father, defying authority, and inviting jealousy and interest.

A resumé of the patient's behavior as it manifestly evolved was considered to be as follows:

1. A regressive anaclitic syndrome at 6½ months—infancy.
2. Phobic, effeminate tendencies in early childhood.
3. Soiling during the day—late childhood.
4. Accident proneness, stealing, lying, effeminacy—puberty.
5. Truancy, school failure, stealing, fabrication—early adolescence.
6. (Sexual deviancy?), fabrication, finagling, religiosity—mid-adolescence.

DISCUSSION

This case has enormous ramifications. The pathology in it touches on all levels of psychosexual and ego development. The delinquent acts of this boy possess a primitive revenge character, such as hiding objects and throwing them away; furthermore, they serve an impulsive, immature discharge function, as is evident in the touching of the little girl. In addition, we recognize in his behavior omnipotent and restitutional aspects, for example, the lying and the telling of tall tales of a family romance. Finally, in reaching a settlement of a tumultous development, he assumes a delusional role: the holy man, the religious leader, the dictator, and the savior. The organic pathology has been investigated and found to be negative.

In the following I want to highlight certain aspects in the case in order to bring some clarity into the picture. The child was not wanted. The pregnancy was denied until the sixth month. The mother seems to have been a rather immature, narcissistic individual. She related to the child on a narcissistic level, desirous of giving the child what she had missed. Her response to her child followed the line: "I understand what my child needs because his needs correspond to my own unfulfilled wishes." She did to him what she desired, and she said, "I gave him everything he wanted; I feel sorry for him." She indulged him—in fact, herself—as much as she could. This woman seems narcissistic to such a degree that she gives the impression of a borderline case. Unfortunately, her condition had not been clarified and we can only surmise a diagnosis. It appears that mother and child enjoyed a symbiotic relationship. There existed total dependency of the child on the mother, whom he feared and hated but on whom he depended on for protection and stimulation. This constellation led eventually to retarded ego development through impaired reality testing and excessive dependency on the environment. Environmental influences substituted for a sense of self which lacked inner continuity. The ego was fragmented. If the boy was put into a camp, he was rather happy. If he was put into a hospital, he stopped soiling. If his mother was not home, he had no life, he might "just as well be dead." There is no continuity in the feeling of self or in the mental representations of objects. If the mother is not present, he does not exist. This is a very primitive way of relating to the environment and to love objects; it is characteristic for the development of a symbiotic relationship, in which case an independent self could not emerge. Where symptoms such as soiling, for instance, change so easily, this disappearance of symptoms might flatter the therapist, but, on the other hand, it should be a warning sign and alert us to the fact that the ego is of such a brittle nature and is so suggestible and malleable that almost anything therapy does with such a patient will remain, for a long time, like writing on water.

This boy experienced an early and rapid pubescence. During this time we witness also an intensification of some pregenital activity. The fact that this boy soiled when forced to visit the mother's beauty parlor and expressed his rage, his hostility, his stubbornness in such a primitive fashion indicates the seriousness of the symptom. The anal sadism is an expression of his aggression against the mother who forces him to sit in the beauty parlor with all the women. It is noteworthy that anal sadism, which was aroused by the forced confinement in the beauty parlor, took the form of soiling and was not expressed on a higher level of mental functioning. Of course, we frequently see in adolescence the arousal of anal sadism; but, although it is derived from anal-zone activity and is associated with aggressive affects, it usually becomes detached from the organ zone and becomes displaced and generalized. We see it, at this age, as estranged from the original body zone, over which the ego has established secondary autonomy, and expressed in behavior modalities of a higher order, such as cursing, murderous fantasies, destruction, stubbornness, resistance, etc. Primitive oral sadism permeates his relationship to the mother and strengthens passive homosexual (feminine) fixation or identification. The mother forced him to be what she wants him or herself to be; she related to him on such narcissistic terms that she emasculated him and forced him into the role of a girl. Why couldn't he resist this? After all, many mothers attempt the same thing.

A factor which is an extremely important one in this case is the role of the absent father. An absent father, an absent parent generally, is always a target for fantasy elaborations. These can never be checked against reality: Who is this father or who is this mother? We see in treatment how absent and dead parents have undergone changes in a patient's mind which have little in common with the original person. This is the reason why the role of the father is important in the genetic picture. The father was a chronic alcoholic. He had fits, and he destroyed furniture. He was violent. But don't let us forget that he was also educated and spoke languages. It is precisely this area in which this boy can apply himself; this ego function is fairly well developed. That this infantilized boy can learn and communicate intelligently at all, that he went as far in school as he did, is indeed surprising. But let us look first at his early childhood. Since the boy was 3 the parents have been separated. The father—what was he? Was he a psychotic? His suicidal attempts and rages strongly hint at the probability. In any case, he was a very threatening, frightening individual for a small child. The child must have seen an enormous amount of violence in which his mother was his only protection. The father was a "good-for-nothing." The wife had to earn the living, she had to play the role of the man, and finally they separated. Of course, I asked myself what became of that father, because he is still this boy's father who plays a most important role in his mental development.

I have seen, so often, a similar family constellation that I feel free to conjecture and say that mothers of this type, in this particular situation, will always warn their male child never to be like their father. As soon as the little boy acts up, he is threatened with the condemnation: "You are just like your father and I don't want you ever to be like him; disavow him as I do!" In this fashion the mother has systematically destroyed the father for the child. This experience leads to an early fusion in the male child's mind between his masculine self-image and the mother's forbidding attitude to never be like the father. What else shall he be then? Like his mother? Such a male child is between the devil and the deep sea. He can never develop a normal oedipal situation because he can never relinquish the bisexual orientation which should find a settlement at the conclusion of the oedipal phase.

It is my contention that this boy desperately tries to preserve a positive father image in order not to become totally feminized— in order not to lose his identity; the sexual identity is an essential part of ego identity, and beyond it we enter the realm of psychosis. I think this boy tried to hang onto a positive father image when he says: "My father was a pilot in the Air Force, my father is rich, my father is powerful, I come from very important people." The elaboration that his father and mother are not really his parents is the typical family romance. The boy describes it vividly, and I think that in this relation the church plays an important role and points out the reason why he finally uses this almost delusional solution of the impasse in which he has been caught. The father is Greek Orthodox. This is precisely, as he says, what his mother does not want him to be. The mother is Greek Orthodox too, but she doesn't care. Then he talks about the family tree and the fact that he really belongs to a royal family. If the Russian royalty would be reinstated, he would have an important position and he would be an important personage. We must understand this in terms of the family-romance fantasy and as a restitution attempt for his disillusionment in his real parents.

When the child finds out that his parents are fallible, he still tries to preserve the belief that they are indestructible and omnipotent, because he derives from it narcissistic gratification and a sense of safety. Finally, the child has to accept the fact that they are mortals—fallible and weak; here the child resorts to the typical family-romance fantasy. In this light I understand the patient's productions under discussion. They are not so unusual in the lives of children; however, in this case, they acquire delusional proportions. The religiosity really became the preservation of a positive father image. Thus the total threat to his masculine identity was averted, and his drifting into a psychosis was forestalled. Religion finally became a delusional restitution—the renunciation of sexuality, the renunciation of all badness, of all that the father was: he was bad, he was raging, he was wild. The boy said of himself: "I am such a monster." The father, of course, was the real monster who, in the eyes of the child, was capable of killing the mother. The child knew that his mother would simply abandon such a monster. Entangled in the symbiotic bond, the fear of abandonment was always present. There was only one solution left—to destroy the monstrosity within himself by religiosity (obsessional defense). We have laid bare an insoluble dilemma which brings the Greek tragedy to mind. There seems no way out except death or insanity, both represented in psychological death or psychosis. The patient became preoccupied with the killing of the monster (negative father image). He will actually have taken on the role of the evangelist when he has succeeded in projecting all his own monstrosity into the outside world. Like a true evangelist he will then say: Repent your sins, give up sexuality, go to your mother, do what she says, go to the beauty parlor, sit down, stop soiling, accept it all. At that moment he can stop berating the mother for not having allowed him to have a father.

I am curious to know why, during the course of therapy, the father was never "dug up." I ask this question because I have good reason to believe that fragmented and ambivalent identification promotes delinquent behavior. A brief case vignette might illustrate this: A 12-year-old boy was brought for treatment because he was aggressive, uncontrollable, truant—in short, he was a predelinquent case. Contrasting with this behavior was the boy's submissive, passive, demeanor. He would yell at his mother, curse her, and throw things at her. Then a change came over him. He would wash the dishes and scrub the floor; he would behave like a good girl. The parents were divorced, and, when the boy was 4, the father had disappeared completely from the child's life. The mother never permitted the child to see the father, because the father was a "bad man." The fragmented ego of this child raised the suspicion of psychosis. It was my hunch that this boy was caught in a dilemma of identification. He perpetuated a bisexual identification in a kind of phasic rhythm. I decided to get the father of this boy into his life. The two had to confront each other in flesh and blood. This was done. The father was not so bad as he had been pictured; in fact, he turned out to be a rather nice man who was interested in his son. It was arranged that the child could spend four week ends with his father and the father's new family. It was interesting to see how the behavior of this boy changed after the reacquaintance with his father. After he met his father, the man and what he stood for could be discussed with the child. He was no longer a phantom; he was a person and not an elaboration of fantasy. The father figure which the mother had constructed for the child became corrected by reality.

References

1. Aichhorn, A. *Wayward Youth*. New York, The Viking Press, Inc., 1935.
2. Benedek, T. Adaptation to reality in early infancy. *Psychoanalyt. Quart.* 7: 200, 1938.
3. Bernabeu, E. P. Underlying ego mechanisms in delinquency. *Psychoanalyt. Quart.* 27: 383, 1958.

4. ERIKSON, E. H. *Childhood and Society*. New York, W. W. Norton & Company, Inc., 1956.
5. FREUD, S. *A General Introduction to Psychoanalysis*. New York, Liveright Publishing Corp., 1943.
6. GLOVER, E. *On the Early Development of Mind*. New York, International Universities Press, Inc., 1956; *The Roots of Crime*. New York, International Universities Press, 1958.
7. MAHLER, M. S. "On Child Psychosis and Schizophrenia," in *The Psychoanalytic Study of the Child*. New York, International Universities Press, Inc., 1952, vol. 7.
8. REDL, F., and WINEMAN, D. *The Aggressive Child*. Glencoe, Ill., The Free Press, 1957.

chapter 8   Truancy and Pilfering
Associated with Bereavement

AUGUSTA BONNARD

The initial diagnostic reports on two cases of truancy and pilfering were selected for presentation together, because of the similarity of their manifest features. These include the immediate and sustained *symptomatic* response by both boys to the analytically orientated insight proffered from the outset. However, whereas Thomas came to see me regularly, at intervals varying from two weekly at the beginning to six weekly or more thereafter, over a period of almost 3 years, John has been interviewed by me only six times in all. Subsequent biweekly therapy arranged for John, at the hands of a trained child therapist, as well as further appointments to see me were rejected by him and his father, as will be described.

The similarities provided by the manifest features of these two boy patients are as follows: They are almost identical in regard to age, John having been 1 month short of his thirteenth birthday at the initial psychiatric interview, while Thomas was 1 month beyond it. Both had been of good character at home and at school before their truancy and pilfering became evident. In each of these cases the surviving parent correctly surmised the coincidence of truancy with recent parental bereavement. Both John and Thomas are above average intelligence. Furthermore, although the clinical data are meager compared with those deriving from full psychoanalytic therapy, the pathological operation of feminine identifications could be discerned in both cases. The similarities come to an end at this point, other than the fact that both these boys, although in need of analysis, would themselves be the first to reject it. (As is well known, the difficulties of successfully "holding" children of this age in full analytic treatment often prove insurmountable, in practice, even when the cooperation of the adults concerned is adequate.) Their feminine identifications, however, are entirely dissimilar in their nature and psychodynamics. They played their distinctive contributory part in the grossly differing response of each boy to such psychotherapeutic facilities as were made available to him at the East London Child Guidance Clinic. Whereas Thomas, an illegitimate boy, identified on a passive homosexual basis with his sister and mother in regard to the latter's subsequent marital choice of a pathogenic husband, John had identified with his dying mother on an introjective, melancholic level.

The one true common denominator between these two cases is not manifest. It pertains to the metapsychology of the nonspecific "lightning-conductor" functions of their truancy and pilfering. Disregarding the differing individual symbolisms contained within these apparently similar actions, the force which detonated them was, in each instance, derived from an unmasterable degree of anxiety. Part of the explosive quality, which Aichhorn[1] describes so well, of this essential unmasterability drew its charge from the fact that there were matters of crucial significance in the lives of these boys which, by their fear-promoting nature, could not be conceptualized, let alone comprehended, through the exchange of spoken words. It is this last factor, whereby the "unspeakability" of certain kinds of fear are added to an existent burden of depression and anxiety, which probably provides the flash point for various types of impulsive behavior, including many instances of dissociality. To coin a phrase, the kind of fears here under discussion, whether preponderately objective or subjective, that is, anchored by ego-disturbing fantasies, would seem to produce an affective state of "intrapsychic panic." It is as if the subject defends himself from this state, experienced as ego disintegrative, by the commission of palpable, that is, externalized, actions of which the consequences do at least pertain to the realms of known "cause-and-effect" sequences. The function of such actions on this level is that of distractive offsetting of intrapsychic commotion; hence, one of the metapsychological mainsprings of Freud's famous characterization of the "criminal through a sense of guilt."[2]

These introductory comments are given in order to emphasize, in advance, such affective and metapsychological features. It is especially necessary because reports of this immediate nature, based on a single, diagnostic interview, cannot but be exploratory gropings and samplings. They inevitably lack many aspects of definition and synthesization.

It is hoped, however, that they do exemplify the rationale of the investigator's approach. In so far as certain operative aspects of the patient's dilemma of circumstantial doubt and fear are correctly evaluated and verbalized to him, the over-all function of the procedure can best be described as "sustaining a child's (or an adult's) sense of reality." It is where the impact of events, whether real or assumed to be real, becomes inextricable from highly charged fantasy constructions that such a combination may prove most pathogenic. But also, it is in situations such as these that "first-aid" work is most cognate, justifiable, and often quite peculiarly rewarding. As the late Kate Friedlander[3] used to say, "Not every case which we know to stand in need of analysis, *could* be analysed." There are, however, many categories of case and of situation, including lack of availability of psychoanalysts or trained child therapists, in which the operative word has to remain that of "could."

In the presentation of these diagnostic-prognostic surveys, that of Thomas remains, essentially, unchanged. John's, however, has had to be rearranged in order to incorporate the content of the two psychiatric reports which were necessary in the resolution of this case. One of the latter had to be written with tact and with some deletions, for the benefit of the family doctor; and the other, in great haste, as always, for the clinic files. Whenever feasible, relevant material, some of which was gained subsequently, has been inserted in both of these reports, in square brackets.

CASE REPORT—JOHN S.

John, aged almost 13 years, was initially referred to the clinic through the London County Council Child Care Committee, at the request of his headmaster, in April, 1958.

In a school report dated March, 1958, the following information was given: John had attended only 1 week since Christmas, and "he had put in very little appearance during the previous term." (No details were given.) John was considered to be a pleasant boy who had become "work-shy." The father had asked that his son be transferred to another school, in the hope of effecting an improvement in his attendance. This, the headmaster informed us, he had refused (quite rightly in my opinion), since he regards such moves during the continuance of truancy to be "bad policy."

Rather unusually, in the area served by the clinic, Mr. S.'s family doctor contacted us and asked for an advance interview with the psychiatrist. When he came, he wanted me to know that, although John was a truant as well as a pilferer from home (the headmaster knew nothing of the latter circumstance) the S. family had always held exceptionally good standards, both before the death of John's mother, the previous July, and since. Therefore, John was not to be handled by us in whatever way clinics are prone to do with delinquents; rather, we should speedily make arrangements for his admission to a good *residential* school. [This last procedure is quite common practice in our welfare state, under which all fees, and *sometimes* the totality of the child's upkeep, including pocket money, may be provided.] The family doctor informed me that he had, so far, advised spankings for John, without therapeutic success. He emphasized that Mrs. S., until being hospitalized for 10 months owing to secondary carcinoma of the bones, had been an exemplary wife and mother. The doctor did remark that, despite his own high opinion of Mr. S., not all of the womenfolk related to the family seemed to like him. He also said that there was some dissension between Mr. S. and his 80-year-old mother-in-law, who lives with him and his children and who still assists in running the home. These were the salient facts and opinions which the general practitioner contributed to the social history.

Because of the necessity of sending a psychiatric report to this somewhat smug family doctor, whom John was immediately to tell me he disliked, both of the reports have been recombined in what follows:

John's *intelligence test* gave him a score of 116. [In Britain it is customary for all children to be examined, at 11 years of age, to test intelligence and aptitudes. According to the results obtained, children are directed into three different levels of education. John had been correctly evaluated and was attending a middle-grade school. Reassessment for upgrading is made possible at 13 years.]

In accordance with our usual clinic practice, the accompanying parent was interviewed first. Mr. S. was a man of extremely burly build, with a frank, open type of face, whose manner created a favorable impression. It soon became clear, however, that he was in a state of fury and despair in regard to John's inexplicable behavior. The only future he said he could envisage for his son was of growing up to become an incorrigible criminal. John was the middle of his three children, the eldest being a boy of 17 and the youngest a girl aged 4 years. Mr. S. stressed that John had, in the past, always been a well-behaved and reasonable boy. Only during the period when his wife was in the hospital had John begun to steal money from home. The father associated, with some certainty, John's continuing truancy, during the past 6 months, to the fact of his wife's death. He was at first extremely dubious, however, about the linkage made by me between John's thieving and his sense of increasing guilt and anxiety, since the pilfering of money from home and the sporadic truancy had begun during his wife's lifetime.

Mrs. S. had been admitted to the hospital following a fracture of the leg. She remained there until her death 10 months later. During the last 5 weeks of her life, when he was told of the hopeless nature of her illness, Mr. S. had spent all his days and nights by her bedside. John's truancy had, however, begun, sporadically, in his previous school, that is, before these last weeks of the mother's life. The father had, meanwhile, been horrified by the discovery that John had been thieving from the home. Owing to Mrs. S.'s absence, it had been the father's practice to leave the week's housekeeping money in some obvious place, convenient for the household requirements. It was only when, on at least two occasions, the entire week's money had disappeared that suspicion finally fell on John. Mr. S. thought it likely that the purloining of lesser sums might have been going on unnoticed for many previous weeks. What had appalled the father even more was how, when John confessed, he had refused to express any remorse. His attitude appeared to be that his father was making an unnecessary fuss. Nor did it become known how John had spent these not-inconsiderable sums of money. There was, however, one singular item which Mr. S. told me. Despite his growing antipathy to John, he thought it only fair to mention his indebtedness to the boy for his voluntary undertaking of much of the family cooking. Furthermore, as his father put it, John had seemed to have acquired this aptitude, including recipes, "as if out of the blue."

After a very long talk with the father on the subject of the traumatic impact on a child of grave parental illness, I told him, to his astonishment, of the likelihood that John felt animosity toward him. I explained how the very nature of John's character changes suggested blame against his father, and in some respect connected Mr. S. with Mrs. S.'s death. He nevertheless promised me that if John would only talk frankly with him he would try to forgive his child. Mr. S. declared his willingness to treat him as he had previously, namely, as a loving son whom he himself ached to be able to love without shame or anxiety. He had, meanwhile, informed me of the thrashings he had administered to John, on his doctor's advice. Mr. S. expressed his distaste for these procedures, saying that he had felt most embarrassed in having to carry them out. He was extremely relieved to learn not only that these were useless but that they were likely to widen the terrible gap of mutual dislike which now existed between father and son. The ground was, therefore, well prepared for what was to ensue, first between me and John, and then between all three of us together. (It might also be mentioned that Mr. S., who fortunately has a sense of humor, asked me rather dryly, as he was about to return to the waiting room while John was being interviewed, "Did you know that our family doctor, who advises me just to go forth and remarry, is himself a bachelor?")

When John came in, the physical resemblance to his father proved most striking. He was of powerful build for his age and, like his father, burly. He had his father's large face and open expression. At first he appeared to be in a cheerful, bantering mood. As our conversation developed, and as it began to turn into surprising channels for John, his facial expression changed. He looked profoundly unhappy and spoke in tones of increasing embitterment.

In this type of stealing and of truancy, there is not only a sense of blame but also some factor in operation, the nature of which is *felt* to be secret. Mrs. S. had had a mastectomy 5 years before, because of carcinoma. Among the beliefs to which John gave utterance was that the trouble started in the mother's breast because of the death of a baby 7 years ago, when aged 5½ months. It would seem unlikely that John had ever previously put such a notion into spoken words. He may, however, have overhead views of this nature expressed by certain womenfolk in the family. John stated, "Because of the baby's death there was milk left unused, and so it all went bad." According to my understanding, John blames his father bitterly for, as it were, enforcing yet another pregnancy, which resulted in Mary, now aged 4 years. She was born about a year after the breast operation. If this supposition is correct, it would seem that John telescopes both of these pregnancies together into that of the first baby, whose death, rather than whose birth, is declared as lethal, that is, by the mechanisms of condensation and reversal. Indeed, for various reasons, of which an important one is more clearly indicated later [John's inverted oedipal situation, pathologically reactivated by the mother's illness and death], Mary's existence as the only girl, combined with her present fate of continued sharing of the father's bed, may have provided the flash point for John's present breakdown into dissociality.

John proceeded to accord further blame on two unexpected but interconnected scores. He says that he and all the family were brought up to be lazy, the mother taking the load of the work and responsibility within the home, as well as shouldering their father's complaints in regard to any of their childish misdemeanors. His father, so John said, did nothing directly for or with the children, but merely grumbled to his wife; that is, John seems to have resented not having become a successful competitor of his mother for the sharing of his father's interest. Furthermore, not only does Mary continue to share the father's bed, but she is very much spoiled by him. Mr. S. had already rationalized this sharing of his bed by telling me that he has to keep a continuous watch on Mary because in the past she had "suffered from too many fits before having a fever." [This statement was subsequently counterchecked with the Children's Hospital where Mary attended. It was learned that the fits were no longer considered to be of any significance, the last one having occurred a year previously. Although the father was urged on two further occasions to cease from keeping this little girl in his bed, it being explained that such an upbringing might facilitate unwelcome character traits in her, he has proved adamant on this point. His rejection of my advice on this score may be one of the underlying reasons why he has subsequently neglected to respond to invitations to come and see me again at the clinic, despite his expressed gratitude and appreciation for the rapid disappearance of John's dissocial symptoms.] John was glad to enlarge on the topic of this little girl, who is well cared for by himself and his brother, Roger, as well as by the grandmother. Mary, despite their kindness, ignores them all as soon as their father comes home. John said that, when Mr. S. is home, "she just keeps on saying 'Let Daddy do it for me' and he does." In this way John once again verbalized his sense of rejection because of Mary's behavior and because she finds favor with his father, with whom, he feels, he does not.

At some point the question of his mother's fractured leg came into our discussion. [The mother had previously been diagnosed as suffering from secondary carcinoma of the bones, and had had regular hospital treatment by deep X-ray therapy. The family doctor was informed of the serious prognosis. It was felt to be more humane to tell the husband that his wife was suffering from severe arthritis. Arthritis is also the condition from which the maternal grandmother, who shares the S. home, mainly complains. It was, as already stated, only in the last 5 weeks of Mrs. S.'s life that the husband was told all of the true facts.] John recalled how two accidents had occurred to his mother, within a week of each other, before her hospitalization. The dog was blamed for the first one, having rushed past her and thus upset her balance. In the other accident, she fell downstairs and fractured her thigh. With tearful passion, John demanded of me why his mother, of all people, afflicted with arthritis as she was, should be carrying a tea tray? Only because they were all lazily abed, said John, did she have to bring early-morning tea to her husband. As can be seen, the implications of the boy's own sense of guilt are here "passed across" to the father, to be his marital and parental burden.

When I remarked to John, in accordance with one of the father's more trivial complaints about his son, that he seems to keep his bedroom unduly untidy, John expostulated, with unutterable bitterness, "Just take a look at my father's room and then tell me if I am untidy." [It should be noted that invitations of this kind, that is, to penetrate into the most private parts of the home, even when made in a rhetorical context, are sufficiently unusual, at first encounter, to be significant. As further knowledge of John showed, not only is such material symbolic, but also he was, indirectly, seeking to tell me "there are things which need to be found out."]

John says that his father is smiling and polite to everyone outside but that he is scowling and in a black mood at home, but only since the mother died. (The implications here are multiple. His father is to be recognized as "double faced." Furthermore, Mr. S. has reason enough to be overwhelmed with guilt. Although in a state of depression on account of the death of his marital love object, she has been superseded by Mary, her own daughter.) It was at this point that tears coursed from John's eyes as he exclaimed, with the utmost scorn, "Just look at the color of my father's hair now, it was dark before that fracture." The ambivalent attitudes revealed by the contradiction between the boy's words and his effective state were most striking. Meanwhile, the things which Mr. S. had been telling me had been explained to John. Just like John, the father had been led to believe that Mrs. S. was suffering from simple arthritis. It was not until I explained the whole march of organic events to John that he seemed to realize that a grave illness had been the cause of his mother's prolonged hospitalization. [The silence by which anxious or bereaved parents and other adults are afflicted, or which they adopt with the best of motives, can produce secondarily traumatizing consequences on the children concerned. There was adequate evidence that John, and no doubt his father, had been defending themselves, via the mechanism of denial, against recognition of the progressive decline of the mother. Indeed, at one stage, John said angrily, "Everyone knew mother was dying, even *she* knew, but no one told me." In critical phases of family life such as this one, adult stoicism or silences may serve pathogenically to reactivate, because of the apparent lack of any refutation, a child's most secret or repressed fantasies. A pathological variant of the oedipal tragedy, whereby the daughter replaces the mother, seems thus to have been proved for John S.] It was within this context that it was explained to John how spontaneous fractures in cancerous bones are an ever-present risk. When told that they could occur, not only in falling downstairs but on the slightest movement, such as turning over in bed, he recalled how just such a fracture had actually taken place in his presence, while sitting with his mother in the hospital ward. [In this parallel manner John was being shown by allusion how he might also exonerate his father from the accusation of doing *intentional* harm, as, for instance, in the primal scene.]

John said he would now let me into a *real* secret. He proceeded to specify the names of certain relatives who do not like his father (as the family doctor had stated), any more than John does. One can conclude from these remarks that some womenfolk in the family have criticized the father in the boy's hearing in regard to Mrs. S. becoming pregnant within so few weeks after a major operation. John continued to be enabled to enlarge on his grounds for hostility toward his father, the additional material proving to be of singular interest. Once again he asked me, in his bitter and rhetorical tone, if the following could be believed. His father has actually threatened to throw his 17-year-old brother, Roger, out of the house for a ridiculous reason. Mr. S. insists that Roger must be home by 10:30 P.M. Roger has a girl friend, and this girl friend has permission from her parents to stay out as late as 10:45 P.M.—a whole quarter of an hour later! Who but his father would threaten a young man who has a girl friend about what time he should come in? The deduction made in regard to this material was as follows: John, in fact, envies his brother, as well as his father, in being the possessor of a responsive love object of his own. The envy, however, is hidden through his apparent alliance with his brother's cause and in his altruistic hostility toward the father. If, however, there is truth in this story, then it does suggest Mr. S. to be a rather severe and restrictive parent.

This reference to the keeping of late hours probably served either as a facilitating recollection or as the associative link with the poignant episode which was to follow. With tears in his eyes, John asked me how it could happen that he should be the only member of the family not to be told of his mother's impending death. He learned the news only by chance, and in the most hurtful manner. One night, because he could not sleep, he went for a stroll with his girl cousin, at about midnight. They encountered the mother of this girl, John's aunt, returning from a party. She asked John how he could possibly go out strolling in the street while his mother lay dying in the hospital. This, said John, was the very first he knew of it all, and it came to him as a terrible shock. The episode was utilized in order to suggest to John that maybe he had found himself unable to fall asleep, and felt restless enough to invite his cousin to come out for a walk, just because he had such strong fears and suspicions concerning his mother's desperate state. John was inclined to agree with me about this. He then recalled a singularly interesting item. John remembered that he too had sustained a fracture (of his elbow) on September 3 of last year, that is, two months after his mother's death. This day was the first anniversary of his mother's leg fracture.

We can see, therefore, how deeply identified and preoccupied this boy was with the full course of his mother's fatal illness. It was actually from the time John sustained his fracture that he began to play truant continuously. This occurred at the beginning of the next school term. Although he was incapacitated in the use of his right hand, there was, of course, no rational reason for remaining away from school. Retrospectively, it seems likely that part of his truancy represented a kind of hysterical enactment through the mechanism of identification with his late mother's continuously failing state and with her absenteeism in the hospital. This would, however, account only for the unconscious motivation of the earlier days or weeks of his truancy. By the time it had been sustained over a period of 6 months, until he was referred to the clinic, it must have come to represent a multiplicity of significances for John. The sum total of his truancy and expression of dislike for school had become that of the symptomatic condition known as school phobia.*

John had been told by now of my having warned his father of the likelihood of his son holding a deep grudge against him. It was therefore suggested that, as he had now been able to express certain of these grievances to me, and as his father had promised his sympathetic willingness to listen, perhaps we could now admit him, in order that all three of us could discuss the situation together. Mr. S. was duly invited to join us. Father and son agreed that they would thresh everything out between them, but this time not in anger or with physical violence. They agreed that each had some justification for blame despite having made some very sad and painful errors about each other. John told his father that he had blamed him for the mother's fracture and for various outcomes of his father's strictness, as well as for favoritism. The conversation was held in my presence, and it was gratifying to see how the expressions of tension and anger left their faces as their *rapprochement* progressed.

Eventually, they left the clinic arm in arm. Before doing so, however, the father was asked to talk with me again alone. He was told of John's response when I asked him why he had become a thief, an answer which I had accepted as the truth. John had responded to my query with a genuinely astonished exclamation: "But I didn't know I was doing wrong!"

In what sense should one understand a sincere reply of this illogical nature, in a boy of John's age and manifestly good reasoning ability? It could only mean that the housekeeping money had come to represent the very substance of John's ambivalent, maternal love object, being as it was, the currency of the parents' relationship to each other and to the family. John appropriated these tokens for himself, feeling that those of whom he was jealous or who did not sufficiently appreciate him were well able to do without them. Reparation as well as identification with the common love object of his father and himself, namely Mrs. S., were together achieved in taking over her important function of cooking for the

* The psychopathology and psychodynamics governing various types of school phobia, have been evaluated by me (to be published). John's case could serve as an illustrative instance of their commonest single factor—fear and anxiety pertaining to the home environment, more often well founded in real events rather than in fantasy-based misconceptions.

whole family. The mechanism of stealing in circumstances such as these, as well as the nature of his feminine identification, illustrates a more profound over-all condition. It represents introjection (of the ambivalently loved and lost object) which has reverted from an intrapsychic process to a material level as concrete as cannibalism. In other words, John's stealing exemplified the operation of a mechanism related to that of melancholia, but by which dissocial actions here described he had sought to mitigate this affective state.

Although complex mechanisms such as these could hardly have been conveyed to Mr. S., their affective consequences could be. With the reassurance that John was not truly dishonest, one could stress how changed John had become in ways other than dissociality. Mr. S. readily agreed that his son's life was barren and that he had withdrawn from social contacts. He knew John to be thoroughly miserable as well as hostile. He also grasped something of the concept of the stolen money serving as a substitutive comfort for the mother which, in his sense of loneliness, John had seized for himself. (In this instance it was not difficult to arouse parental compassion. Whenever one succeeds, whether with parents or teachers, the affective setting becomes so changed through the positive attitudes prevailing that even the acquisition of a modicum of insight seems to go an astonishingly long way.)

Subsequent Data

There were only five more consecutive interviews between John and myself, on three of which he was accompanied, at my request, by his father. The latter also wrote an appreciative letter to me on one occasion, explaining that his work commitments precluded his further attendance.

After the psychiatric interview reported upon, John returned at once to school and soon expressed his pleasure at being in class again. He agreed that there could not have been anything amiss at school, after all. Much had subsequently been talked out together between father and son, and they seemed to be the best of friends. From now on, John was to radiate an air of positive health, both mental and physical. Mr. S. seemed eager and willing to increase and deepen his understanding of the complex mental processes which had dictated his son's disquieting behavior. Many more features were discussed, the emphasis being on guilt, anxiety, and thwarted affection serving as the mainsprings for hostile attitudes.

The father seemed sincerely anxious to be shown how he could suitably modify his handling of all matters concerning his family, including his mother-in-law. The only obvious exception, as already indicated, proved to be the disregard of the advice given for changing the sleeping arrangements of his daughter and himself.

It had become apparent, however, even by the third interview, that John invariably discussed daily events and their significance in two contexts. The one sketched out the reasonable or likely outcomes of interpersonal activities, whereas the other asserted how he was persistently misunderstood or unfairly dealt with. Thus his headmaster soon came to be revealed as possessing many of the obtuse and unappreciative aspects of his father. For example, the headmaster wanted good results in a swimming meet, and John was only too eager to improve his prowess. Owing to pressure of schoolwork and other commitments, John made a special arrangement to practice at lunch time. No sooner had he done so, than the headmaster forbade swimming during this part of the day. When telling me of the foregoing, John's expressions of annoyance and contempt could be seen to be strikingly exaggerated.

Shortly after the initial psychiatric interview, John had expressed a desire to join the Sea Scouts. I already had misgivings about his feminine identifications and the likely paths of their expression. However, when I realized that the Scout company he favored had its club quarters on the riverbank where the father cultivated a vegetable patch as his hobby, John's ambition seemed to me to be a perfect one. It was easy for me to coax his father to agree, in advance, to the purchase of John's complete uniform, provided John applied and was accepted. When John again broached his wish to me, as well as his doubts about being allowed the requisite clothing, it was pleasing to be able to tell him how good his chances were likely to be. Instead of being glad, he suddenly looked sulky. He explained in precise detail how, even if he were to ruin the uniform, provided it were returned to the Scouts, his father would be repaid most of the purchase price. It had already become apparent that John was primarily a neurotic boy in a depressed state—one who stood in need of regular psychotherapy. In the third session, therefore, the father, who by now had no complaints to make of his son's behavior, was informed to this effect. He readily agreed to the offer of biweekly treatment. In the following session, John revealed much more clearly his preoccupation with homosexual attitudes. He giggled coyly in describing how a Scoutmaster had photographed him in his new uniform against a background which had made him look winsome and girlish. John also made quite a number of spontaneous observations on those who might even find enjoyment in the company of "fairies and sissies."

This session was largely spent in introducing the topic, as well as the objects, of psychotherapy. John seemed pleased by the opportunity of participating in more detailed work at the hands of a trained child therapist. He readily agreed that he still had many worries and that he was doing poorly in some of his schoolwork, such as arithmetic. The period covered thus far comprised 10 weeks.

Unfortunately, after a few attendances, John's psychotherapist became ill for some weeks. He therefore came to me during her absence. John expressed his satisfaction with this arrangement and also with his former therapist. Nevertheless, when she returned he repeatedly failed to keep appointments with her. My assumption is that her delicate appearance, along with her becoming ill, had proved too threatening to John in terms of maternal history repeating itself. Written inquiries and appointments, however, made for the father to come and see me, have similarly been ignored. It might be worth pointing out that it is by no means uncommon for a school-phobic child, to shift his phobic reaction away from the original source (home), that is, off the displacement to school and onto the clinic. This, however, is only likely to be a partial or inadequate explanation of John's reaction of avoidance, in which his father now must be included. It is baffling and disquieting to consider what kind of man Mr. S. can be, also, having expressed his profound appreciation of my services, should then ignore all further contacts offered by the clinic. Subsequent school reports nevertheless indicate that John has remained a steady and industrious pupil of unexceptionably good character. He had previously talked with his therapist about his ambition to be trained as a chef. The latest report indicates his success in persuading his headmaster of the suitability of this choice of occupation. John is about to be transferred to another school where his desired vocational training is a part of the curriculum.

If John can sublimate his symptomatic choice of cookery as a lifetime occupation, he is assured of a satisfactory livelihood. He is, however, likely to remain vulnerable in regard to the quality of a depressive reaction which deepened to an introjective-melancholic level. Furthermore, as a part of his defense against his homosexual trends is the classical one of a sense of hostility against (senior) men, and he seems likely to suffer, even if this is concealed, from much social unease. Our immediate interest in this case is, however, the consideration of the question of whether or not John's stealing is likely to recur, whether it might (together with the truancy) have resolved itself spontaneously without psychiatric intervention, or whether he would have best been served by residential placement, penal or nonpenal? My own inclination is to reply "No" to all these queries and, instead, to put forward my recurring plea for the need for effective follow-up, that is, the institution of real research into psychosociological phenomena.

CASE REPORT—THOMAS THOMAS

Thomas Thomas, whose name I have changed in order to preserve his anonymity, aged just 13 years, scores an I.Q. of 130, and, although he does badly in class, he is correctly placed in a grammar school (the top of the three available levels of state scholastic education, as described previously).

If the mother, Mrs. W., is to be relied upon, his truancy and pilfering from shops and the home date back to a period either soon after the death of his father, Mr. Thomas, 1½ years ago, or possibly in relation to her association with her present husband, Mr. W. Mrs. W. states this to be her third marriage. She married again about 6 months after the death of Mr. Thomas. It would seem she had known Mr. W. only 6 weeks prior to being married to him. He is a Polish ex-soldier. According to Mrs. W., her son, who is sometimes known, at his request, as Thomas W., was previously named Thomas Thomas. He was given this duplicated name because he was illegitimate. [Retrospectively, it seems unlikely that his father's surname was Thomas. It is therefore quite probable that the boy was previously known by his mother's maiden name, or else by some surname other than Thomas. Unfortunately, I did not clarify this point with the mother. This feature is mentioned specifically because *inexplicable* changes of surname are always anxiety promoting to a child, as are the *inexplicable* circumstances which usually occasion such changes. Classical fantasies of childhood such as, for example, of being a foundling, are thereby pathogenically reinforced. The problems

concerning the identity of the self may then become of traumato-
philic significance, especially under the instigation of real events,
which, by their obscure or frightening nature, could not or dare not
be verbally conceptualized; that is, they could not be "told back"
to the self.]

There is so much in this boy's and his mother's history of an unfortunate and dramatic kind that they must be regarded as a quasi
unity. Add to this the peculiar quality of impulsiveness which is inherent in the nature of the mother's past and present history, and
one has a situation for a child of actual gross, psychical, insecurity.
The maternal story is as follows: Mrs. W.'s own father was brought
up on a farm. Mrs. W.'s mother, feeling unwanted by her young
stepmother-in-law, who insisted she must live in a barn through
these two years of her married life, then deserted and went to London. Mrs. W. was thus brought up, until the age of 7½, by her
father, together with the people of the farm. These included three
young children born to the step-grandmother (that is, Mr. W.'s
stepmother). During this time, Mrs. W., who says she hated her
father, shared his bed until 7½ years of age. He then rejoined her
mother in London, where her parents cohabited until Mrs. W. was
16 years old. Within this context we must note Mrs. W.'s awareness of her mother's accusation against Mrs. W.'s father of having
attempted to have sexual relations with her mother's mother, that
is, Mrs. W.'s maternal grandmother. The incident was alleged to
have occurred during the time her mother was in the hospital giving birth to the present Mrs. W. I think this readily proffered statement may serve as an exemplification of a kind of displacement.
From what follows, one could either assume that there had been
some kind of sexual relationship between Mrs. W. and her own
father, before or after the age of 7½ years, or that their sleeping
together in one bed had promoted incestuous fantasies which were
pathogenic in their intensity.

At 16 years of age, Mrs. W. became pregnant. She and her
mother then left the father, and went to live elsewhere. It would
seem that either her mother undertook the care of the baby, or
else her future mother-in-law eventually did so. Mrs. W. states that
when the father of this child came back from service abroad (he
was a soldier in the regular Army), they were married. Another
boy was born 2½ years later. She explained the next chapter of
her life as follows: In that, her husband could be considered
promiscuous, and, being again absent on service abroad, when he

returned, it was to find she had had two more children. These were fathered by a man here to be known as "Mr. Thomas." Mrs. W.'s casual suggestion in regard to this situation was that possibly both she and her husband had become "somewhat lax in their morals, while apart." He divorced her, however, and emigrated with her first two sons to New Zealand.

When Mrs. W. found that she was pregnant with Thomas (our patient), she seems to have gone off to "Mr. Thomas's" wife to tell her of the liaison. "Mr. Thomas" then left his wife and cohabited with Mrs. W. Mrs. W. says his wife did not divorce him until 10 years later. About 2 years after being divorced, he died rather suddenly, of a cerebral hemorrhage. Although remaining unmarried, Mrs. W. says that she regards this period of cohabitation as a stable part of her life, with good economic conditions. Thomas also has a sister 2½ years his junior. Mrs. W. feels confident that neither of these children suppose themselves to be other than legitimate.

Within this context, there is a circumstance which seems to be most unusual. "Mr. Thomas" was so enamoured of Judaism as to toy with the idea of becoming a Jew. He was, however, quite definite in his wish for these two children to become converted. To this end, Thomas and his sister have attended the religious-instruction classes held for Jewish pupils in their respective schools. Nowadays, it is Thomas who still insists, so Mrs. W. says, on going to these classes. Presumably, he expresses his loyalty, thereby, to his late father. Mrs. W. also remarked that Thomas has said he hated his late father. There were adequate opportunities to ascertain the contrary. Her statement in regard to her son's sentiments, however, had already been freely used by her in regard to her own father. She also stated that Thomas has always been on bad terms with his sister. This the boy later confirmed. There are, however, items in the Care Committee visitor's report suggesting that the mother does in reality favor the girl and that Mr. W. shares this view.

Of herself, Mrs. W. says that she "has a wicked tongue and a quick temper," and that Mr. W. "is a man of extreme temper." Both of them hit Thomas rather hard and often. She says it makes her feel somewhat nauseated, however, when seeing Mr. W. strike him forcibly. She too, on occasion, has taken the boy's own leather belt and beaten him with it because of theft or truancy. While telling me about her own actions, Mrs. W. became greatly excited, justifying herself in a wild kind of way, and demanding, "What else *can* one do in such circumstances?"

When Thomas was born, Mrs. W. had what she described as "a nervous breakdown in the hospital." Not only did she think she heard him crying all night, but also she was convinced that there were real voices——probably those of the nurses—criticizing her. (It must be remembered, of course, that Thomas was at least her second illegitimate child.) Mrs. W. then had to be transferred to another hospital because of her "breakdown," whence her removal to a mental hospital was advised. (She must have become unmanageable in some degree.) It was then that "Mr. Thomas" intervened and removed her. She says she is sure that, had she been admitted to a mental hospital, where a stay of 6 months had been envisaged, she would never have become sane again.

One of the many interesting items concerning Thomas is contained in his remark that, because the other boys at school are nasty, he gets on best with girls; hence he tends to go about chiefly with girls. It is likely that this type of relationship represents a splitting off of his tender feelings toward his sister onto those of other people. [Only much later on was I to recognize a certain quality of passivity in Thomas, this being feminine in both type and aim.] In this connection it should be noted that, owing to lack of accommodation, his 11-year-old sister shares the bedroom in which Mr. W. and their mother habitually conduct (in the girl's presence) their sexual lives. Mrs. W. was quite surprised to find that I regarded it as more normal, as well as more decent, for a sister to share a room with a brother, at their ages, than with someone who, in more senses than one, was "a strange man." [As, later on, I grew to hear of more and more chaotic episodes of violence and threats (as well as periodic desertions or separations) between Mr. and Mrs. W., a clear picture emerged of the former. As well as being a compulsive and ambitious craftsman in the building trade, he is given to paranoid outbreaks of insensate rage. These could be directed with equal irrationality against one or another member of the household. The longest period of peace ensued when Mr. W. went to live for nearly a year with a bachelor of his own nationality, in an empty house. They had bought it for the purpose of reconditioning and selling it. Not only was there a harmonious, homosexual arrangement between these men, but Thomas became increasingly pleased to visit Mr. W. there, and render himself acceptable to his stepfather.] It is likely that, because of Mrs. W.'s childhood history of sharing a bed with her own father, she regards the present procedure with regard to her daughter as perfectly satisfactory.

At some point I said that I was quite convinced, on the basis of my knowledge of so many cases of this kind, that her son's breakdown into delinquent reactions represented his anger, worry, and puzzlement at not being able to make a coherent story of his own origins, these anxieties being traumatically exacerbated by her sudden and premature marriage to a man of violent moods. It was emphasized that in all cases such as her children's, within my experience, they have been given access, either accidental or intentional, possibly on the part of some ill-disposed adult, to some kind of awareness (1) of their illegitimacy and (2) of all kinds of perturbing deviations within their past life. Indeed, it would seem reasonable to presume that Thomas clings to the idea of becoming a Jew partly because it fosters the notion of achieving thereby a new identity: strange, but at least comprehensible (that is, the new identity). Although the mother denied it when with me, she had told our psychiatric social worker how it was at the boy's insistence that he is sometimes known as Thomas W. To my mind, such a request underlines his reality-based sense of the need to acquire the status of a legal family name.

The impression of the visitor from the Care Committee had been that Mr. W. would continue to refuse to adopt the boy owing to his misbehavior. The surprise elements in this case continued when, quite by chance, the mother mentioned, in her casual way, that a court hearing of both children's case for adoption is imminent. In her estimation there is just one stumbling block. Mr. W., being a Catholic, will be required to sign a declaration of his willingness to let Thomas continue in his present faith, this being Protestantism. The unique difficulty which threatens is that Thomas (as he was to repeat to me) will insist in court that he be inducted in the religion which was preferred by his late father, namely Judaism. Mrs. W. supposes that neither her husband nor the court would be likely to accept such a proviso. [Thomas was 15 years of age, when we recently parted. So far, he has not been adopted, much to my satisfaction.]

The offer was made to Mrs. W. of my meeting Thomas in her presence, as our first introduction. My purpose would be to discuss matters with him in such a way that she might learn in direct fashion (1) useful leads she could later follow at home in order to explain the complex circumstances of his and his sister's ancestry and (2) how much more than she supposed, he already knew or had surmised. She accepted my proposition willingly, especially as she was now pleased to be able to tell me of Thomas having boasted to her, in advance, that he would neither tell me anything nor answer any questions. The opposite turned out to be the case, as the motivation of such a statement often implies.

A child, so placed, knowing there was so much being hidden from him, or else which he is adjusted to ignore or keep silent about, is constrained to deny or refute en masse. As the boy and I talked together, with his mother sitting by quiet and controlled, the tears were hardly ever absent from his eyes. His state of mind seemed to be one of complete sincerity and complete desperation. When asked how many times his mother had been married, he replied, to her discomfiture, that he had no idea of the frequency. The implication was that she had changed husbands repeatedly. He knew with certainty of there being a brother somewhere, and he also supposed "there were lots more, besides." When we stolidly worked through the childbearing range he had assigned to his mother, he seemed quite unmoved by the chronological facts which would have made her give birth at 11 years of age! That such an intelligent boy should be able to "hold" a variety of confused half-convictions, of which this is an example, suggests that he must have done much pondering, but the final outcome of it must always have been the same, namely nonsense. When, then, his mother intervened to confirm that she had been 16 years of age when her first son was born, he was aghast to learn she could have been so young! He was quite astonished to be told that there is merely one more half brother to take into account, and that both were in New Zealand with one former husband. At this, Thomas said he had always assumed that her children had gone to Canada. When interchanges of this kind are made, in this instance between place names, which to Thomas share similarities because both are in the British Commonwealth and both are remote, one can usually assume that the one named serves as a guarded admission of knowledge of the other. The alibi of over-all ignorance must remain in cases such as these, because it is less threatening to the ego than is unauthorized or secret knowledge. When Thomas agreed with me, in his mother's presence, as to his worry about the secrets in their lives, he was assured that she had promised henceforth to explain all his queries, and thus he could expect to find that all kinds of puzzling items would, "click together and begin to make sense."

In due course, Thomas and I talked alone. Although he continued to agree that he had many worries, he would not, in fact, answer any more leading questions. [At this stage Thomas could only permit himself to divulge that which the mother's presence allowed of being decensored.] The common channel which could be freely traversed in her absence was that of religion. When he again asserted his determination to become a Jew, it was suggested that such a change-over was quite unnecessary until he had reached an age when he could make up his own mind with full knowledge and genuine freedom of choice. Thomas was advised to take full advantage of being so young, thereby automatically belonging to the religion (Church of England) in which he was baptized and which, it was emphasized, his own father had never forsworn. The indirect purpose of these abjurations, together with the display of my lack of enthusiasm in regard to his impending adoption, was to inform him that his present identity seemed real and reasonable enough to me—an outsider. I casually remarked that there would be no legal compulsion for him to remain with Mr. W. after Thomas reaches his sixteenth birthday. (In clinic practice, one sometimes has occasion to verbalize that which may seem to a grownup to be such common knowledge as to be self-evident. Telling a child who has reality reasons for despairing of happiness within his home that he has individual, legal rights of protection or redress of one kind and another is often quite peculiarly salutory. Thereafter, depending on the child and his circumstances, many seem much better able to harness their anxieties, and even to cope with the present, on being clearly told that its continuance can be curtailed at their own will. The psychodynamics of what amounts to the child as a kind of award of ego autonomy, that is, by way of *mutual* recognition, are by no means simple.) Thomas was also told how, when he has fewer preoccupations and worries, his capacity for schoolwork will improve. [His later mediocre school records were to remain disappointing, although understandably so in the light of his continuing alarms and worries.]

It should be noted that both the psychiatric social worker, on a previous occasion, and I on this one, agreed on her description of the behavior in the waiting room of mother and son as "being loverlike."

The outcome in a case of this kind is extremely chancy, because such a woman is an acting-out fantast whose seductive quality of impulsiveness promotes, in the dependent and immature child, libidinized states of suspense and excitement. In addition, the attachment of this boy to his mother is profound. Unfortunately, much of it is based on competitive jealousy exacerbated by the traumatogenic arousal, through her actions, of his scoptophilic curiosity.

Résumé of Three Subsequent Years

At the next interview, Thomas was accompanied by his mother. Subsequently, she came only once, and then was in a great hurry. [There is no doubt that the headmaster's influence helped to consolidate the reliability of Thomas' attendances. It included his making Thomas, after discussion with me, eligible for an additional financial grant. As I was to realize, Thomas became not so much a wheedler as a charmer where advantages of personal maintenance were concerned.] Mrs. W. said she had faithfully implemented all my advice, including putting both children in the same bedroom. She made it plain that no good would come of my notions. On the one hand, she had overheard Thomas explaining to his sister, "As I am a bastard, so are you. We both are." She wondered if the whole district were to be similarly enlightened by him. [It was not.] On the other hand, the two children now chatted as late as 10 P.M., so that her daughter would henceforth have even less rest than when sharing her mother's bedroom.

Quarrels still ensued between her husband and the boy. Many of these, she said, were precipitated by Thomas' refusing to speak in response to Mr. W.'s peremptory mode of address. [As I came to realize, with the passage of time, there seemed always to be angry scenes created by Mr. W. Alternatively, an apprehensive silence reigned. The latter came either as an aftermath of a quarrel or else because of the stepfather's objection to anyone speaking while he pursued his technical studies in the family's midst. At this time, and for a few months to come, Thomas was recognized as rebelling against Mr. W., in the way any self-respecting person might do. Whenever his mother made another of her final decisions to end her marital association, Thomas expressed his relief, during this earlier phase. Later on, however, his well-founded incredulity was succeeded by a kind of submissive despair, during which periods of crisis the boy looked exhausted and in poor condition. This phase merged into a different one, to be described.]

Thomas, having talked to me in a lively fashion, told me of a skill which he has successfully fostered. He has taught himself to "fall asleep at will, practically standing up." He expressed pride in his ability to remain sleeping for unconscionable periods of time. Such a description, which we know so well from Pavlov's dogs, of sleep bespeaking a physiological attempt to absent oneself from the unavoidable (as well as his mother's "wrong-in-advance attitude" toward my efforts, and much else) led me to suggest a residential placement for Thomas. What I had in mind was a remarkable school opened by the London County Council for boys of good or excellent intelligence. Although run on the lines of the best private schools, it avoids the dangers of social mixing together and manifestly denying the differences between boys from materially and culturally well-endowed homes and boys whose backgrounds are more usually the opposite.

As time passed, however, I dropped the idea, with the agreement of Thomas, so he never left his present (excellent) day school or his home. My reasons were both rational and subjective. Thomas is a very good-looking boy of somewhat aristocratic appearance and refinement of manner. Such an appearance, especially if regarded, as it often tends to be, as a recommendation in itself to place a boy in a school of especially high middle-class standards, may sometimes activate something of an "imposter" attitude. It is harmful, whether the boy "slides" into it, or whether he strengthens his superego, usually in punitive ways, to operate against himself or the family environment with which he feels himself inextricably identified. To my mind, a faulty placement imposes a special hazard on certain of these children whose problems of identity are such as to make them unable to "process" proffered advantages in an egosyntonic manner.

[Apart from the foregoing considerations, it had become increasingly clear that Thomas and his sister were serving as the main bulwarks of each other in terms of safeguarding the realities of their common past and of their future. As Thomas put it to me, "I can see she is going to become my chief relative." The question of exacerbation of an undue sense of guilt in Thomas, were he to "desert" his sister, also had to be considered. If the sister, whose life at home was unhappy, were to break down, who could be blamed, and what would be her fate? Should boarding school be advocated for her, too, and, if so, what would be the final outcome in terms of their mother's next episode? There was no doubt that Mrs. W. took both pride and strength from the presence of her two children. These issues, as well as the boy's quick response to having a grown-up friend in the clinic with whom he could freely discuss his life circumstances, kept him in London. As will be seen from what follows, it might well be argued, even by myself, that my change of decision was a mistake. There were, however, to be only minor complaints, so Thomas was to tell me, of his home behavior henceforth.]

There was, however, one very ugly incident about 1½ years later, which he was unable to clarify for me. He had lost his temper one morning, or maybe had been fooling with his sister and gone beserk, in consequence of which he had so winded her that she arrived looking pale, ill, and anxious at school. Meanwhile, however, I had been hearing of frequent ugly scenes between Mr. and Mrs. W. These included violence and brief desertions by either of them. Mrs. W. always seemed to be on the point of expelling her husband, for the last time, from the flat of which she would have been the operative "householder," were it not that their entire tenancy was "under cover" and illegal.

I knew that Mr. W. was a paranoid man, in a permanent state of incipient anger. Thomas told me how, one day, he happened to laugh at some comic episode on the television screen. Mr. W. turned from his perpetual engineering home studies to smash his fist at the boy's face. His assumption was that he was being laughed at behind his back, on this occasion, by Thomas. As to whether the brutal episode between Thomas (who is a most unviolent boy) and his sister represented the enactment of the mechanism of "turning passive into active," or, still more important, that of switching of roles between "masculine" (sadistic) and "feminine" (masochistic) could remain only guesswork.

With the passage of time, it emerged that Mrs. W. would agree to remain with her husband on condition that he purchased a suitable house. Thomas often said, thereafter, that he behaved himself purely to further his mother's ends. He began to pursue a policy of ingratiating himself with Mr. W. This man needed geometry and algebra for his (perfectionistic) studies. Thomas became his instructor, until higher trigonometry entered into the curriculum and defeated the boy's undistinguished attainments. There was one halcyon year for the family, already mentioned, when Mr. W. moved off, apart from brief returns, to a distant part of London. He shared an empty house with a Polish bachelor. Thomas cycled back and forth on errands or on social visits, which included his being a coach in mathematics. The homosexual aspects of the whole arrangement became manifest. The boy was greatly intrigued to find himself so acceptable and to be amicably treated in an all-male setting. By contrast, Thomas had continued to take his summer vacations in another part of the country with his maternal grandparents, eventually camping out in their garden. He proved most scrupulous in his budgeting of expenses and in any financial commitments he made with them, all paid out of his own earned resources. When, however, Mr. W. did buy a new house this year, outside London, Thomas immediately dropped his, hitherto, convenient grandparents, even though the family's move was yet to be accomplished.

The only known recurrence of stealing happened 7 months after his initial referral to the clinic. With some trepidation on his account, I had at that time left London for a prolonged trip to the United States. Three weeks after my departure, he stole a bottle of lemonade from a delivery cart in the street, and was immediately caught. He was placed on probation, as I was glad to learn in this particular case, with the court's knowledge of his being a patient at the clinic.

Throughout, whenever life was going reasonably well with Thomas, his manner toward me was bantering and casual. He behaved as if he tolerated me and my ways, as being in the nature of yet another of his chores. At other times, when he would look pale and drawn, he could usually be persuaded to recount just how badly their affairs at home were going. On these occasions it was clear that I was his only adult confidante; above all, one who needed neither introductions nor reminders of the texture and quality of the chapters of his life. One of the disquieting features in this boy's character structure is a combination of passivity, to which the term "fatalism" would be appropriate in many contexts, as well as his apparent lability of mood. He was weary in the face of psychic pain, but vastly optimistic about its total banishment as soon as current events seemed more favorable. One could clearly distinguish the similarities between his mother's and his own attitudes to the flux of events provided by a capricious fate, of which her role was that of receptive controller. Part of my function was to remind him that the current state, whether good or bad, would be unlikely to be final.

As the new house, purchased before completion, in a newly built-up part of the countryside became an imminent fact, he warned me that he would not be seeing me much longer. His scholastic achievement was not sufficient to justify remaining at his London school as a senior pupil. Thomas said he would, in any case, refuse to make long journeys daily. He had few ideas about the choice of future employment. His expressed intention was to wait and see what jobs might be available in the new area of residence. When I sought to persuade him to come and see me again, possibly after the passage of a few months, he refused and said he saw no reason for so doing. Furthermore, since he would then be working, the fare money would have to come out of his own pocket.

I had long realized how important it was to him to ensure that he was obtaining, as he often told me his mother had made clear she was doing, maintenance in exchange for services in kind. Eventually, he used to joke about Mr. W. being quite a convenience because he provided for all their basic needs. Only when the last interview came to the point of good-by did tears appear momentarily. Thomas was clearly in the process of closing one of the last doors, not only of his childhood, this being a common reaction or initiatory rite on leaving school, but on his previous identity. To move out of London to an area where all were newcomers meant for him that the whole community-to-be would be starting "from scratch." He admitted, on pressure, that it was his intention to be known in the new locality as Thomas W., adding "And why not? It's his house, isn't it?"

Letters have been exchanged, since Thomas left school recently, between his headmaster and myself. Both of us feel that he is still in a vulnerable psychic state which, nevertheless, might well be subject to safeguards. What we would have wished would have been the passage of more time within the safety of his familiar school routines, or at least that he remain in the sphere of influence of well-tested authority figures.

One of the chief characterological danger points for this boy is his combination of passivity and suggestibility. In practice, these are seen most clearly via his mechanism of identifying with the *aim* of his mother's marital behavior with Mr. W. In many ways the present-day Thomas can be compared with the agile, parasitic mouse in the lion's cage, snatching morsels from under its mane. By being able to bolt out to, or in from, the liberty beyond the bars, he gives teasing reminders of that which is denied to the lion. But since this mouse is assured of no certainties of sustenance other than those to be found in the lion's cage, it has to go on taking its chances, together with its satisfaction of needs and its provocative pleasures.

My real concern for Thomas is that he will, unconsciously, seek to appear as the perpetually charming and effete youngster. So beguiling would be his charm that strong men will be satisfied to give without thought of imposing a libidinal return. Since pubertal changes are still only beginning, however, biology may yet work sufficiently in his favor to sweep him back to the level of masculine potential which once was his. Previously, it was its traumatically enforced paralysis which eventuated in panic and the breakdown products of impotent rebellion.

Discussion

It could be argued that both of the lads here reported upon might, in time, have "grown out" of their truancy and thieving, regardless of their handling. This might even be my own guess, with certain reservations. But, whatever the present nature of their psychic vulnerabilities, these would, in my opinion, have been much greater if they had not been afforded some degree of insight into the *predisposing* and fantasy elements of their conflicts. Furthermore, that which they learned pertained not to criminology nor to penology (nor even to morals) but to their individual symptomatology. The importance of the distinctions between these approaches is great in terms of the individual's self-esteem, nor can their life-long impact be overemphasized. To know oneself to be a "reformed delinquent" (that is, in those, be it noted, who never lacked a superego) imposes a load, in perpetuity, on the ego. Knowing oneself to have received help as an anxious and perturbed youngster, who had sought faulty relief by way of undesirable conduct, requires much less psychic accommodation. Indeed, in cases of this type, we need set our therapeutic sights no higher than on making our best efforts to "hold" or restore the child in his useful possession of whatever socially acceptable ego-defensive forces he had at his command before their operation became impaired. Therapy and maximal accuracy of diagnosis are, therefore, inextricable.

REFERENCES

1. AICHHORN, A. *Wayward Youth*. New York, The Viking Press, Inc., 1935.
2. FREUD, S. "Some Character Types Met with in Psychoanalytic Work," in *Collected Papers*. London, Hogarth Press, Ltd., vol. 4.
3. FRIEDLANDER, K. *Latent Delinquency and Ego Development in Searchlights on Delinquency*. New York, International Universities Press, Inc., 1949.

chapter 9 The Suicidal Adolescent

HENRY I. SCHNEER AND PAUL KAY[*]

The incidence of threatened suicidal intent and of attempted suicide increases markedly after childhood. Not infrequently, children playfully refer to or even play-act suicide. Obviously intended, nonaccidental suicide, however, is rare among children. Schechter[21] indicates that suicide is rare in the child because "the child is still so dependent upon his love objects for gratification and, as the process of identification has not been completed, turning of the hostility against and destroying the introjects within himself is too painful and too frightening." Among adolescents, especially under 16, the incidence of completed suicide is very small, but there is a high frequency of suicidal threat (hospitalized cases) and attempts. It behooves the adolescent, as compared with the child, to loosen the ties to the parents. This occurs under the impact of intensified sexuality, physiologically engendered, which revives the oedipal struggle for its "second" crucial resolution. The settlement demanded of the psychic apparatus may result in suicidal behavior. Zilboorg[24] stated: "Suicide in puberty represents an acute explosion in the oedipal difficulties wrapped in the castration problem and homosexuality, particularly as it pertains to males." Sigmund Freud,[10] in discussing the suicidal attempt (by jumping) of a homosexual girl of 17 after having lost her loved one (an older woman), concluded that, in addition to the conscious motive of despair over the loss, there were two other motives: "It was the fulfillment of a punishment (self punishment) and the fulfillment of a wish. As the latter, it meant attainment of the very wish which, when frustrated, had driven her into homosexuality—namely, the wish to have a child by her father, for now she 'fell' through her father's fault."

In psychoanalysis, adolescence has been compared with states of

* With the help of Dr. Morris Brozovsky, Clinical Instructor, State University of New York, College of Medicine, and Dr. Carl Rosengart, Department of Psychiatry, State University of New York, College of Medicine.

being in love and in mourning. The adolescent ego, likewise, as in these opposite states, has to contend with the overwhelming force of the object (the introjected parent for the adolescent). Anna Freud[9] said that "adolescents may defend themselves against the love experienced for their parents by reversing the affect into hostility. The hostility may then be displaced from the parent to the self leading to depression and even suicidal wishes may be carried out." The psychoanalysis of depression (Freud,[11] Abraham,[1] Rado,[20] Gero,[12] Lorand,[18] Jacobson,[14] etc.) has taken into account the turning of hostility against the self—against introjected objects which are part of the self—and the orally regressive phenomena involved. Adolescents are frequently depressed but may, as often, be manic. On the question of suicide, Lewin[17] presented the thesis that suicide was "not necessarily depressive but could just as often be manic. The manic does not kill himself for the purpose of dying but on the contrary to live in fusion with the ego ideal."

Adolescent suicide appears to us to be the omnipotent, regressively infantile behavior in coping with an explosive oedipal conflict involving loss (destruction) of the sadomasochistic, narcissistically invested object. The parents engender a sadomasochistic attitude in the child. Then, at adolescence, after a profound sense of rejection was experienced (through death, prolonged departure, illness, etc.), separation, whether provoked by the adolescent in the independence bid for an identity or whether initiated by the parents, constitutes too severe a narcissistic mortification[6] for the emerging adolescent ego. The suicide, in promoting "sleep" (surcease from restless, emotionally labile adolescence) enables fusion with the object (mother). The adolescent's struggle with frustration can be ended.

Erikson's[8] concept of "negative identity" yields further help in elucidating the dynamics of adolescent suicidal behavior, particularly among "juvenile delinquents." He states that negative identity is "perversely based on all those identifications and roles, which, at critical stages of development had been presented to the individual as most undesirable or dangerous, and yet, also as most real." "To be a suicide, although it is a negative identity, is, nevertheless, an identity choice in itself." As such, the adolescent manages to obtain narcissistic gratification, "self-esteem," as a "suicide." It is, however, "carrying regression in the service of the ego to an extreme" (Erikson[8]).

Detailed psychoanalytical case studies of suicidal adolescents are scarce in the literature. Mason[19] described 4 adolescent girls (3 diabetics) who used their organic illness as suicidal attempts in coping with incestuous drives. Bosselman[4] reported the suicidal attempt of an 18-year-old girl and stated the motive to be guilt owing to repressed hostility.

An adolescent girl and a boy who attempted suicide and 2 other illustrative cases from our study of 84 adolescent suicidal patients will be given with regard to predisposing conditions, motivation, and meaning of the suicidal behavior.

DESCRIPTIVE PSYCHOPATHOLOGY OF THE SUICIDAL ADOLESCENT

The description is derived from a study of 84 suicidal adolescent patients who ranged in age from 12 to 16 years. They constitute a series of patients out of a total of 653 adolescent admissions to Kings County Hospital during 1956 and 1957. Most of the suicidal adolescents were in their fourteenth and fifteenth years of age. Annually, the approximate rate obtained was 12 suicidal adolescents per 100 admissions.

The series studied consisted of 34 "threat" patients and 50 "attempt" patients. Patients admitted for suicidal threat were included in the study, because our material indicated the similarity with patients making attempts. Threats and attempts may be regarded as phases of a continuum of suicidal behavior which could end in death. Stengel[23] is at variance with this view. He holds that completed suicides have a different personality structure.

There were more than twice as many female as male adolescent suicidal patients (58 girls and 26 boys). Among the girls, 20 were "threat" cases and 38 "attempt" cases. Among the boys, 15 "threat" cases and 11 "attempt" cases were recorded.

The categories by religion and race were calculated as follows: adolescent admissions by religion or race during 1956 and 1957 were divided by total admissions of adolescents by religion or race during those years. Thus the total of 44 white suicidal girls divided by the 173 white girls admitted yielded 25 per cent—one fourth of the white adolescent girls were admitted to the hospital for suicidal behavior; 14 Negro suicidal girls out of 119 Negro girls admitted yielded 12 per cent—about one eighth of the Negro adolescent girls were admitted to the hospital for suicidal behavior. Other calculations were as follows: white suicidal adolescent boys, 9 per cent (22/261); Negro suicidal boys, 4 per cent (4/99). By religious category the suicidal rate was 26 per cent of Catholic girls (38/148), 23 per cent of Hebrew girls (7/30), 12 per cent of Protestant girls (14/111), 18 per cent of Hebrew boys (11/62), 5 per cent of Protestant boys (5/98), and 4 per cent of Catholic boys (8/192).

Less than one fourth of the patient group was found to be unequivocally psychotic. If, however, the category "very disturbed" is used to describe the adolescents' behavior, then more than half the patients would be so considered. Balser and Masterson[3] indicate that, for adolescents, there is a closer relationship between schizophrenic reaction and suicidal attempts than between affective disorder and suicidal attempts. Bakwin,[2] in his survey of children and adolescents, found that mental illness is a factor in only 10 per cent of the cases of adolescents. Hertz,[13] in her Rorschach study of 24 suicidal adolescents, stated that the group gives evidence that neurotics have suicidal ideas and make attempts.

Less than half (about 40 per cent) of the patients were moderately to severely depressed. One fifth of the patients had phobic symptoms. About 10 per cent of the patients were symptomatically recognized for lying and stealing, and as runaways. Habit disorders were manifest during the childhood of at least half of the patients.

School achievement was generally of a low order. About a third of the patients were truants. In all but 2 of the patients, the biological mother had physical but varying (variably emotionally absent as well) contact with the patient, and in a high percentage of the parents the biological father was absent.

Frequent illnesses, operations, and accidents were found in the life histories of the patients.

The suicidal form of behavior was mainly by ingestion. All of 10 suicidal attempts by adolescents reported by Jacobziner and Raybin[15] made the attempt by ingestion.

CASE REPORT—A FEMALE ADOLESCENT SUICIDAL PATIENT

The mother of 15-year, 10-month-old Carol, a second-year high-school student, was called to a party at a Jewish Center where Carol had fallen into a coma. She was taken to the hospital and remained in coma about 40 hours. Among diagnostic considerations at the hospital, the girl was thought to have had a subarachnoid hemorrhage. Provident gastric lavage made her revival possible. During her delirium she said, "Daddy I didn't take all the pills. I left some for you." She also expressed fears that her girl friend would think her crazy and not like her. Upon awakening she asked if "Mommy" would "punish" her. She stated: "She [the mother] thinks I'm a genius. I'm not a genius." Her 95 school average had fallen to 79. It was discovered that she had taken 17 of her father's Doriden capsules and told no one about the suicidal attempt. It was discovered, much later, that a week previous to the ingestion of capsules, she had sniffed a carbon tetrachloride bottle with the thought of suicide, but she did not like the fumes.

What had consciously or manifestly led to the suicidal attempt?[22] It appeared to be the feared parental wrath on the disclosure of a forbidden act. The school principal had asked to see her mother because Carol was caught smoking in the bathroom at school. But 3 weeks previously she was caught smoking in the bathroom at home and was told by her mother "not to make a habit of it until [she was] 16." (The toilet smoking may have been a substitutive gratification and reaction-formation against the smelling and/or sniffing of carbon tetrachloride and the oral route for the suicidal attempt. The number of pills, 17, has as a possible derivation and wish to be older, in defiance of the mother's dictum that "not until 16" could she indulge herself.)

Other possible precipitating events during the months prior to the attempt may have been that she had a secret date and her father surreptitiously followed, scolding her on her return home and striking her for lying. Subsequently, she refused to kiss her father. Her schoolwork was becoming impaired, and she was forgetting things on examinations. There was a constant sense of shame in not meeting the scholastic ideal of her mother. She was also separating from her close friendship with a girl who was not as interested in dating as she was. At about the same time she also witnessed the scene of a mangled body of a man struck by an automobile. This became a day residue for recurrent images of blood, murdered people, and mangled bodies which would disappear on opening her eyes. (The closing of the eyes, her sleep problem, insomnia, the assaultive attitude of the father, and the taking of the father's sleeping tablets may now be linked for the latent meaning of the aggressive, libidinal intent in the suicidal behavior.)

The manifest precipitating factors such as the disclosure, the reprimands by parents, separation from friend .and family, with interest in dating, and slipping in schoolwork are found frequently in adolescents who do not commit suicide.[22]

The following events and reactions in the patient's life yield additional determinants for evolving the meaning and motivation of the suicidal behavior.

Carol's mother wanted a second child but would have preferred to "wait awhile longer." She already had a son about 2 years old. When she became pregnant with Carol, however, she had recurrent dreams of falling into a void. During her pregnancy she said she "lived on carrots." Carol was a small baby, 5½ pounds, born by Cesarian section, at which time the mother also had her fallopian tubes tied. The mother was bedridden for a month, and Carol was attended by a practical nurse. At 8 weeks of age Carol had bronchial pneumonia, requiring oxygen, a blood transfusion, and a rib resection. She was said to have been famous as a first candidate for penicillin. Apparently in reaction to the illness, she slept excessively during the day and was often awake at night. Throughout most of her life there has been a sleeping problem. She tosses and moans. At 9 months she was banging her head on the pillow before going to sleep, and she still does this occasionally. After beginning to walk at about 1 year of age, she suddenly stopped and did not resume until about 18 months of age. At 2 she fell downstairs. The mother seemed to relate this to a myopia and astigmatism. There was a vague hint of feeding difficulty in that the mother gave the child milk by a spoon. (She was bottle fed to about 1 year.) Speech developed adequately, and she "beat" her brother in talking at 1 year. At about 2½ she would demand to be changed immediately if soiled. An infant seat was used for the toilet. At 3 a tonsillectomy and adenoidectomy were performed.

When Carol was 5 the mother worked and the child was cared for by the maternal grandmother. Previously, the mother had worked sporadically, taking Carol with her. During her subsequent childhood we only know that she rocked in bed, which was passed off as a "natural rhythm." She also engaged and still does in hair twisting and pulling. Recently, she pulled her mother's hair, playfully referring to her as an "old hag." She liked horror movies. The mother recalled her having had a nightmare but was not told the content. An outright phobia was not elicited.

Up to the seventh grade she was referred to as a model child. At about the age of 9 she attended Hebrew School, and only because of the insistence of the parents since she was so rebellious did she receive a diploma.

When she was 10 she no longer slept in the same room with her brother. There was much wrestling with her brother, and she was said by the mother to have confided in the brother.

Her menstruation started at 11½ years. She was unconcerned, although the mother worried about her irregularity. For about 2 years now she has menstruated every 3 weeks. Although her mother restricts her own activity when menstruating, Carol is symptom free and feels more energetic at such times. Temporally,* she menstruated 2 weeks before the suicidal attempt.

Genital masturbatory activity was not elicited, although the equivalents of hair pulling and bed rocking were noted. When her mother learned of her discussions with friends about sex at the age of 10, the mother prepared her for menses. Subsequently, during her puberty the mother informed Carol, in connection with dating, that she and the father, who was very passionate, were often tempted to engage in intercourse before marriage but were happier and more respectful of each other as a result of not succumbing to temptation.

At about the age of 13, in the eighth grade, the mother said of Carol that she "found her tongue." She was involved in a school incident of hitting a colored female student with an umbrella. The incident reached such proportions that it was brought to the attention of the superintendent of schools. At this time Carol was associating with companions the mother believed undesirable. The mother felt that this spoiled Carol's school achievement and her chances for scholarship. Nevertheless, Carol got the biggest part in the school play, but the mother was again disappointed that Carol was not valedictorian. The mother also hoped that Carol would make up for the brother, who did not pursue engineering as had been hoped. Also, about this time the mother forced Carol to see a doctor because the acne on her back was "disgusting."

As Carol was turning 14 her dating intensified, and her mother was also taking a more intense interest in her social activity. Her bond with a girl friend was loosening because of the dating. Carol would go as the only girl, platonically, with four or five boys of the good type (mother's preference) to a park but secretly would go with a "fast boy" (sexually aggressive). Coinciding with her dating at 14, her father became irascible in connection with chronic somatic complaints, bursitis, and unemployment. He became abu-

* We have found no direct consistent relationship between suicidal behavior and menstruation among our cases.

sive and shouted at the patient, calling her a bastard. As previously stated, the father followed her on a date and then struck her for lying. Afterward, she became morose. The mother states that "Carol knows father loves her to distraction." She was also "heartbroken" that she could not get a school office-work job and was not accepted in the school chorus. She was having trouble in schoolwork with history and geometry.

In regard to her family, the mother is 47 years of age, of Polish birth, older than her two brothers. The maternal grandmother, 72, is considered by Carol to be prying and by the mother to have always been neurotic and having "had everything cut out of her." The maternal grandfather is referred to by Carol as a "prince." Severe mental illness in the family is not reported. The father is 51, of Polish birth, and 1 of 8 children. The paternal grandmother has arteriosclerotic brain disease. The mother maintained that the marriage had been essentially stable and happy except for financial problems. When the father became ill a few years ago, she admonished him that if he did not stop "aggravating the family," she would have to take action to separate. The father had Asiatic flu followed by dizzy spells and anemia. Tuberculosis had to be ruled out. A peripheral bursitis impaired his work capacity and financial status. The mother has been working regularly in a factory.

How did our patient come to find a use for her energy in self-destruction? Neutralized energy available for sublimation was diminishing. Note that her decreasing achievement in school was given manifestly as an event leading to the suicidal attempt. Also, her chance for office work at school, to be imitative of the mother, was lost to her. Her dream life was fraught with horror and mutilation. Sexually, her outlet had to be secretive and defiant. There was a prevalence of aggressive energy rather than libidinal, erotic cathexis. Boys were categorized into the "good ones" of her mother's choice and the "bad ones"—her choice. She would tease boys but leave at the point of being "hot and bothered." She would attempt to belittle boys ("rank them"), implying their homosexuality. Information as to genital masturbation was not obtained, but masturbatory equivalents in the form of rocking and hair twirling were elicited.

As with adolescents whose egos are caught between intensification of the instincts on the one side and conscience demands on the other side, so our patient's ego was affected by the surge of sexual interest and the demands of her parents—her mother's insistence on high scholastic average to make up for disappointment in her son, and the father's abusive interference with the patient's heterosexual inclinations. The patient was compellingly pulled further into a family situation of increasing oedipal stress. This was a grievous complication for our patient's adolescence.

The aggressive instinct was strongest with our patient. A love relationship had not materialized. Then, to follow Freud's indicator for a meaning of the patient's suicidal behavior, "that the object cathexis is withdrawn from the object" and turned upon the self, the apparent object to be turned upon during her adolescence was the father. More accurately, the object consisted of the parental image, a phallic mother and less adequate father. When the patient was about 12½ years old, the father became ill, less attentive, but sporadically abusive. A struggle over withdrawing her cathexis from him was occurring. For instance, she would no longer kiss him after he spied on her when she was with a boy friend. He would slap her for not eating cooked potatoes. Her food fad was raw meat and raw potatoes. Although the mother protested that the father loved his daughter to "distraction," our patient "knew," as every adolescent girl does, that she is rejected by the father because he has a wife. And our patient's anger over the rejection was multiplied by the father's abusiveness.

In narcotizing herself in her suicidal attempt, we noted the link to her father, namely, that his sleeping capsules were taken. In narcosis, a condition of withdrawn object cathexis, she became the avenger as well as the avenged. With her eyes closed the patient saw bloody, mangled body images. The mother spoke of her daughter's having had a rib removed during infancy. The mother also spoke of the maternal grandmother's having had everything cut out of her. The mother, during the patient's childhood and during her adolescence, worked while the father was unemployed. The mother, furthermore, stimulated competition with the brother. An aggressive, masculinized identification with a phallic mother was developing. Thus in narcotizing herself, the sadomasochistic wish and her bisexual identity could be regressively, omnipotently, and hallucinatedly gratified. Unconsciously, she was doing to herself, as an object, what her phallic parental image was doing to her consciously (aggressiveness).

The aggressive nature of her sleep had earlier foundations. She was an insomniac throughout her life. In infancy there was separation due to her own bronchopneumonia at 8 weeks of age. From that time on there was head banging of the pillow, later, continuance of the same accompanied by rolling in bed to sleep. The aggression in this rhythmical motility pattern is apparent and would seem to be an outcome of frustration in regard to separation. In recent years she would assert proudly that she felt no fatigue, although she slept only a few hours. Often she would awake at 5 A.M. and go into the kitchen to look at the clock. Frequently her father would be in the kitchen. (The conflict with her father over her oral sadistic food fad has already been noted.) Last year she had a dream of two brothers trying to attack her sexually. (She slept in the same room with her brother.) Yet she rationalized her insomnia as the result of a fear of oversleeping.

Preoedipal, oral, and anal sadistic (aggressive) impulses were also manifest in the bathroom smoking episode. The public-school bathroom smoking, in particular, indicated the struggle of her ego for an identity, albeit a negative identity. The fear of disclosure of her defiant smoking triggered the suicidal attempt. Yet there must have been the wish to be seen (an exhibitionistic, "phallic" impulse), since it was a public-school toilet. The dangerous climax for the patient in the smoking episode was the "contact" between reawakened pregenital urges and newly acquired genital ones. The negative identity which she assumed as the tough, smoking, defiant, phallic girl, opposite to the demanding ideals of the parental image, only carried the regression in serving the ego to an extreme.

As an oral-nasal respiratory process, the smoking recapitulated the infancy of the patient. We may postulate a cathexis of the oral–nasal-organ tract in that the patient required oxygen inhalations for her bronchopneumonia during infancy. This was also a time when she was separated from her mother. The sniffing and inhaling of the carbon tetrachloride as a suicidal gesture is conceivably linked. At 15½, as in infancy, there was angered frustrated separation from the mother. The inhalation of the fumes and the ingestion of the capsules point to a primitive, magical (oral) solution for her necessary although frustrated adolescent anti-incestual isolation from the parents.

The toilet smoking and sniffing of fumes are referable, as magical sadomasochistic trends, to fixations at the anal phase. During her toddler period she demanded to be changed immediately if soiled. This was already showing a fear of feces and a rejection or banishment of an aggressive part-object identification. It is significant that on Rorschach Card X, she referred to a detail as, "this looks like underwater coral." On inquiry she said, "I don't know what color it is . . . looks like brown. . . . I once saw coral. It is supposed to be green!" It is interesting to note that by a minor change in letter sequence the "brown . . . underwater coral" could stand for Carol (patient's name). A further sign of her soiled sadistic self which evoked punishment is indicated by the mother's compelling her to see a doctor because the acne on her back was said to be disgusting. The patient also became embroiled at the age of 13 with a colored girl whom she attacked with an umbrella at school. The colored girl may have been the projected brown image for the sadomasochistic solution to the conflict between pregenital urges and emerging genital urges and as to the bisexual conflict in her process of identification.

Psychological Test Results*

The patient, during her hospitalization, showed high average to superior intelligence (WISC, verbal 124, performance 104). Although she was not considered to be on the verge of schizophrenia, evidence of defect in ego structure was noted. There was a difference of 20 points on the performance part of the I.Q. test, yet there were excellent information, very good comprehension, and good abstract reasoning. There was an overclose quality to her responses, however, on the Word Association and on the Rorschach tests. Oppositional tendencies in the form of white-space responses are just as lacking as are contrast words. She is unable to maintain consistently any degree of appropriate objectivity. She cannot develop an adequate measure of detachment to give considered judgment as a basis for her acts. On the Rorschach there was no single human response, no human-movement response. She "spills over" far too much on the color side. For example: "This is just a blotch of paint, this is made up of blotches of paint." So, despite evidence on the intelligence test for good abstract reasoning, in an unstructured situation just the reverse occurs. When seized by an impulse, she is likely to give way.

Some of her word-association-test responses were:

Man: "That's a good one! Two faced! You realize there's nothing personal in that?"

Hard: "Hard-boiled egg."

Home: "Any place you find love and you can come to."

* The authors are grateful to Mr. I. S. Yudelowitz, Dr. S. Machover, and Mrs. K. Machover for the psychological tests and their interpretations.

Mother: A mother—what can you say about a mother? A person that takes care of you, a parent."

Father: "Does the same thing as mother. He is a parent to you. Brings you up. Gives you advice, same as mother. Besides going out to make a living."

Death: "Heart attack."

Suicide: "Fear."

Long reaction times to her responses on different test items indicated depressive tendencies.

In analyzing her handwriting, it was observed that she could not maintain a straight line. She wrote half above and half below the line. When she completed the sentence, "I get angry . . . " with, "when I make mistakes," she crossed out the "I." The "I" destroys itself. When she wrote "I hate," she went below the line. It was not a characteristic "I." Her characteristic "I" in other contexts went differently. It suggests that, in a depressive context, hostility may be turned against herself.

On the House Tree Person drawing and the Machover test, the lines had a heavy, slashing quality and dug into the paper; if one considers graphomotor movement as going into space, she was stabbing into space. A sadistic attitude was thus indicated and, by the sloppiness of her lines, an anal sadistic character. The drawing of a female was not very feminine, not very different from the male drawings. Both the female and male lacked feet, and the hands were concealed. She was unwilling to draw facial features. The attempt to make a female was the pinching of the waistline, but the lines were strong and the shoulders wide and masculine. She tends to put on feminine hair, but it is phallically curved (like "the proboscis of the rhinoceros" she saw on Card I of the Rorschach). The figures were small for her age, suggesting low esteem and depressive aspects. It was also noted from the drawings that her sociability is superficial, characterized by a considerable amount of hostility. Her figures also flowed off to the left upper end of the page, suggesting a regressive kind of movement away from the environment. The development of an acceptable identity is much retarded. She cannot commit herself to a definite imprint in the drawings. On the Rorschach, problems in sexual identity emerged. On Card I she saw elephants with trunks, then a rhinoceros with a proboscis. By card V her involvement with sexual fantasy takes on a paranoid flavor. She saw a bat on Card V but, because of the projections which she felt to be exaggerated, she raised questions:

"Are you sure you don't follow a pattern?" On Card VI, of strong phallic suggestiveness, she looked at it, turned it around several times, and said, "Oh my, what is this about? Are you sure you don't follow a pattern?" Her anticipation of phallic arousal is plain, but is she anticipating sexual assault? Will it become a paranoic erotica, anticipating assault from every man, or a problem in sexual identity? The undersea response with "brown coral" on Card X indicated a response of derogation (a reference to anal fixation, as already alluded to) and a place of regression. (The male patient, Fred, to be discussed next, also had an undersea-coral response. Undersea responses are not infrequently present in alcoholics.) The undersea response indicates a wish to return to the mother, but it is a dangerous wish. Also, that Carol saw coral in this undersea place may indicate not only the anal derogation but the sharp, risky phallus with which she identifies.

CASE REPORT—A MALE ADOLESCENT SUICIDAL PATIENT

Fred, 13, attempted suicide by the ingestion of about "25 pills," some of which consisted of the antihistamine that he had been taking for his asthma and some of his mother's sedative, phenobarbital. He then put on his new suit, lay down on the floor of his room, and told everyone that he was going to die. This occurred after he had first threatened to kill either his mother or himself. Fred then fell asleep. He was brought to Kings County Hospital by a neighbor, his stomach was lavaged, and he recovered quickly. He was signed out on contract to his mother on the day of admission. He had been making occasional threats of suicide for some time previously, as had his mother. This attempt followed the refusal of his parents, just prior to his *bar mizvah*, to grant him immediately his wish that he be given the bicycle promised to him as a *bar mizvah* gift.

The attempt was the climax of a long history of friction between Fred and the rest of the family. Prior to the age of 3, Fred was noted to have become sensitive and resentful about his father's open partiality to his newborn sister. This sensitivity and resentment were both preceded and accompanied by frank jealousy. His mother was hospitalized for a hysterectomy soon after the sister's birth, and, although there are no data to show what specific reaction Fred had to this hospitalization, it is likely that it played a part in his resentment. At the age of 3, he is said to have thrown a bottle at his sister. There is no indication that his sister was seriously injured. Some time after this event, the mother was hospitalized again, this time for cholecystectomy, varicose-vein treatment, and repair of cystocele and rectocele. We have no data to indicate any particular response on the patient's part to this separation, but in the following year, his fifth, his personality is said to have changed radically. He became demanding, domineering, assaulted his mother, father, and sister, and developed temper tantrums. The latter occurred whenever his demands, which were usually excessive, were not met. His asthma started at this time. At the age of 7, his mother was hospitalized again, this time for a "broken back." Fred and his sister were placed with another family since the mother's hospitalization. Fred became so unmanageable that no one wanted to care for him. Most disturbing to his family and relatives was his fire setting and his throwing a knife at a girl. On his mother's return, Fred continued to have uncontrollable outbursts of anger, at times taking the form of hitting his mother and father with the mother's crutch.

About a year after the mother had been last admitted to the hospital, she had her first heart attack. Fred was not 8 years old. He became the leader of a gang which wrecked his father's truck.

The mother's next hospitalization occurred when Fred was 10. She was then hospitalized, because of a stroke, for 3 months. About this time, Fred's conduct in school deteriorated, although he continued to get good grades. He had always been a good student, as far as the work was concerned. Schoolwork has had particular significance for Fred, because it has been an important area of competition with his sister, who was superior to him in winning awards.

Other significant features in his history were that he was a normal, full-term baby, although his mother had suffered from toxemia of pregnancy, necessitating a cesarian section. He matured rapidly in regard to sitting, walking, and talking. He is said to have achieved bowel and bladder control by the age of 1 year. Between the ages of 1 and 2 he developed a fear of the dark, but this was apparently transitory. His thumb sucking, which is still present, began at this age. Apparently, even as a child he was friendly and attractive to other children, whom he dominated easily. His difficulties commenced on a background of poor relationships between the parents. The mother, a massive woman who weighed about 250 pounds, is domineering and runs the family. The father, a short, thin man, has been helpless against the domination of his son and wife, with both of whom he has frequently and apparently impotently argued. The mother and father have had little affection for one another.

The mother has shown some affection to Fred's sister, but apparently neither she nor the father has ever shown any affection toward or recognition of Fred. Fred complained to his parents about his mother having to be hospitalized so often, and because his father never did anything with him, such as going to ball games together.

The father makes no attempt to hide his hostility to Fred. The family life in general was marked by constant fighting and was dominated in this respect by Fred's hostility toward the entire family and the fear with which the family tried unsuccessfully to anticipate his next move.

Psychological testing revealed very superior intelligence, impaired concept formation, and the use of rationalization, intellectualization, and denial as defenses. His depression and need to act out are related to his identification with his mother and the oral deprivation he experienced because of her. On account of his poor self-concept, he views himself with contempt, that is, castrated. He has a need to manipulate people to maintain his self-esteem.

By examining the manifest events and conscious ideation[22] which led up to and constituted the suicidal attempt in terms of Fred's life's experiences and development, we may now begin to understand, from a psychoanalytic point of view, the preconditions, the motivation, and the meaning of his suicidal behavior.

Taking as our starting point Fred's peremptory, inappropriate request for the promised gift, we can immediately recognize the onset of this demanding, omnipotentlike behavior as early as his fifth year, when his personality changed. He became domineering (and later, obese) like his mother, suggesting an emphatic identification with her during the oedipal period. The data suggest several motives for this identification. By far the most prominent would be the need to hold fast to a mother who had already disappeared from the home several times and who was threatening in size and manner—that is, identification with a disappearing aggressor. The feminine identification probably also represented his attempt to wrest from his father the latter's attachment to his mother and sister, whose appearance on the scene provoked his jealousy and diffuse rage. These motives, of course, would have been strengthened by excessive guilt and castration fears arising out of the oedipal conflict owing to his father's frank rejection of him. (The psychological test data indicate that he "perceives his father as an inadequate model.")

His thumb sucking, which started in the first year, his excessive demands, his asthma, which began at the time of his change in personality, his trumpet playing, which also started in the latter period, and his assaultive rages when frustrated—all testified to the oral deprivation, fixation, and regression on which the feminine identification was based. (The trumpet playing probably represented an attempt at the sublimation of oral sadism.)

The next event leading to the suicidal behavior is the mother's refusal of his request. Actually, the refusal came from both parents, but the mother's decision carried the weight. Undoubtedly, this is what Fred desired: to prove to the world that his mother refused him the love he had long wanted. This was his attempt to master actively a deprivation which was, originally, passively endured.

The next element to be considered is the choice of the gift he demanded—a bicycle. We do not know if he was the one who had originally asked for such a gift, but, at any rate, his excessive feelings about the bicycle tempt the following speculations, for which, unfortunately, no data are available. A bicycle represents an object on which one performs rhythmic movements of the legs and which one keeps between the legs. Therefore, riding a bicycle suggests the idea of the masculine role in heterosexual intercourse, and the bicycle itself, between the legs, evokes the idea of a penis. Fred's wish for the bicycle then leads to two possible meanings: for example, the wish for a penis as a reaction to his feminine identification connected with his oedipal strivings, and the wish to use that penis as a man. We can assume that, in his identification with his phallic mother, he regarded himself as having a penis, but only as a woman.

The refusal of the bicycle then led to Fred's threat to kill his mother or himself—a threat whose precursor was most likely his assaulting of his parents in childhood when refused anything. The threat further suggests the identification with the mother, the precarious nature of his perceptions of the boundaries of his self, and his unstable sense of identity. The threat also suggests the ready displaceability of his anger and therefore the fact that his ego, in this respect, is characterized by primary process functioning.

Finally, killing himself or his mother strongly indicates, since the one could stand for the other, killing both, that is, being united in death.

The threat is followed by the suicide attempt, the ingestion of his mother's and his own pills. Early in childhood, oral frustration led to a temper tantrum. Now the frustration leads to a suicidal attempt. Both have similar features—an exhibitionistic display of rage directed at the world (mother) and the self. The temper tantrum, however, is involuntary and self-limited; the suicidal attempt has an initial voluntary component but may lead to death. Fred's attempt led to sleep. Sleep, in his instance, may be likened to a temper tantrum in that the sense of identity is temporarily lost. There is a confusion between self and nonself, and the aggression is vented. The aggressive quality of the sleep of our female patient, Carol, may be recalled. In this particular instance the wish to return to a state in which the distinction between self and nonself is lost through a suicidal attempt has a sadistic component. Fred later said he did it to scare his mother. By means of the magic of the pills, Fred retreated into this extreme state of passivity and helplessness, omnipotently coercing others to rescue and nurse him. He made his mother come and get him. What he could not get in the way of libidinal satisfaction from his mother as a *bar mizvah* boy, he could get as a helpless infant, having given up his struggle for sexual identification and the achievement of a sense of identity.

The ingestion of the pills not only brings up the idea of the oral incorporation of mother and the wish to fuse with her in sleep (death) but, on a preoedipal level, owing to a regression from genitality, it is possible that the ingestion of "poison" (if, for the moment, we equate the pills with the idea of poison in Fred's mind) represents taking mother's milk and sadistically leaving her as she left him. (From the point of view of Fred's identification vis à vis his phallic mother, we have also considered the possibility that the ingestion of pills represents the incorporation of the mother's phallus and therefore oral impregnation.) This orally induced sleep brings up two other considerations: first, the likelihood that such a sleep is analogous to the sleep induced by nursing and the sleep which follows genital orgasm, and second, that this sleep represents a megalomanic method of coping with overwhelming problems of sexual identification, identity, and the handling of aggression.

The next piece of manifest content to be considered is the putting on of his new suit, the *bar mizvah* suit, and lying on the floor of his room, announcing his wish to die. Two meanings stand out—exhibitionism and the attempt at identity. The *bar mizvah* suit is his exhibition of masculinity. The giving up of the erect posture (under these circumstances) and the lying down represent a surrender to a passive, feminine position. The *bar mizvah* suit may also represent his search for an identity—he is Fred, the *bar mizvah* boy, arrived at manhood.

This point brings us to a crucial datum—the impending *bar mizvah*. The *bar mizvah* is one of the institutionalized forms of pubertal initiation rites. Arlow[1a] notes the function of such rites: "They dramatize the transition to biological and sexual maturity." They mark the granting of adult privileges and responsibilities to the youth; they help resolve the hostility between the old and the new generations, arising out of oedipal rivalry, and they allow the youth to identify with the group. Arlow[1b] notes that at one point in the *bar mizvah* ceremony, the boy is called to the Law (Torah) as "the *bar mizvah* groom," a procedure which is also followed by the bridegroom in orthodox communities 1 week before the wedding. Comparing the significance of the *bar mizvah* to that of the menarche in girls, Arlow states: "The Bar Mizvah ceremony serves as a sharp reminder to the boy of his new biological status and forces him to re-examine his attitude toward his masculinity . . . [it] is . . . ambivalent because of the "feared hostility of the older generation."

What might the *bar mizvah* have meant to Fred that his suicidal attempt occurred at that time? Retranslating for the sake of our discussion, we could ask what dangers faced Fred at this time that the public announcement of his manhood should be associated with the desire to hurt himself to the point of annihilation? The clinical data offer certain clues to the answers of this question. During Fred's seventh and eighth years, for example, he set fires, deflated automobile tires, threw a knife at a girl, assaulted his parents with one of his mother's crutches, and, with the help of his gang, wrecked his father's truck. This behavior suggests, among numerous possibilities, wishes to castrate and kill his father (and mother and sister) and the wish for sexual intercourse with his mother (and sister) on a sadistic level. Looking at these wishes from the point of view of the oedipal rivalry with his father, and assuming that they were intensified as the *bar mizvah* approached, we can surmise that an extreme sense of guilt because of these wishes contributed very heavily to the self-punishing suicidal behavior which, as we have already pointed out, also represented in a condensed form his regression to infantile libidinal and ego states, in fact, to temporary annihilation of the personality. Noting the excessive nature of his aggressive behavior, we can add that the wish to castrate, which probably represented one of the unconscious determinants of that behavior, was very likely associated with, or arose in reaction to, castration fears. Intensified at puberty, such fears, like the guilt to which they indirectly gave rise, could be avoided by the suicidal attempt. Bearing in mind Fred's change in personality and behavior at the age of 5, which continued essentially unchanged to puberty, we may consider the suicidal behavior and the circumstances under which it occurred as a dramatic and tragically exaggerated version of the faulty resolution of the initial oedipal conflict.

Fred could be neither man nor woman with sufficient gratification and lack of anxiety. The final solution of the quest for sexual identification was to become, by way of reversing the death wishes toward the mother (and father), the omnipotent infant at one with the world (his mother) and cared for by the world (mother and mothering figures).

Comparison of Cases

In addition to the anxiety of exaggerated guilt and aggression, the loss of or separation from one or both parents, in varying degrees, at crucial periods in libidinal and ego development (the preoedipal, oedipal and revived oedipal conflict at puberty) predisposes the adolescent to suicide.

The two adolescents who made suicidal attempts, chosen for elucidation in this chapter, came from families which were always intact. Among the other adolescents in our series there was greater frequency of family disruption.

Parental separation in Carol's instance was chiefly on the basis of a mother absenting herself by working in a factory. There were hospitalizations of Fred's mother which were traumatic separations. To be identified with a disappearing aggressor (as in Fred's case) was to have to disappear oneself although the aim of that very identification was to prevent the mother (and oneself) from disappearing.

Among the other male adolescents where the separation factor was less intense, the erotic intimacy with the mother was more frequent. Among the other female adolescent patients, physical abuse and interference with relationships was greater than in Carol's instance. Carol and Fred were much less afflicted by extrinsic factors than the other adolescents in our series. The other cases, furthermore, indicated a more archaic expression of conscience and a more primitive mode of handling aggression. The bisexual dilemma of adolescence was severely prevalent among all of our cases by reason of faulty identification.

The high ratio of suicidal girls to boys in our series may be explained, in part, by the increased opportunity for aggressive acting out by boys and the less complicated oedipal problems that boys have, as compared with girls.

ETHNOMYTHICAL AND LITERARY REFERENCES

The connection between the failure in masculine identification and suicide has also been pointed out by Erikson[7] who describes what customarily happened to an American Indian boy faced by that situation: "If such a boy does not prefer to commit suicide, he must give up the career of warrior and hunter and become . . . a man woman who dresses like a woman and does woman's work— a berdache."

According to Japanese government statistics, as given in the *New York Times*, page 24, March 12, 1959, suicide is the leading killer between the ages of 15 and 24. The glorification of suicide in Japanese literature and drama is given as the psychological inducement to self-destruction. Social commentators blamed the intense competition for the Japanese boy, who may be left behind at any stage in high school, with an end to career ambition. In Tokyo (1958) 175 boys and 37 girls ran away from home after failing to pass university entrance examinations. Kleinschmidt[16] gives an account of the death of Elpenor in the Odyssey. Elpenor's self-destruction is analyzed as due to Odysseus' rejection of him, and the revival of repressed incestual drives and thwarted aggression toward Odysseus and Circe, fantasied parent substitutes.

Classical is the double suicide of Romeo and Juliet, wherein hostile attitudes on the part of their respective families interfered with fulfillment of their heterosexuality. Juliet's father insisted on her marriage to a much older suitor (an oedipal threat).

Hedwig, an adolescent girl of 14 in Ibsen's *The Wild Duck*,* committed suicide after being told of her illegitimate origin. Upon the suggestion that she kill her wild duck pet (which "came from the depths of the sea") in order to give sacrificial proof of her love for her stepfather and to keep him from leaving the house, she shot herself instead. In the novel *Jude, the Obscure*, by Thomas Hardy, Jude, 19, jumped into a pond after learning of the suicidal drowning of his mother when he was a baby. This suicidal attempt took place during the period of the dissolution of his marriage. Here the theme of loss of the mother by the boy, oral frustration, and identification with the mother was apparent.

SUMMARY

Adolescent suicide represents an active attempt to master, by magic and omnipotence, passively endured trauma in the pre-oedipal and oedipal period. The suicidal behavior is translatable by recognizing the revival of primary process thinking and acting with energized aggression against the internalized sadistic object, mainly a phallic, narcissistic mother image. The wish for sleep, in the suicidal behavior at adolescence, represents a megalomanic method of coping with overwhelming problems of sexual identification, a sense of identity, and handling of aggression, which explosively rids the adolescent of the oedipal struggle.

REFERENCES

1. ABRAHAM, K. "Manic Depressive States," in *Selected Papers*. London, Hogarth Press, Ltd., 1948, chap. 26.
1a. ARLOW, J. "Bar Mizvah," in *The Psychoanalytic Study of the Child*. New York, International Universities Press, Inc., 1951, vol. 6, p. 185.
1b. ARLOW, J. "Talmudic, midrashic, and Cabbalistic literature," "As a bride or beloved woman," *ibid*.
2. BAKWIN, H. *Am. J. Pediatrics. 50:* 749, 1957.
3. BALSER, B., and MASTERSON, J. F., JR. Suicide in adolescents. *J. Am. Psychoanalyt. Assoc. 116:* 400, 1959.
4. BOSSELMAN, B. C. *Self Destruction*. Springfield, Ill., Charles C Thomas, 1958.
5. DESPERT, J. L. Suicide and depression in children. *Nerv. Child. 41:* 378, 1954.
6. EIDELBERG, L. The concept of narcissistic mortification. *Internat. J. Psycho-Analysis. 40:* Parts III–IV, 1959.
7. ERIKSON, E. H. in *Childhood and Society*. New York, W. W. Norton & Company, 1950, p. 136.

* Paul Kanzer called attention to this reference.

8. ERIKSON, E. H. The problem of ego identity. *J. Am. Psychoanalyt. Assoc.* 4: 1, 1956.
9. FREUD, A. "Adolescence," in *The Psychoanalytic Study of the Child.* New York, International Universities Press, Inc., 1958, vol. 13, p. 270.
10. FREUD, S. *Collected Papers,* ed. by Strachey, James. London, Hogarth Press, Ltd., vol. 10, p. 162; vol. 19, p. 252.
11. FREUD, S. "Mourning and Melancholia," in *Collected Papers.* London, Hogarth Press, Ltd., 1925, vol. 4.
12. GERO, G. "An Equivalent of Depression: Anorexia," in *Affective Disorders,* ed. by Greenacre, P. New York, International Universities Press, Inc., 1953.
13. HERTZ, M. R. Suicidal configuration in Rorschach records. *Rorsch. Research Exchange & Journ. of Projective Techniques.* 12: 3, 1948.
14. JACOBSON, E. Depression: Oedipus complex in the development of depressive mechanisms. *Psychoanalyt. Quart.* 12: 541, 1943.
15. JACOBZINER, H., and RAYBIN, H. W. Attempted suicides in adolescents. *New York J. Med.* 59: 862, 1959.
16. KLEINSCHMIDT, H. J. Death of Elpenor. *J. Hillside Hosp.* 3: 4, 1956.
17. LEWIN, B. *The Psychoanalysis of Elation.* New York, W. W. Norton & Company, 1950.
18. LORAND, S. Dynamics and therapy of depressive states. *Psychoanalyt. Rev.* 24: 92, 1937.
19. MASON, P. Suicide in adolescents. *Psychoanalyt. Rev.* 41: 48, 1954.
20. RADO, S. "Hedonic Control, Action Self and the Depressive Spell," in *Depression,* ed. by Hoch, P. H. and Zubin, J. New York, Grune & Stratton, Inc., 1954.
21. SCHECTER, M. P. "On Recognition and Treatment of Suicide in Children," in *Clues to Suicide.* New York, McGraw-Hill Book Company, Inc., 1957.
22. SCHNEER, H. I., KAY, P., and BROZOVSKY, M. "Events and Conscious Ideation Leading to Suicidal Behavior in Adolescents." *Psychiat. Quart. In press.*
23. STENGEL, E., and COOK, N. G. *Attempted Suicide,* Maudsley Monographs. London, Chapman & Hall, Ltd., 1958.
24. ZILBOORG, G. Contributions on suicide, with particular reference to the young. *Am. J. Orthopsychiat.* 7: 15, 1937.

chapter 10   Psychosomatic Disorders

MELITTA SPERLING

✳ Puberty and adolescence are crucial phases in the life of young people, during which their ability to renounce the attachment to the original love objects and to form new relationships with persons of the same and of the opposite sex is being tested. The influx of sexual energy at this period of life disturbs, to a considerable extent, the precarious balance which the child has been able to establish during latency. It is well known that many neurotic and character disorders have their onset at this particular period of life. It is less well known that a variety of psychosomatic disorders also begin during this period. This is probably due to the fact that youngsters who appear organically sick are usually not referred for psychiatric treatment. An additional reason may be the fact that there exists a reverse reciprocity between psychological and somatic manifestations in a psychosomatic disorder, that is, the more apparent the somatic manifestations are, the less apparent is the underlying neurotic structure. During the phase of active somatic illness, the individual does not appear neurotically sick, and there is little incentive for the parents or their advisers to have such a child treated psychiatrically.

Coming from general medicine and pediatrics, it seems that I have retained an interest in "sick" people. Having worked for many years in a general hospital setting, I had the opportunity to see and treat a considerable number of psychosomatically ill children and adolescents in the hospital. The additional fact that I was in a position to select my cases from the wards made it possible for me to work with patients who ordinarily would not be treated by a psychiatrist or psychoanalyst.

The disposition to react with a psychosomatic disorder to a particular life situation is acquired early in life. The conflicts motivating such an individual are conflicts of the preoedipal phases, and the fixation points and regression in psychosomatic illness go back to the oral and anal phases of development. This disposition is

202

rooted in a specific mother-child relationship, of which the out-standing feature on the part of the mother is her need to keep her child in lifelong dependence for the satisfaction of vital emotional and bodily needs. The complementary specific feature in the child is an unconscious compliance with these needs of the mother, that is, to be sick and dependent.[8] The specific somatic symptoms of the child, in these cases, are structured similarly to neurotic symptoms in which both the forbidden wish and the punishment are executed at the same time. In the psychosomatic symptom, both the compliance with the unconscious wish of the mother and the rebellion against it are expressed simultaneously. Although most investigators in the field of psychosomatic medicine consider rejection of the child (by the mother) as the significant feature of the mother's personality, I could, with the help of a specific research method which I used for the study of such cases, namely, the simultaneous psychoanalytic treatment of mother and child, arrive at a different conclusion.

In the simultaneous psychoanalytic treatment of mother and child, in which the interaction between the unconscious wishes of the mother and the responses of the child can be observed and treated analytically, I found that the mother rejects the child only when he is well and attempting to assert his independence, but that she rewards him when he is sick; that is, when he submits to her wishes.[10] Low tolerance of frustration and emotional immaturity have been described as characteristic features of the psychosomatic patient. These features, however, are not specific for these patients; they are also characteristic for psychopaths, addicts, impulse-ridden characters, perverts, and other pregenitally fixated individuals. The specific characteristic feature of the personality of the psychosomatic patient, namely, that feature which differentiates him from the above-mentioned categories, is the specific structure of his superego. This, in turn, is the outcome of the specific mother-child relationship operating in these cases. During certain phases of the treatment, the behavior of psychosomatic patients may temporarily become that of impulse-ridden characters.[12]

I am emphasizing this point because I want to indicate that the decisive factor is not so much the difference in the ego, particularly its strength or weakness, which accounts for the psychosomatic reaction, as it is the different structure of the superego of such patients. The afore-mentioned changes in the behavior of a psychosomatic patient occurring during treatment can be understood as resulting from changes in his superego. That means that his superego has become more permissive and less punitive and not that the ego has become weaker in the treatment process.

CASE REPORT*

This report is given to illustrate what may appear to be, but is not, a psychosomatic disorder.

A 12-year-old Jewish boy, a seventh-grader in junior high school, was referred to the Kings County Hospital Child Guidance Clinic by the Kings County Hospital Pediatric Department after a 10-day diagnostic hospitalization failed to disclose organic pathology. His symptoms were overweight and "colitis." His mother was not precise, but she felt that soiling was the problem. She said, "He had celiac disease when he was a baby. The doctor said if he lost weight the soiling would go away too." She continued, however, to refer to "colitis." She expressed concern that he had no friends because of the smell. Almost daily, he has a bowel movement in his trousers.

From the report of a psychiatric interview with the boy, he was observed to be markedly obese, friendly, but constantly making self-reassuring comments and seeking approval. Whether complaining or not, his smile presented the same quality of bland acceptance. His soiling and eating were discussed in the same passive manner. He blames his trouble on being lazy—"but I can't do anything about it."

He recalled his life by school grades, for example: "In the first grade my mother went to work. . . . " "In the fifth grade I broke my leg. That is the year we had four teachers. I hate that. Getting used to new ones."

Of his soiling, he had this to say: "I get cramps and I have to go. I can't wait. It happens any time. No special reason. It's because of the colitis. There is nothing I can do about it."

He would like to be thinner but not "skinny" like one child they call "the stick." He overeats and cannot stop—"not because I'm hungry, I just want to eat."

His family consisted of an obese mother, 43, and his father, 46, described as a "giant," "6 feet tall, 300 pounds" who was able to load 350-pound packages of fish at the market. The father was considered to be impulsive, impatient, and generous, and he would

* Prepared by Dr. Roy Lilleskov under supervision of Dr. Henry I. Schneer.

strike the children when annoyed. During her marriage the mother had a surgical repair for a pendulous abdomen. She also has been diabetic for the past 5 years. She described with much guilt how she would become enraged over the patient's soiling. For her diabetes, the patient would inject her in the morning and the older son would perform this service in the evening. The older son, 17, is tall and slim, not as bright as the patient, and "spoiled" owing to childhood allergies. The patient feels that he is always picked on by the brother. There is a 22-year-old married daughter of whom little is known. A maternal grandmother, incontinent of urine and feces, lived with the family during the patient's second and third years of life.

Concerning the patient's development, he walked and talked at 10 months. The mother attributed feeding difficulties to "severe food allergies" of her children. When the patient was 13 months old, he had a severe diarrhea during which he lost weight. For months he continued to have three to four stools a day, loose and filled with mucous but not foul. Celiac disease was diagnosed. He was placed on a banana-and-rice diet, and, by the time he was 2 years old, he recovered his weight. Coincidentally, he was having a recurrent tonsillitis between the first and second years. When he was 2 years and 4 months old, he had a tonsillectomy. He weighed 27 pounds then. When he was 3 years old he weighed 77 pounds! The voracious eating since the tonsillectomy has now culminated in a weight of 210 pounds in a boy 5 feet, 3 inches tall.

For several years the mother was concerned with the small size of his genitalia. He was given androgen injections. Last year, however, a leading endocrinologist said that there was no sign of an endocrine problem, and that hormone therapy should cease. In regard to his sexual history, the mother took pride in the lack of modesty in the home. When the father is shaving, the mother may be in the bathtub while one of the children uses the toilet.

At school, the patient is considered "very intelligent." He is in an advanced class.

Psychological testing of the patient placed him in the superior range of intelligence. The Rorschach, TAT, and figure drawings did not reveal any indication of a psychotic break.

DISCUSSION

I do not consider this case a true psychosomatic disorder. The mucous colitis of this patient, on closer investigation, reveals itself to be really a form of soiling. I do not consider obesity a psycho-somatic disorder, and the structure of the superego of the obese patient confirms my view. In the case of this boy, too, the structure of the superego is that of an impulse-ridden character. The out-standing feature in his case is a lack of instinctual control. My diagnosis of this boy would be: a character disorder closely re-lated to addiction. As you may know, in some cases of obesity, the treatment is actually like that of addiction, for the obese patient behaves toward food as an addict does toward a narcotic.

Here, again, I want to stress the fact that I consider the differ-ences in the structure of the superego to be of primary etiological significance. I did not find the ego of these addict-type patients particularly deficient. In fact, in certain aspects these patients re-veal particular abilities in manipulating reality and people. In the Rorschach test of this boy, there was no evidence of psychosis. The superego originates from the incorporation of parental prohi-bitions, interdictions, and commands. The family history of this boy reveals a very permissive, seductive environment and parents who were lacking in emotional control themselves. We would ex-pect that, by identification with the parental figures, he would de-velop a superego of the kind which would permit the behavior described in the case history.

In psychosomatic patients, however, the superego is very harsh. The psychopath or delinquent permits himself to release his de-structiveness and his aggression externally to the outside world and to the objects in reality. Therefore, they attract much atten-tion. The literature on adolescence deals mainly with the problems of delinquency. The psychosomatically sick adolescent does not attract very much attention because he suffers, whereas the de-linquent adolescent makes others suffer. The element of suffering is essential to justify the diagnosis of psychosomatic illness. It is not mental pain or manifest anxiety which the psychosomatic pa-tient experiences. These are the very feelings which he tries to avoid at the price of bodily suffering. There is a great deal of suffering involved in psychosomatic illness which, in some cases, may even lead to what I have called "psychosomatic suicide."

A beautiful illustration of this is the following observation re-ported by the internist Cullinan.[3] A young girl, gravely ill with ulcerative colitis, was receiving the last rites. The priest told her of the suffering of her parents, how they grieved and cried. Shortly after the priest left her, the patient got off the bed and said that she thought her parents had suffered enough. This was the end of her ulcerative colitis attack, which had not responded to medical treatment.

In this connection again, the differences between the personality structure in psychopathy and psychosomatic illness are of interest. The psychoanalytic concept that, unconsciously, every suicide represents a murder is a familiar one. Neither the psychosomatic nor the obsessive-compulsive nor the depressive patients are prone to commit murder. This can be understood on the basis of the structure of the superego, which does not permit the acting out of destructiveness in reality but which prompts them to turn this destructiveness inside and toward themselves. These destructive impulses, in the case of the psychosomatic patient, are then released through the bodily symptoms.

The concept of profiles in psychosomatic diseases, introduced by Dunbar,[4] is of interest. According to this concept, certain personality types are prone to develop certain psychosomatic disorders, such as the peptic-ulcer type described by F. Alexander.[1,2] The problem of specificity of symptoms should also be mentioned here. It has been found that the same patient can develop different psychosomatic symptoms at different times, and also that persons of different personality types can develop the same psychosomatic syndromes. This would seem to contradict the concept of specificity of symptoms. The phenomenon of change of psychosomatic symptoms in the course of treatment has been described by Engel and myself.[11] Just as, in a psychoneurosis, the symptoms may change when the underlying unconscious fantasies have been analyzed but the basic conflict has not yet been resolved, so the same can occur in a psychosomatic disease. Concerning the fact that different personalities can develop the same psychosomatic disease, careful analytic study of such cases revealed, rather, the significant basic similarities in these patients.

PSYCHOSOMATIC DISORDERS IN ADOLESCENCE

In describing some of the psychosomatic disorders most frequently encountered during adolescence, I shall use the conventional approach and classify these disorders according to organ systems. Most frequent are the disorders of the gastrointestinal system, comprising the mouth, the intestines, and the anus. The mouth is the organ for intake and, in the infant, the primary organ for contact with the outside world. The first object relationships are established through the mouth, so to speak. In the unconscious, food and mother remain associated all through life. The mouth is also an important organ for the development of reality testing and differentiation between the inside and outside worlds. Ernst Simmel,[5,6] a well-known German psychoanalyst of the old guard, suggested that there may be a libidinal organization preceding the oral phase which he called the gastrointestinal libido organization. In this way he was stressing the significance of the whole gastrointestinal system in the early instinctual development and not only that of the mouth, which is considered to be the most important and earliest erotogenic zone. I think it may be of interest to learn how Simmel arrived at this concept: Simmel was the man who founded what can be considered the first psychosomatic hospital in Germany during World War I. In this hospital he treated his patients with the psychoanalytic technique, and it was as a result of his experiences with these patients that he formed this idea.

The respiratory system is another organ system to be afflicted frequently with psychosomatic disorders. The psychologic mechanisms operating in certain psychosomatic diseases of the respiratory system are similar to those which we find in the disorders of the gastrointestinal system. The physiological processes of inhaling and exhaling can be used symbolically by the unconscious to express conflicts of separation and fantasies of taking in or letting go.

Disorders of the circulatory system are not too frequent in adolescents.

The skin, owing to the fact that it represents the boundary of the body from the outside, becomes the seat of a number of psychosomatic disorders which, from a psychoanalytic point of view, can be understood as expressions of conflicts between the inside and the outside.

One of the most frequent disorders of the gastrointestinal tract found in puberty and adolescence is anorexia nervosa. It can be a very serious condition. There are patients who have to be hospitalized and fed artificially. This behavior toward food is similar to that of patients suffering from depression. We actually find, in the psychoanalytic treatment of patients with anorexia nervosa, a very close dynamic interrelationship between anorexia and depression. In some instances anorexia has been described as an equivalent of depression, the refusal to eat being an outstanding symptom in severe depression. Anorexia nervosa occurs more frequently in girls but is also found in adolescent boys. From a dynamic point of view, one should think in such a case of an unconscious feminine identification as an important dynamic factor. Very often anorexia is associated with nausea and vomiting. Unresolved sexual problems and unconscious pregnancy fantasies and wishes also are significant dynamic factors.

In anorexia nervosa there is a severe inhibition of the oral instincts to the extent that the patient stops eating and may have to be fed artificially. The exact opposite is true for obesity. In these cases, overeating and excessive gratification of oral instincts in reality are common. It is for this reason that I do not consider obesity as a psychosomatic disorder. I consider obesity as an impulse disorder and would place it, together with drug addicts and alcoholics, in the category of impulse-ridden characters. The decisive difference between this type of patient and the psychosomatic patient is precisely that the impulse-ridden character gratifies his impulses in reality with a disregard of the consequences of his actions for himself and others, whereas the psychosomatic patient, consciously unaware of his impulses, can gratify them only partially and in a distorted way via the somatic symptoms. In the psychosomatic symptom, as in the neurotic symptom, the need for punishment is gratified in the pain and suffering associated with the illness. As one patient suffering from chronic ileitis put it, "This [the ileitis] makes me a martyr and not a maniac." In his case, and this is so in every case, the illness brought essential gains. It was the key to the heart of his wife. Had he shown his true feelings in his overt behavior, it certainly would have brought him not sympathy but disapproval from his wife and others.

The alternative in these cases, however, is not either to be sick (a martyr) or to act out destructive impulses in reality (a maniac) as this patient presented it. It is possible for these patients in psychoanalytic treatment to achieve the adequate instinctual control necessary for healthy functioning.

Ulcerative and mucous colitis are psychosomatic disorders of the lower gastrointestinal system, frequently occurring during adolescence. Abdominal cramps and diarrhea are characteristic features in both conditions. Ulcerative colitis is the more serious illness and is associated in most cases with fever, anorexia, and bloody diarrhea. The onset is generally sudden. The course of this illness is characterized by spontaneous remissions and exacerbations and often leads to chronic invalidism and even death if not treated.

For detailed studies on this subject I refer to my publications. I can only summarize here some of my findings.[7]

In its severe form, ulcerative colitis is the somatic equivalent of a melancholic depression. The fixation and regression are primarily to the oral-sadistic level. In it's milder forms it can be understood to represent the somatic equivalent of certain perversions or severe character disorders. In these cases the fixation and regression are primarily to the anal level of psychosexual development. The specific quality of object relationship in ulcerative colitis and its etiologic and dynamic significance have been demonstrated and emphasized in my studies of this illness. Since I intend to present in more detail a case of mucous colitis in an adolescent boy, I shall not discuss this condition now. I should mention here that gastric and duodenal ulcers occur in older adolescents and that the same unconscious conflicts have been found to be at work in these conditions as in young adults.

Another condition seen not too infrequently, particularly in adolescent boys, is hemorrhoids. Of course this does not mean that every case of hemorrhoids in an adolescent is a psychosomatic disorder, but there are some instances in which this condition is a true psychosomatic disorder, that is, the somatic expression of an unconscious conflict. I am thinking of one case, that of a 17-year-old boy who developed acute and severe hemorrhoids during his analysis. Since the boy was suffering badly, his father had arranged with the proctologist for surgical removal of the hemorrhoids. I was able to get a postponement of the operation so that we had a chance to understand, in the analysis, what had happened. After resolving the conflict and becoming conscious of his fantasies, the hemorrhoids cleared up as dramatically as they had appeared. The proctologist was so baffled by this that he wanted to know what medication we had used so successfully. He could not understand that merely talking could have such an effect upon hemorrhoids.

I shall now mention some of the disorders of the respiratory system, such as hay fever, rhinitis, nervous coughing, sneezing, etc., referred to as "allergies of the upper respiratory system" occurring in adolescents. In this connection it may be of interest to learn that the psychoanalytic treatment of certain allergic conditions, while freeing the patient from his allergic reactions, does not change the (constitutional) allergic condition. After treatment such patients may be found to be sensitive to the allergens, for example, in skin tests, but when exposed to these allergens they show no clinical manifestations. This phenomenon demonstrates the significance of the emotional factor which, in these cases, apparently is a specific factor to trigger off the allergic clinical reactions. I have observed this phenomenon in cases of hay fever, bronchial asthma, and food allergy in adolescents.

Of the disorders of the circulatory system, angioneurotic edema and migraine headache occur not too infrequently during adolescence. I had an opportunity to treat also an adolescent girl with hypertension. On follow-up 7 years later, it was found that her hypertension did not recur even in situations of stress.

Of the disorders of the skin to be found in adolescents, dermatitis and eczema are the most frequent. In my material there was a preponderance of girls in whom the dermatitis was associated with a particularly severe itch and uncontrollable scratching. Because of some of the dynamics unfolded in the psychoanalytic treatment of these girls, I am inclined to think that girls may be more prone to develop dermatitis. Although psychological factors undoubtedly play a role in acne, I would not consider acne to be a psychosomatic disorder. It would, rather, seem that acne is secondarily used in certain conflicts of adolescence and may be aggravated and maintained by this.

This will have to suffice as an outline for psychosomatic disorders in adolescence. I shall now proceed with the presentation of a case of mucous colitis in a 12-year-old boy.

CASE REPORT

This boy had been suffering from severe diarrhea, of unknown origin, for 2 years prior to the start of treatment. He had undergone a series of tests and examinations, including rectoscopy and X rays. He had been diagnosed as a case of mucous colitis. All medical treatment and the many dietary regimes prescribed during these 2 years had been ineffective, and his condition became progressively worse. He also had many phobias which, together with the diarrhea, incapacitated him so that he could not attend school.

It was found that he had been very insecure with his mother and phobically attached to her ever since he could remember. He was very much afraid of his father and felt that his father looked down on him. Whenever he attempted to leave the house without his mother, he would get cramps and have to turn back immediately and run to the bathroom to move his bowels. He had not been able to stay in school for this very reason. He had not been doing so well in school because of the diarrhea and because he worried so much. He was very much afraid of infection; a little cut or scratch would throw him into a panic, and he worried that he would die from septicemia. He feared that the slightest cold would result in pneumonia. He could not concentrate in school, and when he failed he worried about his bad marks and feared that he would be left behind. He thought that the children and teachers were laughing at him, and he therefore withdrew from the children altogether. He sat at home by himself, listened to the radio, and modeled airplanes, which was his only occupation.

Whenever we discussed his relationship with his mother, he reacted to this with an immediate urge to leave the room and go to the bathroom to move his bowels. "It seems I cannot talk about my mother without having diarrhea," he said.

When I interpreted to him that this meant that he was really very angry at her, he said, "She does prefer my brother." He then complained that his mother was holding up his brother (who was 5 years older) to him as a model boy and a superior student, and also that his mother gave a great deal of attention to his younger sister. He recalled that he had a severe attack of diarrhea right after his sister was born, when he was 7½. He remembered that he was very unhappy then, because, shortly before his sister was born, his grandmother, who lived with the family and who was taking care of him, had died. He had been very much attached to her. He had also lost his pet dog at that time. He remembered that he had attacks of diarrhea before that too—at the time when he started school. He didn't want to go to school and leave his mother.

Perhaps I should make clear here why I am stressing these facts. First of all, although the diarrhea for which he was being treated (and this is true for other psychosomatic symptoms) occurred for the first time in adolescence, it was possible for the patient, during his treatment, to remember that there had been earlier episodes. Second, these episodes had occurred at certain significant phases of his life, such as separation from his mother, the start of school, the birth of his sister, the death of his grandmother, and the loss of his dog. All of these situations represented specific traumata to the boy, to which he reacted with this particular symptom. When he started having trouble at school and was afraid to go, his father would bring him there forcefully and stay by the window and watch to see whether he would run out.

He remembered an episode which occurred when he was 3 or 4 years old. He was in a room with his brother, who showed him a globe. He remembered that he ran out of the room, panic stricken, to look for his mother. When he found her, he pleaded with her to promise him that if he should have to die she would hold his hand and die with him. And if she should have to die, he wanted to hold her hand and die with her.

When he was still younger he used to have temper tantrums. His mother would punish him and hit him for this, and so he became a good boy and very much attached to his mother. He had a sadomasochistic relationship with his mother. Of the sadistic attitude he was unconscious; it revealed itself in his phobias and in the diarrhea. The masochistic attitude was very much apparent and brought him rewards in reality, because in this way he could keep his mother close to himself. He had the feeling that he was a moron and really crazy, and that his mother rejected him and considered him crazy.

These feelings had a basis in reality, although they were exaggerated and neurotically distorted. From his mother I learned that she had not wanted the child at the time he was born, that she had particularly not wanted another boy, and, that she had had some sort of a nervous breakdown in reaction to his birth. She disliked him intensely, and she considered him a very homely child. This was a narcissistic hurt to her. She had been very impatient and punitive with him and had put a great deal of emphasis on toilet training. She was a compulsive woman.

During the first year of his life his grandmother had taken care of him and apparently had succeeded very satisfactorily. But then his mother took over, and from then on things did not go right. He could not be trained and he had diarrhea. He was already disturbed then, but she would beat him until he became clean and obedient.

He had the recurrences of the diarrhea later, in the situations mentioned. He had many colds as a child, and pneumonia when he was about 2½ years old. He was so sick then that he could have easily died. This was also an experience which contributed to his becoming a quiet and good boy. His mother was annoyed with him because he would not go to sleep unless she would lie down on the bed with him, and because he clung to her at all times. She was always comparing him unfavorably with his older brother, and when his sister was born she turned toward the little girl.

In proportion to his awareness of his repressed hostility and death wishes directed toward his mother, and in proportion to his increased ability to tolerate frustration without immediate discharge, his entire behavior, but particularly his diarrhea, improved. He could understand how much satisfaction he had derived from this behavior, which was so disturbing to his parents and which brought him important secondary gains—primarily, the attention he got from being sick.

He liked to scare his mother by talking about an irresistible urge to kill his brother. Actually, he once sprained his brother's wrists in a fight. In fights with boys he would become very violent. The breakthrough of destructive impulses in these cases is a factor to keep in mind during treatment. It is important not to release such impulses too suddenly but, rather, very gradually. Once he almost killed a boy who teased him. He banged this boy's head on the sidewalk, and he had to be separated from him by force.

The dynamics of his phobic clinging to his mother and the fear of letting her out of his sight, as well as his diarrhea, became clear during his treatment. In the phobia, he was holding onto his mother, protecting her, as it were, against his own unconscious death wishes. If she was there near him, then he had the reassurance that he hadn't killed her yet (by the magic of his unconscious wishes). That was why he would wait at the window when she had gone out and hadn't come back on time. In the diarrhea, he was giving her up unconsciously as feces. This was the only way in which he could separate himself from his mother, namely, by the unconscious equation of feces = devaluated object = mother. After we had analyzed this meaning of the diarrhea and of his destructive impulses, his diarrhea stopped completely. This was after he had been under treatment for 4 months.

The precipitating trauma which had caused the disturbed behavior and diarrhea when he was 10 years old could be traced back to an experience which occurred then. The paternal grandfather, who was sick and in need of care, came to live with the family. Up to that time the patient had shared a room with the brother and had enjoyed very much their wrestling and playing at bedtime. When he talked to me about this phase of his life, he related at first that he had shared a room with his grandfather and his brother had gone to sleep in the parental bedroom. He remembered being very unhappy about this arrangement, which deprived him of the playful wrestling with his brother, and that he had to be very quiet in order not to disturb his grandfather, who suffered from a cardiac condition. He also recalled that he would stay up nights listening to see if the grandfather was still breathing. Later in the treatment it was found that this memory had been falsified and that he had an amnesia for what had actually happened during that period. When this amnesia lifted we learned that it was he and not his brother who had moved into the parental bedroom. This was confirmed by his mother. She also told me that at that time she had noticed that the boy had become very much disturbed, and that he had developed a severe sleep disturbance, with nightmares which kept him and them up for most of the night. His sleep disturbance made them decide to move him out of the parental bedroom and into the room with his grandfather. It was found that between the ages of 10 and 11 he had been exposed to primal-scene experiences which reactivated his oedipal conflict and intensified severely his masturbatory conflicts. He was thrown into a state of acute anxiety, with sleep disturbance and nightmares. He rescued himself from this very threatening sexual situation by regressing to the anal phase to which he had been strongly fixated.

The meaning and the psychodynamics of the mucous colitis could be understood in the following ways:

1. As a retreat from the genital to the anal level of libido organization, it provided this boy with the possibility of discharging aggressive and sexual impulses (masturbation substitute).

2. By releasing sadistic impulses immediately through a somatic symptom, he was trying to protect himself from the overwhelming anxiety stemming from his own destructiveness (conversion on a pregenital level).

3. The experience in the parental bedroom had revived his oedipal conflict, which he had been unable to resolve originally and which had caused him to regress to the anal sadistic level.

4. He was devaluating the frustrating object (mother) to feces and giving her up in the physical symptom. The diarrhea, therefore, which would appear to indicate helplessness and inability of control, unconsciously represented sadistic control over the mother. The secondary gain derived from the illness supported such a magical belief. He could stay home with his mother, take her away from the others, and have her accompany him wherever he went.

5. The punishment for this was executed upon himself by the physical suffering and restriction imposed upon him by the diarrhea and fears.

This case was presented in order to demonstrate the psycho-dynamics of a psychosomatic disorder (mucous colitis) in an adolescent boy. More details and a follow-up of this case are given elsewhere.[9]

REFERENCES

1. ALEXANDER, F. Fundamental concepts of psychosomatic research: psychogenesis, conversion specificity. *Psychosom. Med.* 5: 205, 1943.
2. ALEXANDER, F. *Fundamental Concepts of Psychosomatic Research: Psychogenesis, Conversion Specificity: Psychosomatic Medicine.* New York, W. W. Norton & Company, Inc., 1950.
3. CULLINAN, E. R. Ulcerative colitis: clinical aspects. *Brit. M. J.* 2: 1351, 1938.
4. DUNBAR, H. F. *Emotions and Bodily Changes: A Survey of Literature on Psychosomatic Interrelationships.* New York, Columbia University Press, 1946.
5. SIMMEL, E. "Pregenital primacy and intestinal stage of the libido organization." *Internat. Ztschr. Psychoan.* 19: 245, 1933.
6. SIMMEL, E. The psychogenesis of organic disturbances and their psychoanalytic treatment. *Psychoanalyt. Quart.* 1: 166, 1932.
7. SPERLING, M. Psychoanalytic study of ulcerative colitis in children. *Psychoanalyt. Quart.* 15: 302, 1946.
8. SPERLING, M. The role of the mother in psychosomatic disorders of children. *Psychosom. Med.* 11: 377, 1949.
9. SPERLING, M. Mucous colitis associated with phobia. *Psychoanalyt. Quart.* 19: 318, 1950.
10. SPERLING, M. Psychosis and psychosomatic illness. *Internat. J. Psycho-Analysis* 36: 1, 1955.
11. SPERLING, M. The psychoanalytic treatment of ulcerative colitis. *Internat. J. Psycho-Analysis* 37: 1, 1957.
12. SPERLING, M. "A Study of Deviate Sexual Behavior in Children by the Method of Simultaneous Analysis of Mother and Child," in *Dynamic Psychopathology of Childhood,* ed. by Jessner, L., Pavenstedt, E., New York, Grune & Stratton, Inc., 1959.

chapter 11   Adolescence and Schizophrenia:

Problems in Differentiation

HYMAN SPOTNITZ

The identification of schizophrenia as a childhood illness, with dynamic manifestations, diagnostic criteria, and therapeutic indications distinguishable from those of adult schizophrenic reactions, did not actually get under way until about 10 years ago. A few cases were reported in the literature in 1929 and 1933. Compared with 54 items concerning dementia praecox in childhood, which appeared from 1936 to 1946, Bellak and others[3] report that the technical literature from 1946 to 1956 contained 515 items related to the broad field of childhood schizophrenia and related disorders. Only 2 of the 54 earlier reports—that is, 4 per cent—dealt with therapy, and by therapy is meant chemotherapy—the use of Metrazol; there was no report at all on the use of psychotherapy. In the following decade, 190 of the total of 515 items—that is, 40 per cent—were therapeutically oriented, and 90 of these 190 items were psychotherapeutically oriented.

Schizophrenic reactions are loosely related disorders replacing the formerly recognized disease entity of dementia praecox, and they comprise a wide range of disturbances. Among these are the simple, the hebephrenic, catatonic, paranoid, schizo-affective, acute undifferentiated, chronic undifferentiated, residual, and childhood types. All are vaguely described in the *American Psychiatric Association 1952 Diagnostic Manual* as "marked by a strong tendency to retreat from reality, by emotional disharmony, unpredictable disturbances in the stream of thought, by regressive behavior, and in some by a tendency to deterioration." These schizophrenic reactions may or may not be of a psychotic nature.

Until the last 10 or 15 years, most of the observations of these various pathological conditions were confined to their manifestations in adult patients. Since descriptions of the various symptom pictures in adults have dominated the literature, it is relatively simple for the psychiatrist to make a diagnosis of schizophrenic reactions of one type or another in the person who has achieved at least physiological maturity.

ADULT SCHIZOPHRENIA

When the clinician perceives a strangeness about the adult facing him, he quickly begins to explore the possibility that he is observing some type of schizophrenic reaction. The patient will generally seem withdrawn and will exhibit an emotional flatness and lack of drive. His affect will also be inappropriate, his thought processes confused, and in one or more respects his behavior will seem incongruous or even bizarre. If he is suffering from simple schizophrenia, he will convey the impression of a general slowing down in his physiological functioning, sometimes to an extreme degree. If he hallucinates, one may associate this with the catatonic, hebephrenic, or paranoid form of the disease. If this is actually present, the adult will also show some marked defect of ego functioning, such as stereotyping, posturing, disorientation as to time and place, and a pathological degree of self-preoccupation matched by his reluctance to associate with other people.

In establishing a diagnosis of schizophrenia, one takes into consideration many different factors, and the more of these factors one has knowledge of, the easier it becomes to reach the clinical diagnosis. These include such functions of the patient as his general performance and behavior in his life situation, any disturbances of control, relationships to others, thinking, memory, learning, perception, reality testing, etc. It is in the early stages of the disease, when one is most likely to lack information on these various aspects of functioning, that the principal mistakes in diagnosis occur. Estimates of incorrect diagnosis reportedly range from 16 to 50 per cent, and appear to indicate that women are more frequently misdiagnosed than men. The most common mistakes reported are to categorize the illness as one of anxiety reaction, hysterical and phobic reaction, a manic-depressive or depressive reaction, a neurasthenia, or a psychopathic personality.[19]

The study of diagnostic criteria for the establishment of schizophrenia in the patient who has not reached adulthood leads us into a much more uncharted area than when we are dealing with the disease phenomena in the older patient. Least ground has been broken in the study of schizophrenia in adolescents. Let us approach it through the territory of childhood schizophrenia.

Why should we do this? Because, in the same way as adolescence is the meeting ground of childhood and adulthood, adolescent schizophrenia is the meeting ground of childhood schizophrenia and adult schizophrenia. To recognize the picture of adolescent schizophrenia, one has to know the childhood and adult pictures of the disorder, as well as those of adolescent psychosis and adolescence itself.

CHILDHOOD SCHIZOPHRENIA

Although a great deal of nosologic confusion still exists and a tendency to overdiagnosis is still noted, much has been done recently to facilitate the development of diagnostic criteria for the schizophrenic reactions of childhood. Most helpful in this respect have been the clinical pictures delineated by Lauretta Bender, Leo Kanner, and Margaret Mahler—that is, Kanner's concept of early infantile autism, Bender's investigations of childhood schizophrenia, and Mahler's hypothesis about symbiotic psychosis.

According to Bender,[4] childhood schizophrenia "involves a maturational lag at the embryonic level characterized by a primitive plasticity in all areas from which subsequent behavior develops."

Eisenberg and Kanner[7] regard extreme self-isolation and obsessive insistence on sameness as the primacy diagnostic criteria in early infantile autism. These lead to derivative characteristics such as mutism or abnormalities in language development, unusual apathy, and failure of the autistic child to respond to the approach of people, rage reactions over attempts to alter his mechanical way of living, interest in spinning objects, and tendencies to relate to things rather than to people and to parts rather than to whole objects.

The conjoining of innate and experiential factors produces the clinical picture of this syndrome, Kanner has recently concluded. Early infantile autism is basically determined, in his opinion, by the child's own psychological structure, resulting from inherent factors combined with the dynamics of child-parent relationship.

Mahler[15] classifies symbiotic psychosis into three groups of symptoms. The primary group includes panic reactions brought on by extreme organismic distress; alternating and unpredictable outbursts of violently destructive behavior and apparently pleasurable excitement; symptoms indicative of the fusion of the self with the nonself leading to a confusion between inner and outer reality; lack of differentiation between animate and inanimate reality marked by a tendency to devitalize the animate world; attachments to adults; and conspicuous evidence of dereistic thinking and feeling, and dereistic actions. Psychotic defense mechanisms representing attempts at self-integration comprise the group of secondary symptoms, and defenses akin to neurotic mechanisms constitute the third group.

Mahler[14] sharply differentiates this condition from autistic psychosis. She traces symbiotic psychosis back to pathological vicissitudes of the normal symbiotic period of infantile development. As a result, the brittle ego of the child broke down and fragmented in the process of leaving the mother outside the omnipotent orbit of the self.

In addition to the difficulty of diagnosing childhood schizophrenia, numerous general difficulties in diagnosing psychotic illness in children have long been recognized. One is caused by the unreliability of the histories given by parents. Even the fully objective and detached observer may have trouble detecting emotional illness in a child, because of the fluidity of a symptom complex in a psyche whose capacities and tendencies have not yet completely emerged. Moreover, the severity and significance of sudden changes in disposition and behavior are difficult to diagnose in the relative absence of adequate criteria for differentiating normal from deviant aspects of maturation in this period. The early behavioristic reports of schizophrenic children tended to obscure one important differentiating factor between adult and childhood schizophrenia. This is the fact that the child's symptoms have a special meaning in relation to his developmental and maturational age level.

From a pathognomic point of view, Ekstein's[8] concept of fluctuating ego states is a major diagnostic feature in all types of childhood schizophrenia. Marked and frequent fluctuations in the ego states of many schizophrenic children under intensive clinical observation led to Ekstein's hypothesis that there were similarly fluctuating ego states in the children in response to the stimulation and reactions emanating from their relationship with the significant mothering figure. Ego regression alternating with progression characterized the functioning of the extremely sensitive and fluid ego organization of schizophrenic children. In their regressed state, they produced markedly oral fantasies with such underlying themes as fear of separation, abandonment, or bodily disintegration and distortion of body image. Fantasies of giants devouring their victims, and primitive outbursts of rage were also characteristic. These fluctuating ego states are especially marked in adolescence.

The multiple symptoms and paradoxical picture of acceleration alternating with retardation of development have led to various other theories. Bender's concept of the plasticity underlying the schizophrenic manifestations has already been mentioned. There is Hartmann's[12] concept of dedifferentiation—that a reversal of the normal course of ego differentiation takes place. Bergman and Escalona[5] conceptualize a precocious ego undergoing fragmentation in the course of stressful development and experience. Erikson[9] presents an interesting concept of interference with the psycho-embryological schedule of ego functions.

Adolescents and Adolescent Schizophrenia

Concepts such as these often prove helpful to the clinician who has to make a difficult differential diagnosis in the case of a child. When he is dealing with an adolescent, however, he has few such accepted guideposts. In comparison with the now abundant literature on schizophrenia in adult life and in childhood, he does not find many directional signals to facilitate his entrance into the territory of adolescent schizophrenia. To compound his difficulties, what he would have to regard as an extreme manifestation of psychiatric disorder in the adult is apt to be no more than a normal phenomenon of development in the adolescent.

The following passage will suggest the nature of the difficulty. I include it, before identifying the author and the subject, as an exercise in differential diagnosis. The subject "lives in an atmosphere of great anxiety, high elation, deep despair, quickly rising enthusiasms, utter hopelessness, burning—or at other times sterile —intellectual or philosophical preoccupations. The yearning for freedom, the sense of loneliness, the feeling of oppression by parents, the impotent rages or active hates directed against the adult world, the erotic crushes—whether homosexually or heterosexually directed—the suicidal fantasies. . . . "

Yes, this is adolescence as it appears to Anna Freud.[10] She goes on to say that "in general, the adolescent upset and its manifestations are not predictable. . . . Adolescence is by definition an interruption of peaceful growth. The adolescent manifestations come close to symptom formation of the neurotic, the psychotic or dissocial order and verge almost imperceptibly into borderline states and initial, frustrated or fully fledged forms of almost all the mental illnesses. . . . Such fluctuations between extreme opposites would be deemed highly abnormal at any other time of life. At this time they may signify no more than that an adult structure of personality takes a long time to emerge, that the ego of the individual in question does not cease to experiment and is in no hurry to close down on possibilities. If the temporary solutions seem abnormal to the onlooker, they are less so, nevertheless, than the hasty decisions made in other cases for one-sided suppression, or revolt, or flight, or withdrawal, or regression, or asceticism, which are responsible for the truly pathological developments described above."

All of this adds up to the idea that an adolescent may temporarily appear like a psychotic and *not* be psychotic. On the other hand, this picture may actually reflect the beginning of a psychosis.

Another concept which I have found helpful in understanding adolescence was suggested to me by a passage in a paper written by Freud[11] in 1905. In modifying his earlier views on the significance of adult memories of sexual seduction during childhood by parents or older children, Freud points out that recollections of this nature, which could not be corroborated, probably represented fantasies of seduction. It appeared that between the symptoms and the infantile impressions, Freud went on, were interpolated the patient's fantasies, fantasies created mostly during the years of adolescence. To these fantasies, Freud gave the name "memory-romances."

Memory romance is a term which, in my opinion, beautifully characterizes the period of adolescence. I have the impression that adolescents are less dependent than either the child or the adult on external objects for emotional gratification; perhaps this is because adolescence is a pinnacle where one may enjoy striking new glimpses of the panorama of childhood and also stargaze at will into the future.

Though life has to be lived forward, it can only be understood backward. The Danish philosopher Kierkegaard made that statement a century before we entered the era of dynamic psychiatry. Some adolescents seem to be less interested in living forward than in understanding backward. As gonadal and other physiological changes of puberty (such as rapid growth, the reawakening of pre-genital impulses, and stimulation toward genital dominance) begin to affect the adolescent's psyche and heighten his sexuality, he seems to derive much satisfaction from going back in memory to the family romance of the oedipal period and reliving it in a way that will restore to him some of his infantile sense of omnipotence. Elaborating on his memory traces of the family romance, he spins it out endlessly into the richly embroidered romantic fantasies of adolescence. There is a line in a play by James Barrie to the effect that God gave us our memories so that we might have roses in December, and adolescence is the December of childhood.

Certainly, adolescence is a time of great emotional yearning. The adolescent has a great hunger for the approval of his family, the acceptance of his peers, and popularity with those of the other sex. He needs favorable recognition for his performance at home and in school, on the athletic field, and in social situations. When such emotional gratification is not forthcoming, however, the adolescent appears to have a greater facility than either the child or the adult to derive from fantasy life the satisfactions which his real life denies to him. Within reasonable limits, romancing with oneself provides some desirable relief amid the too brief satisfactions and stormy vicissitudes which the process of being socialized may bring. Loving oneself is at least the beginning of a lifelong romance, as Oscar Wilde pointed out.

An adolescent's great emotional hunger is not invariably due to an absence of gratification in his life. The hunger may reflect primarily some inability to absorb and assimilate emotional satis-factions which actually are available to him. Hypersensitivity, tend-encies to overreact to certain stimuli will make it difficult for him to tolerate the company of other people, let alone to obtain the normal quota of satisfaction from associating with them. In that case an adolescent will tend to spend much time alone or with a relatively constant, nonstimulating figure—a twin image. Or he may withdraw into a life of fantasy, of memory romancing. In extreme cases he will attempt to deny the existence of the un-gratifying outside world and search for nirvana in an all-inclusive psyche, an ego device which Silverberg[16] calls the schizoid maneuver.

The fact that the adolescent is able to derive a great deal of gratification from his self-preoccupations may help to explain why schizophrenic breakdown is less likely to occur in early adolescence than in its later years, or in early adult life. Sooner or later, though, he may reach the point where his fantasies become too pallid, too worked out to give him further gratification. As he moves toward that point, more and more frustration aggression develops, and what the adolescent does about this is a crucial factor. When the satisfaction value of the memory-romance period has been exhausted, the adolescent has two choices. The first is to establish new sources of satisfaction in external objects. That is the choice of the healthy adolescent. The other alternative is to run the risk of ego breakdown from lack of emotional satisfaction and from the psycho-toxic effects of his undischarged frustration aggression.

Since it is about as difficult to prove the presence of a schizophrenic reaction in an adolescent as it is easy to suspect it, how does one differentiate between typical adolescent defenses and true schizophrenic reactions? There is virtually complete agreement that the persistence of a symptom picture is one of the most reliable differentiating criteria. Periods of seclusiveness, despondency, and sexual or philosophical preoccupations do not last long or lead to a break with reality if the ego is an essentially healthy one which is undergoing one of the transient states of fragmentation normally associated with adolescence. If such behavior is prolonged, however, one must investigate the possibility of a schizophrenic reaction. Pervasiveness as well as the persistence of the symptom picture, and also its apparent inexplicability, are other diagnostic criteria which are mentioned by Herbert Weiner.[19] And one must also examine the history for previous disturbances of personality and relationship in the patient and his family.

How the adolescent handles his frustration aggression seems to me to be an equally important key to the differential diagnosis. If he demonstrates a strong tendency to attack his own ego rather than his object, this is an important indicator of his vulnerability to a schizophrenic reaction.

The first male adolescent schizophrenic I treated was a youth who used to go through a bizarre routine of singing, dancing, wisecracking, and showing off whenever he was in the presence of girls. Since he did not enjoy their company, this clowning helped him to keep his distance and to get some of the admiration which he craved. He could always admire himself, at least, even if he didn't impress the girls. Needless to say, they would try to avoid a repeat performance.

The differences between behavior such as this and behavior within the range of normality for adolescence are primarily quantitative. Adolescents traditionally go through stages when they are over-stimulated by the presence of the other sex, and act accordingly. A normal youth who was treated by a girl as the patient I have just discussed was treated might make some other attempts to get her to know him better and to like him, but, after a few weeks at most, he would write her off as "lousy" and find himself another girl. Occasionally, my patient would describe a girl who shunned him as "rotten," but it was always himself whom he treated as "rotten." He consistently attributed any failure in social relation-ships to some defect in himself, and the defect was his own feeling. He clung to the idea that if he just made a great effort to change his feeling, the girl would eventually come to like him. In other words, he had a strong tendency to attack the feeling rather than the external object causing it. When such attitudes last for many months, or even years, they are certainly to be regarded as deviant.

The great need for admiration and attention—for emotional gratification—drives the adolescent schizophrenic to extreme lengths in his attempts to make a favorable impression on those around him. Fully anticipating rejection, he tries to forestall it with demon-strations of his right to a place in the sun. Hence, boasting and bragging, verging on outright mendacity, are prominent aspects of the schizophrenic reaction in adolescence. To one adolescent I treated, talking about the inventions he was completing seemed to be a good way to attract attention. But inventing was no more than an idea of his; if this bid for admiration failed, he would seek satisfaction in fantasy and masturbation. In his attempts to gain popularity, the adolescent schizophrenic may unwittingly disclose more than he intended.[1] Sometimes, he shows an eagerness to share the benefits of his own inexperience with others. For example, a schizophrenic youth in basic training boasted to his squad mates that he and his girl friend "used to take a shower together every Friday night."

"And then what did you do?" Jimmy was asked by his expectant buddies.

He could only flatly reply, "Why we dried each other."

Adolescence itself does not precipitate schizophrenic reactions, in my opinion. What it does, rather, is to expose young people to special pressures—social pressures and those attendant upon rapid growth and personality changes—which typically lead to fleeting states of ego fragmentation. These accumulating states of episodic ego fragmentation may serve as the straw that breaks the camel's back; that is, they may suffice, in certain situations, to push a fragile and defectively functioning ego over the threshold into the schizophrenic reaction.

How hard or how easy it is for this to happen depends on how high or low the threshold is. I have the impression that each person has a highly specific threshold for the development of a schizophrenic reaction. This is determined by three interacting factors—heredity, constitution, and life experience. A person's upbringing, and especially what he learned to do in his childhood with his frustration aggression, is a crucial aspect of the life experience. If, in the absence of adequate emotional nourishment, he discharges his frustration aggression into his body, for example, he will develop some psychosomatic complaint. If he discharges frustration aggression into his superego, this will produce depression. It is when he does not discharge the frustration aggression, but tends to mobilize it and let it accumulate in an emotionally impoverished ego that the optimal condition exists for the development of a schizophrenic reaction. It is primarily the corrosive effects of frustration aggression mobilized in the stunted ego, rather than the lack of emotional gratification, which breaks down the ego—interrupts or reverses the growth process—and, if severe enough, produces the schizophrenic reaction. Securing the release of frustration aggression is, therefore, the crucial element in the treatment of the schizophrenic patient. This requires a favorable environment, and, of course, a certain degree of emotional nourishment, but I have found that the emotional gratification itself is a secondary factor in the treatment process.

The following case is presented in considerable detail because of the many diagnostic possibilities it presents.

CASE REPORT*

A 13-year-old white Jewish girl had four admissions to Kings County Hospital Psychiatric Service. Her first admission was at 6½ years of age and was occasioned by the implication of the father by the mother in the sexual seduction of the child. She was diagnosed as a child with "multiple symptoms consistent with the diagnosis of conduct disturbance with neurotic traits." Stealing,

* This case was prepared for presentation by Dr. Lewis Ward, under the supervision of Dr. Henry I. Schneer.

temper tantrums, and exhibitionism were manifest, as well as phobias, nightmares, and somatic complaints. The child's illness was considered to be reactive to the mother. Although therapy for the mother and child was recommended, there was little likelihood that the mother would change.

The second admission was at the age of 8 years. The mother alleged two sexual episodes: "The man next door took out his penis and took out dirty pictures." She also said that the child was molested at school. The child also was said to have put iodine in her urine, telling her mother it was bloody. The mother brought the child to the hospital "to get her away from sex."

She remained for 3 weeks, and part of her mental-status examination is as follows: "On coming to the interview, she stood back and appeared to be reticent before any rapport could be obtained. A period of time had to go by in which she played with a mechanical toy and was flattered for her proficiency. Her speech was clear and to the point, and her emotional responses were appropriate. Some depression appears to be present. Innate intelligence is at least average, and the child can read and do arithmetic. Later on in the interview, she told me she did not like me, and said that I reminded her of someone else, but she refused to elaborate. She guessed that I knew about the incident of an elderly neighbor exposing himself, and she feels that this is the reason why she is now in the hospital. She stated that this was a horrible experience and that she has had no interest in such things. She stated that her mother had told her that the devil comes into men at night and they do terrible things; that men are made to do bad things. She stated that if she went out into an alley a man would be likely to put something around her neck and strangle her. No thinking disturbance is elicited. The hallucinatorylike phenomena that were present 1½ years ago she now feels were her own imagination and occurred mostly at night. With help, she recalled these phenomena in which some womanlike creature supposedly was telling her that her mother was to leave her, and after she would hit at it, 'things would come out.' "

On the ward she was initially depressed, refused to eat for several days, and created conflict between her mother and the hospital with tales of unjust treatment. She engaged in provocative sexual play which she tried to deny and for which she tried to place responsibility on others. An attempt to suggest placement was refused by the parents who, though mutually loathsome to each other, agreed to remain together and took the child out against advice. At that time it was felt that her diagnosis included adjustment reaction of childhood, conduct disturbance, sexual behavior, neurotic traits, and anxiety reaction.

The third admission occurred at age 13 when a finding of neglect was made and the patient was remanded to the hospital. In the years since the last hospitalization, the patient was achieving at school, but the home situation steadily deteriorated. The mother was in group therapy at Kings County Hospital for 1½ years, and the patient was seen in group also for about 2 years. During this period the therapist felt that the patient was in need of residential treatment, and she began to press for it. Receiving no cooperation from the parents, she eventually instituted neglect proceedings against the parents in November, 1958.

The mother related incidents preceding this event which described the friction between mother and daughter. The mother said that she would tear up the patient's books if she was up late. The patient began to use vulgar language to the mother and father, who, the mother stated, was still attempting to sexualize his relationship with the patient. The patient inquired of her mother about her sex life. She refused to let her clothes touch her mother's in the closet. She "got too clean," and the mother "couldn't take it." At the same time the father was coming in at midnight, waking up the patient, and offering her pizza and ice cream. In October, 1958, during an argument, the patient was burned on the left arm by an iron which the mother says she was handing over saying, "If you want it, here it is."

A note on the patient's mental status was as follows: She related very poorly, alternately laughed and cried, and productions in general were coherent but irrelevant, rambling, and marked by loosened association. No hallucinatory experiences were elicited. Content was concerned with her feeling that she has first to experience suffering before she can experience pleasure. She became frightened that she would be examined by a man, because this would make her ashamed. She talked of her parents as being unfit, later changing this. She asked that I not interview her now because later she might be sorry for what she said today. She plans not to eat, and only to take medication by force so as to punish herself. When asked why, she responds that she has pride and that it was humiliating to be dragged in by ambulance. She pleads not to be sent to Ward G41 with girls her own age but at first cannot tell me why, then says that she really feels much superior to those other tramps and bums. She plans to be a psychiatrist because she has such great sympathy and understanding for other patients. Mood was apprehensive, tearful, and depressed as well as agitated. Affect was labile and not appropriate to expressed ideation.

Psychological tests supported a diagnosis of schizophrenia, and the patient was placed in the custody of her aunt to await placement. She was taken to her mother's house, against the express order of the court, for 2 weeks before going to the treatment center where the hunger strike and this history started.

Her fourth and present admission to Kings County Hospital was occasioned by a hunger strike which started immediately after she arrived at a residential treatment center to which she had been sent by the Children's Court. She was making an apparently good adjustment except for the refusal to eat. This was not complete, however, since she occasionally took liquids and sweets. She lost 8 pounds in 7 days, and early signs of dehydration were noted during physical examination. She refused to be examined by a male physician, refused to remove her skirt when examined by a female physician, and refused to submit a urine specimen. Concomitantly, according to the Center's psychiatric report, she developed "marked introspection and seemingly compulsive thinking with regard to her spirit." She constantly referred to the various transformations which the spirit goes through in leaving the body. She visualized various positions over one's body best suited for the spirit both entering and leaving the body. There was more than veiled intimation of the relatedness of suicide to the spirit leaving the body.

Some similar distortion of thought processes was also seen during the psychiatric interview when, knowing that if she did not eat and went to Kings County Hospital she would be forcibly fed, she said, "It is terrible to think that they will forcibly save my physical body but will leave my spirit die." For some minutes after making this statement, although she knew that she would have a psychiatrist seeing her at Kings County Hospital, she seemed markedly agitated and depressed. She also showed marked preoccupation with illness and with what cancer does in terms of the nature of the disease and the nature of the crippling symptoms.

Of her hunger strike at the treatment center, she said that she had taken this action in order "to get even with the court" because the court couldn't make her do what she didn't want to do.

But then she ambiguously added, "I can't begin to eat at the Center because I had another reason for going on a hunger strike but I forgot that reason. I don't think I'll ever remember the reason and so I won't ever be able to stop being on a hunger strike." At another time, she said that she wanted to be on the adult ward at Kings County Hospital because "you meet so many interesting and intelligent people."

On the ward at Kings County Hospital her predominant mood was an anxious depression. She spoke in superlatives of her stay at the treatment center and how she loved her social worker. She said that her urgency to be on the adult ward was to avoid being seen by a girl whom she knew at school. She denied hallucinations, and no delusional system was elicited. She made a vigorous denial that her starvation was suicidal.

The patient's family constellation consisted of her two parents and a half brother from her mother's previous marriage. The mother, 46 years old, has been recognized by several observers to be "aggressive, demanding, impulsive, provocative, functioning on a borderline level." The father, 61, appeared passive, withdrawn, and given to periodic outbursts of anger. The mother came from Russia at the age of 6. She failed several times in grade school. She said she was "cross-eyed and didn't have glasses." She blamed her mother for poverty, deceit, and promiscuity. Her older brother had a "nervous breakdown" at 57 and was given electric shock treatment. She had three marriages previous to her present one. She has accused her present husband of molesting her son as well as her daughter.

The mother supplied few facts relative to the patient's early life. She felt that the child was born out of sin because she did not marry the father until the child was 6 years old. Difficulty with feeding or toilet training was not recalled. The half brother, who was 14 years older, diapered the patient and even "baby sat" on his honeymoon.

DISCUSSION

In making the differential diagnosis of the 13-year-old girl who is the subject of our case report, I considered it necessary to investigate five diagnostic possibilities before reaching a decision. The four disorders which were suggested more or less strongly by various symptom pictures, but which were successively ruled out, were anorexia nervosa, reactive depression, reactive psychosis, and affective depression.

The hunger strike this girl started after the court ordered her placement in Pleasantville obviously suggested the presence of anorexia nervosa, a condition found almost exclusively in adolescent girls and young women. This condition begins most typically as an attempt to lose weight through dieting, and will have been preceded by demonstrations of hysterical tendencies and, perhaps, minor obsessional traits. A family history of mental illness or psychopathy is also associated with the condition, and its course will be marked by amenorrhea or other menstrual disturbance, which in some cases predate the most obvious signs of lack of appetite. Peculiar reactions to food and disturbances in bowel functioning are other signs mentioned by Sandor Lorand.[13] In a case of anorexia nervosa, reported by Lorand, the patient lost her appetite and taste for food—indeed, had a definite disgust for it. Other symptoms were dryness of the mouth, gagging at the sight of food, and periodic vomiting, all of which were aggravated if she forced herself to eat. Depression was also present.

Some of the information in our own case report would sustain a diagnosis of anorexia nervosa. Besides the refusal to eat, I am alluding to the family history of mental illness and such constitutional factors as the earlier demonstration of hysterical tendencies and minor obsessional traits. The girl may also have suffered from amenorrhea, though no mention of menstrual disturbance is made in the case report itself. What seemed to me to differentiate this case most strongly from anorexia nervosa, however, were the indications that the girl's refusal to eat was motivated by her consciously revengeful and self-punishing attitude rather than by any peculiar reactions to food or loss of appetite. Unconscious fantasies of self-punishment and revenge are not necessarily inconsistent with a diagnosis of anorexia nervosa, but these would not be so open and pervasive—not the important elements they are in this case. This seemed to me to be the most important differentiation.

There was, moreover, no conclusive evidence about an actual loss of appetite in connection with the hunger strike. The case report notes that the girl occasionally took liquids and sweets at the residential treatment center; her awareness that she would be forcibly fed on her return to the hospital if she went on with the hunger strike is also noted. Be that as it may, anorexia nervosa would not have accounted for the evidence of deep-seated personality disturbance, the thought disorder, and the pervasive nature of the oral regression, and it was quickly dismissed from the list of diagnostic possibilities.

There was also some superficial evidence that would permit one to entertain a diagnosis of reactive depression—that is, a neurotic reaction precipitated by the immediate trauma of separation from parents and home when this girl was sent to the residential center. Against such a finding, however, it was necessary to weigh the long history of disturbance before the court ordered her transfer to Pleasantville. In view of the longitudinal nature of the girl's disturbance, the environmental and family background, and the diagnostic picture at the time of her three preceding admissions to the hospital, depression over the situational change could hardly be regarded as the major factor of the illness. Somewhat more diffuse depressive episodes had been reported in the earlier history of the illness.

Rather than stressing a fixed depressive reaction to the separation from home and parents, the case material suggests somewhat ambivalent reactions to the stay at the Center and at the hospital. At the Center, the girl insisted that she wanted to go back to the hospital; back at the hospital, she is reported to have spoken "in superlatives about her recent stay at Pleasantville." From this point of view, in addition to the fact that a reactive depression would not have accounted for the intensity of the thought disorder, her condition was differentiated from reactive depression.

Another possibility to be considered was that this girl was suffering from a reactive psychosis of adolescence. Warren and Cameron[18] have described 6 such cases, involving youngsters from the ages of 11 to 16; they had transient episodes of psychosis which proved very difficult to diagnose. All were model children who yearned for parental approval and were fearful of criticism. In each case the psychotic episodes had an acute onset and were followed by much anxiety, insomnia, and pervasive night fears or concern about the parents' welfare. In this condition, from which the patients just referred to eventually recovered, the early history of development and maturation as well as the adjustment to the home were favorable, and the thought disorder was relatively insignificant. Reactive psychosis would not begin to explain the multiple and sustained symptoms in this case, let alone the developmental history, the progressive nature of this girl's disorder, and the disturbances in her thinking and affect, so that it was not seriously entertained as a diagnostic possibility.

Affective psychosis is a label which is sometimes attached to patients whose refusal of food cannot be fully accounted for by inertia of their digestive and metabolic systems and seems, rather, to be just one aspect of a more generalized depression. Patients suffering from a depression of this nature may give evidence of strong convictions about their own unworthiness and may express suicidal wishes. In a case of affective psychosis, however, one does not see obvious reactions to what is going on around the patient, as were observed in this girl; her overreactiveness to the environment and extremely labile affect would argue against a finding of affective psychosis. For this and other reasons, her disturbance has to be differentiated from affective psychosis.

There were present, on the other hand, many factors which would justify a diagnosis of schizophrenia and certainly no presenting symptoms which would preclude such a label. Let us consider, for example, the most obvious presenting symptom—the hunger strike. Early in the century, Bleuler[6] pointed out that "in no other disease does complete refusal of food occur so frequently and so persistently as in schizophrenia." Anyone who has observed schizophrenics in the hospital wards knows how difficult it is to get some of them to eat. The necessity of tube feeding some of these patients, especially if they are in a catatonic condition, is recognized.

I have already called attention to an equally persuasive sign— the tendency of the emotionally malnourished ego, overwhelmed by the weight of undischarged frustration aggression, to punish itself instead of the object. This kind of self-punishing attitude, the essence of the schizophrenic reaction, is strongly manifested by our patient. Her statement that she can't remember why she went on the hunger strike, so she has to stay on it, is typical schizophrenic thinking.

Her family history, her own developmental history, and the many traumatic events in her life which are detailed in the case report are familiar precipitants of such an illness. We find prominently represented the three elements which Weiner[19] found to be precipitating factors in many cases of schizophrenia: domestic discord, the frustration or deprivation of emotional needs, and emotional alienation or separation from others.

Is this case of schizophrenic reaction new in onset, or has it existed since childhood? This question, because of its significance for the prognosis and the form of treatment required, ought always to be answered when one diagnoses schizophrenia in an adolescent or preadolescent. The longer the history of this, the longer the treatment required.

In my opinion, this girl's schizophrenic tendency has been developing since childhood and was accentuated by normal pubertal changes and the traumatic environmental factors reported in the case. The three which seem most significant to me are the apparent sexual seduction by the father, the quarrels with her mother, and the group therapist's intervention which the girl probably experienced as an act of rejection, since it led to her forcible removal from her home and her therapy group. I want to make it clear that this assessment of the therapist's move is based entirely on the case report, and might not be borne out by direct and more detailed information. Hence, it is mentioned tentatively, in the absence of more complete, and possibly contradictory, information. In any event, there were the two other precipitating circumstances involving the parents. The seductive behavior of the father and the quarrels with the mother were also experienced by the patient in her childhood; but the cumulative effect of these relationships and the girl's greater vulnerability in the period of pubertal change could explain the frank outbreak of the disease at this time.

The case report strongly suggests that this girl's parents are both potentially schizophrenic individuals, and reference is made to the mental breakdown of an uncle at the age of 57. But, whether or not there is any hereditary disposition for the disease in the family, the patient's developmental history supports the hypothesis that there was an experiential transmission of the disease. One is tempted to speculate whether she was already a schizophrenic at the ages of 6½ and 8, on her first two admissions to the hospital.

In that connection, it will be noted that she was then diagnosed as having a conduct disturbance with neurotic traits. Various forms of overt aggressive behavior, which probably protected her against a schizophrenic reaction, are mentioned in the first diagnostic report. The diagnosis made on her second admission refers to "anxiety reaction," to reticent behavior, evidence of depression, and to the difficulty of establishing rapport with the child. When she was 8, she spoke about devils taking possession of men's bodies at night and making them do terrible things, an idea of splitting implanted by her mother. There is no information about how the girl was handling her frustration aggression during this period, but, from the first two diagnostic reports, her condition certainly appeared to be one of neurosis.

On the third admission, however, a tendency to bottle up her frustration aggression was evident. Now, on the fourth admission, following her return from Pleasantville, she is well bottled up, and the growth process appears to have been interrupted by the undischarged aggression. Now she gives evidence of oral regression and of typical schizophrenic thinking and attitudes.

One sign that this girl may not be irreversibly ill is that she does well at school. Given the kind of treatment that is needed to get her growth process under way again, the prognosis would, in my opinion, be favorable. The vital factors in her treatment would be small doses of emotional nourishment and the development of outlets for the release of frustration aggression. What made her schizophrenic was not emotional hunger but the psychological consequences of that hunger, which allowed the frustration aggression to be mobilized and, thus, to damage the ego.

The presence of such aggression, and in some cases an unconscious fear of it, gives some therapists the feeling that they cannot get into contact with a schizophrenic patient. In my experience, however, the patterning of adequate outlets for the release of aggression in feelings and language, combined with an ego-strengthening process of emotional nourishment, will generally lead to the resolution of the schizophrenic reaction.[17] Then the sole vestige of the illness is the scarring caused by the healing of the defective ego.

The prognosis in a case does have some significance for diagnosis. The fact that the diagnostician has sound reason to anticipate that a patient will deteriorate without therapeutic intervention does tend to confirm a diagnosis of schizophrenia. I would vigorously challenge the notion, however, that such a diagnosis is disproved if the patient responds favorably to treatment, or that it is confirmed if he fails to respond. Failure to respond merely indicates either that the therapy itself was inadequate or that the environmental situation was so unfavorable that it prevented or seriously interfered with therapeutic progress. My impression is that the schizophrenic reaction can be resolved if the patient secures the kind of object he needs, a setting conducive to emotional reactiveness, and the right kind of retraining and life experiences.

SUMMARY

The concept of schizophrenia is traced as it is historically understood, and also the newer concepts of schizophrenia in childhood as they have recently been recognized. Adolescent schizophrenia, as it appears clinically, is some combination of the less familiar child-hood schizophrenic reaction with the more familiar adult schizo-phrenic reaction.

Finally, in differentiating normal adolescence from the schizo-phrenic reaction, it is pointed out that schizophreniclike adolescent states are transitory, continuing at most for a few hours or days. If such states persist over a period of weeks or months, there is justification for the impression that one is dealing, not with an adolescent state, but with an adolescent schizophrenic reaction which may go on to develop the clinical picture of a psychotic state.

REFERENCES

1. ARTISS, K. L. (ed.) *The Symptom as Communication in Schizophrenia.* New York, Grune & Stratton, Inc., 1959, p. 108.
2. BALSER, B. H. (ed.) *Psychotherapy of the Adolescent.* New York, International Universities Press, Inc., 1957.
3. BELLAK, L. (ed.) *Schizophrenia: A Review of the Syndrome.* New York, Logos Press, 1958, pp. 556–557.
4. BENDER, L. Schizophrenia in childhood; its recognition, description and treatment. *Am. J. Orthopsychiat. 26:* 499, 1956.
5. BERGMAN, P., and ESCALONA, S. "Unusual Sensitivities in Very Young Children," in *The Psychoanalytic Study of the Child.* New York, International Universities Press, Inc., 1949, vols. 3–4.
6. BLEULER, E. *Dementia Praecox or the Group of Schizophrenias.* New York, International Universities Press, Inc., 1950, p. 162.
7. EISENBERG, L., and KANNER, L. Early infantile autism, 1943–1955. *Am. J. Orthopsychiat. 26:* 556, 1956.
8. EKSTEIN, R., and WALLERSTEIN, J. "Observations on the Psychology of Borderline and Psychotic Children," in *The Psychoanalytic Study of the Child.* New York, International Universities Press, Inc., 1954, vol. 9.
9. ERIKSON, E. H. *Childhood and Society.* New York, W. W. Norton & Company, Inc., 1950.
10. FREUD, A. "Adolescence," in *The Psychoanalytic Study of the Child.* New York, International Universities Press, Inc., 1958, vol. 13, p. 275.
11. FREUD, S. *Collected Papers.* London, Hogarth Press, Ltd., 1940, vol. 1, p. 277.
12. HARTMANN, H. "Contribution to the Metapsychology of Schizophrenia," in *The Psychoanalytic Study of the Child.* New York, International Universities Press, Inc., 1953, vol. 8.
13. LORAND, S. *Technique of Psychoanalytic Therapy.* New York, International Universities Press, Inc., 1946, p. 158.
14. MAHLER, M. S., and GOSLINER, B. J. "On Symbiotic Child Psychosis: Genetic, Dynamic and Restitutive Aspects," in *The Psychoanalytic Study of the Child.* New York, International Universities Press, Inc., 1955, vol. 10.

15. MAHLER, M. S., Ross, J. R., JR., and DeFRIES, Z. Clinical studies in benign and malignant cases of childhood psychosis (schizophreniclike). *Am. J. Orthopsychiat. 19:* 295, 1949.

16. SILVERBERG, W. V. The schizoid maneuver. *Psychiatry 10:* 383, 1947.

17. SPOTNITZ, H., NAGELBERG, L., and FELDMAN, Y. Ego reinforcement in the schizophrenic child. *Am. J. Orthopsychiat. 26:* 146, 1956.

18. WARREN, W., and CAMERON, K. Reactive psychosis in adolescence. *J. Ment. Sc. 96:* 447, 1950.

19. WEINER, H. "Diagnosis and Symptomatology," in *Schizophrenia: A Review of the Syndrome,* ed. by Bellak, L. New York, Logos Press, 1958, pp. 107–173.

chapter 12   Treatment of Adolescents

SANDOR LORAND

In *Three Essays on the Theory of Sexuality* Freud[9] described, as the most significant and most painful psychic achievement of the adolescent, his detachment from parental authority. Indeed, in our observation of the adolescent, whether normal or maladjusted, we see a continual struggle with this problem. The strong conscious drives for independence, and at the same time the unconscious need to maintain dependence on the parents, result in various degrees of confusion, exaggerated by the fact that the adolescent is at this time going through biological as well as psychological changes. The continuous, strong tensions which the adolescent experiences during bodily changes and this phase of emotional development bring many new hardships in adjustment, particularly in the sexual sphere. All of these problems set difficulties in the way of ego growth and expansion, which starts to take place on a larger scale, in adolescence, and which may therefore be seriously affected.

In 1922 Ernest Jones,[14] in an important paper, drew attention to the manifold problems which confront the adolescent, but, with the exception of Bernfeld[2] and Aichhorn,[1] neither psychoanalysts nor psychiatrists followed up these early studies to contribute further material until about a decade ago. At that time a number of essays began to appear containing clinical reports on the therapy of the adolescent, as well as theoretical conclusions. Until then, however, examination and clarification of the depth psychology of adolescent behavior had been neglected.

The chapters in this volume deal with these topics and are intended to help clarify the dynamic and theoretical formulations of adolescent problems as well as to illustrate the concepts with clinical case studies. They give valuable insights into the many complex problems of the adolescent.

Before entering into a discussion of the various therapeutic approaches used with the adolescent, let me summarize again the problems with which we have to deal in treating the adolescent. Many of the problems described are present in normal adolescent development as well as in the troubled and neurotic. What makes the difference is the degree of emotional tension, which results in overt behavior deviating from what we look upon as normal. In addition to psychological difficulties, the adolescent also has the important problem of body consciousness, which is by no means a less important source of disturbance. Some boys and girls feel awkward in their growth; they feel unattractive; they try to hide or are ashamed of their developing physiques, the signs of maturation. Their attitude and the behavior they exhibit show clearly the conflict between being partly children who are having difficulties growing up, and partly young adults trying to be independent and to imitate father, mother, or older siblings.

The problem of the adolescent is intimately connected with problems of ego functioning. The expanding young ego is pressured from many different sides. The adolescent is not ready to adapt to the overwhelming pressures and demands of reality adjustment. Confused by demands of reality for adaptation, they become impatient and impulsive; they attempt to regress and run away, frightened of the problems and of the consequences which taking the responsibility for growing up involves. Their confusion and anxiety caused by these tensions lead to various defenses. When attempts at grasping the situation and satisfying reality demands meet with failure, various defenses are developed against progress and growth.

Corrective attempts on the part of parents or authority figures in school will fail because the young adolescent has no insight into his difficulties and no comprehension of what causes his impulsive behavior; he cannot cope with his moody, passive attitude at one time and with his impulsiveness and his acting-out behavior at other times. He is confused about his schoolwork, which he frequently cannot master. He is self-centered, shy, and absorbed in his daydreams; he is easily hurt and feels as if he does not belong, as if he were an outsider.

THERAPEUTIC APPROACHES

The therapeutic approach is always a difficult one in the early phases of adolescence because of the adolescents' lack of insight into their problems, and the difficulty in communicating with them and making clear what it is that disturbs them. They feel troubled by fear and guilt, which they resent discussing; this is true also of their sexual problems and their preoccupation with masturbation fantasies. If they are willing to come for therapy, they are characteristically impatient, demanding quick results. They are intolerant and refuse to cooperate in the therapeutic setting, all of which makes it appear, at times, that the adolescent cannot be treated at all. Difficulties in this initial contact with the adolescent may discourage the therapist from trying to improve the relationship or creating a therapeutic atmosphere.

In the various essays written about adolescent problems and therapy, there are many contradictory suggestions as to the types of approaches appropriate to the treatment of adolescents. Adolescence is a phase of development which extends from about the age of 12 up to and including 18; therefore, when talking about adolescent development, it is important to think of it as consisting of many age levels. Hence, when talking about the therapy of adolescents, we must keep in mind the fact that different therapeutic approaches will be called for at the different stages of development. Therapy must be adjusted to the age level of the patient. Papers written on the subject of therapy in general and of psychoanalytic therapy with adolescents, by Anna Freud,[5] Leo Speigel,[18] Maxwell Gitelson,[11] and others, all emphasize the difficulties involved in using the various kinds of therapy. In a detailed paper, Elizabeth R. Geleerd[10] discusses the various stages of development and the type of psychoanalytic therapy useful at each stage.

Therapy must try to create a dependency relationship on the part of the adolescent patient to the therapist. In creating this relationship, an atmosphere is provided in which the patient *can* be more dependent, more trusting, and more reliant on his therapist than he can be in his outside environment where he feels criticized, misunderstood, and unsupported. This may open the way for the young patient to start communicating more easily. What can also be done at the beginning is to enlarge upon and to explain in understandable language what his problems with his environment and with his reality situation may be.

The therapist cannot expect that his young patient will often acquire even partial insight at the beginning of treatment. The gaining of insight usually comes later, as therapy progresses. The patient then can understand more about himself and will be ready to verbalize and communicate more readily. Transference will develop, and manipulations of the transference relationship will be possible. Creating a positive transference is difficult, and the therapist will have to be versatile if he is to make the patient trusting and to an extent dependent, which also includes the beginning of identification with the therapist. To control the acting-out, impulsive behavior, the therapist will have to exercise a great deal of tolerance; he must have skill and elasticity in addition to empathy and sympathy with the patient's difficulties. At the same time, the therapist will have to be objective, avoid taking over the patient's parents' attitude, and, instead, be a different type of parent substitute—understanding, but also firm when needed. Success in establishing a therapeutic relationship with the patient depends to a large extent on the therapist's personality, ease, self-assurance, and patience, and especially on flexibility in using all types of psychotherapy.

Psychoanalysts hold widely divergent opinions about the possibility of a more or less classical analysis of adolescents. It is generally agreed, by those who are treating adolescents psychoanalytically, that analysis cannot be carried out along strictly classical lines and that one should not attempt to conduct it that way. Variations in the technical approach and modifications must be employed in order to achieve therapeutic success. Moreover, analytic treatment of any sort in some cases is impossible. In the later phases of adolescence, when a boy or girl already has some insight into his or her difficulties and wants to be helped, psychoanalysis can be applied, but even then with modifications. Some psychoanalysts advocate analytical therapy in specific phases of the therapeutic process. But the distrustful, rebellious attitude, the noncooperation of the adolescent who is usually brought to therapy, makes the degree of success of the therapy uncertain.

Therapeutic goals in treatment of adolescents are not very clearly defined in present-day literature. It appears that the center of the therapeutic goal is ego expansion, thus strengthening the ego to cope with the various ramifications of and vicissitudes in the adolescent's adjustment. The continual pressure of new kinds of experiences arising out of the adolescent's changing relationship to the external world, his aggressive strivings, ambitions, and his sexual experiences and feelings—all have to be directed into a unifying channel in order to provide the basis for permanent character structure in later adulthood. In trying to enable the adolescent to control his behavior, one has to make him realize what his actions mean, and the reasons for his acting as he does. Under the guidance of the therapist, the adolescent has to acquire a stronger ego in order to master his current problems and to control his strong tendencies toward acting out, which are connected with tendencies to regress to an earlier phase of development when he was not expected to behave in the controlled manner now required of him.

Therapy is frequently adjusted to the patient's needs. The various therapies may all have their value and bring practical results if used with caution, and if the therapist knows well what his aim is —namely to make the patient able to bear anxiety and discomfort, which will then open the way to improved emotional stability. The therapist has to keep in mind that, however difficult it is for the adolescent to express himself, however rebellious he may be in expressing himself, however difficult it is for him to be able to see his problems in the proper light, his main difficulty psychologically is that he is really helpless and wants to be dependent, while at the same time trying to prove himself independent. His rebellious and acting-out behavior may by itself indicate his inner feelings of the need to be helped, to depend, and to be advised. That these feelings should be present is quite natural, for adolescence is, to a great extent, a revival of earlier phases of emotional experience transposed, which interfere with the adolescent's attempts to adjust to new experiences.

The therapist has an important role in the strengthening of the adolescent weak ego by giving him a better ego ideal with which to identify. One type of approach will work with one patient or with one therapist, and another type of technique will work with another patient and another therapist. This is why, at times, we see cases where better results are obtained after a patient changes therapists.

Should adolescents be analyzed at all? Some authors speak about a first, second, and final phase of adolescence and suggest that in only one or another of these phases is analysis possible. We can say definitely that certain types of adolescents can be treated with psychoanalytic therapy, but that this therapy will never be the so-called orthodox analysis. As a number of authors have pointed out, various psychotherapeutic approaches may have to be used; much re-education and a more positive, directive attitude will be involved at certain stages than is possible in classical analysis. The therapeutic approach selected will depend, to a great extent, on the maturity or weakness of the patient's ego, especially from the standpoint of ego control. Treatment of adolescents really begins when the young patient has some insight into his problems, when he feels he has difficulties and wants to be helped.

To illustrate some of the theoretical formulations, clinical problems, and therapeutic approaches to the general problems of adolescence, I am presenting two cases of "delayed" adolescence which I had the opportunity of analyzing for a number of years. In both cases the early adolescent problems, in all their intensity, were re-enacted by the patient, revealing the struggle which these young people had to go through not only in the various phases of adolescence but from infancy up to adolescence. In the course of therapy there was opportunity to investigate and understand the earlier phases of development which were instrumented in creating the neurosis and which resulted in the patients seeking treatment.

In the transference relationship they re-experienced all the emotional upheavals to which their home environment and early schooling exposed them. Especially important were their dreams. Nearly all dealt with home, parents, siblings, early schooling, abandonment, anxieties, and sadomasochistic sexual tendencies. The dreams were of great assistance in reconstructing the forgotten earlier phases of childhood and thus helped to recall the repressed past where the pathology originated. The analysis of these patients differed a great deal from the analysis of adults. There was constant acting out and impulsive behavior which not only had to be interpreted but, at times, actively blocked. Thus modifications of classical analytic techniques had to be used at times.

CASE REPORTS

A young man of 18, who had just left college in the middle of the term because of inability to concentrate, came with great reluctance for a consultation because he had been told by psychiatrists that he was urgently in need of therapy. He resented the diagnosis; it made him feel pushed into therapy. Nevertheless he came, and his initial symptom was to talk not about his school difficulties but about how well he was getting along with his professors and his classmates and how much they liked him. He conceded, however, that he was backward in his studies, that he could not concentrate, and hence would not get along at college.

His friends had originally all been in the city where he lived, and it would have been possible to go to college there. He felt that he had been forced by his parents to go out of town to college. He admitted that, at times, his behavior at home was not the best, but he insisted that it wasn't so bad as to deserve being sent away from home. One of the reasons his parents wanted him to go away from home was that they hoped he would go for treatment. He had refused to go for therapy in his home town. When home, he was constantly arguing with his father and trying to correct his father's attitude toward him in all kinds of matters—the amount of his allowance, whether or not his father should buy him a car, etc. (He was a sports-car enthusiast and talked for hours about cars and drivers.)

The young man also had a bad relationship with his mother. At times, days would pass without his speaking to her. Later in therapy it was revealed that this behavior was a defense against expression of his sexual fantasies about his mother, with which he was still struggling at the age of 17, just before he left for college. Talking to his mother would have meant contact, and from that would have sprung a desire to establish a closer contact. Therefore he avoided his mother as much as he could. Even when sitting at the table with her, he did not speak to her or greet her.

Very soon in the analytical therapy, it turned out that he was really not in great favor with his friends. He talked well and could make people interested in him, since he was clever and well informed, but he was incapable himself of really liking anybody. On the surface he seemed well adjusted to people, but there was no real warmth in his relationships with his friends or parents. This maladjustment showed itself particularly in his sexual life.

Two important problems presented themselves quite early in analysis; they were the problems which had actually motivated him to come for treatment. One was his sexual problem; he was a chronic masturbator, with masochistic fantasies which amused him to the point of laughing about them. Another important symptom was his "wanderlust" which drove him to compulsive walking for long hours at night.

In his fantasies he was preoccupied with homosexuality but, although attracted to boys, he never had homosexual experiences. He went out with girls and, on many occasions, was on the verge of having a sexual relationship at the girl's instigation, but he always managed to avoid it. Attracted to boyish girls, he was very defensive against becoming strongly interested in any of them.

Parallel to his masochism, was the counterpart: a strongly sadistic attitude toward girls, with his masochistic behavior serving as a defense against his sadistic tendencies. He fought people off by not becoming concerned, or looking through them as if they weren't there, giving them the "silent treatment," as he frequently did with the analyst. He was afraid of getting into fights with men or with friends of his, but he enjoyed the company of girls. The achievement of making them fall in love with him, and then abandoning them, was a source of gratification.

He fought his parents in a calm, composed way, insisting that his will be carried out, contradicting them, and attempting to prove them wrong at every step. He forced them to keep him at home by accepting psychiatric treatment. At the same time, he refused to go to college here, because he had left college in the middle of the term and was waiting until the next term started. He insisted that he wanted a job and that, in order to go to work, he needed a car, which he demanded that his parents give him. He spent his days sleeping late. He did nothing around the house except telephone friends and make dates; evenings he spent out.

In analysis he complained a great deal about the situation with his parents, and cited memories from childhood and early adolescence, when his father and mother were often away. This was especially true in early childhood. At that time he had a continually changing succession of nursemaids, some of whom punished him severely. Thus, his contrary, defiant attitude toward his parents developed early.

He related many dreams, all of which dealt with childhood memories and experiences. Among them were frankly incestuous dreams referring to his mother and his desire to be nursed and to be taken care of by her. He consciously denied, however, all need to depend on anyone or be taken care of. All thoughts of becoming attached or involved emotionally with a girl, or, for that matter, of forming close friendships or confidential relationships with any of his male friends, he avoided. His external, adultlike behavior was purely imitation and acting. His dreams showed confusion between heterosexual and homosexual drives. The following short dream will illustrate the nature of his conflict and confusions concerning sexual involvement, or any deep emotional involvement with either young men or young women: "I had two visitors, a husband and wife, and the husband grabs one of my legs, pulls it out, and runs away with it, and I have quite a time running after him on crutches to get my leg back. I screw the leg back on and then the woman grabs my leg and runs away with it, and I again have to make difficult efforts to retrieve my leg. Then I wake up."

His associations to and discussions of the dream are too lengthy to reproduce here. They expressed his fear of forming deep attachments to either men or women because he might be damaged (castrated) or they might take advantage of him. On an earlier level the dream naturally referred to his father and mother competing as to who would be able to alter his behavior, and his distrust of them and fear of becoming attached to either one because of the fear of a repetition of the disappointments of childhood, when he felt abandoned by them. The dream illustrates the concept of the adolescent as being at a crossroad and not knowing what direction to take; whether to go ahead and take an adult attitude, adjusting to adult life in all respects (adult object relationships and independence of parents), or whether to remain a youngster, an adolescent, so that the threats and responsibilities of adult life and the dangers of frustration and sexual involvements can be avoided.

In another case, a girl of 19 felt ready for treatment because it involved getting away from her home city and her environment. From the age of 9 she had been under the care of physicians and psychiatrists because she was always in trouble. Her home situation had become unbearable because of antagonistic relationships with parents and siblings. The oldest of a large family, she had felt rejected from an early age, with added emphasis each time a new sibling arrived. Her behavior toward her parents and governesses, and later at school, was antagonistic, defiant, and spiteful in every respect. With regard to eating, she did the opposite of whatever she felt was expected of her. In elementary school, when urged to be temperate, she became very fat from overeating. When away at boarding school, she threw the food down the toilet and became emaciated. She had to spend a great deal of time in the infirmary and could not attend classes. Eventually, she had to be taken home, which was her conscious aim. She suffered from a mild form of anorexia nervosa which, with occasional remissions, was still present to a mild degree during her analysis. In her early adolescence, 12 to 14, she was a tomboy, excelling the boys in diving, swimming, and other sports. Socially, at this period, she did not get along well with either boys or girls. She had few friends and was rather aggressive toward everyone. Her pleasure was to make fun of others and to torture them. When the other girls began to date, she was not asked. At this time she began to be troubled by feelings of inferiority, especially with regard to her body. She felt she was too strong and muscular, too much like a boy and not like a girl.

The patient had trouble establishing a menstrual cycle. Her menstruation started late, and for months at a time she did not menstruate at all, which made her feel that there was definitely something wrong with her. She developed all kinds of fears concerning feminine functioning. When she menstruated, she feared that she might bleed to death. If she did not menstruate, she felt she was abnormal. Her ideas about sex were very much distorted and were connected with notions of illness. Pregnancy, she thought, was dangerous and might kill the woman. She thought that by kissing anyone, including her parents, she would get germs in her mouth, so she had to keep away from affectionate embraces or contacts with everyone. She was angry at boys and men, and was aggressive toward them, being consciously envious of their masculinity and the greater liberties they enjoyed. These attitudes, forms of behavior, and thoughts (they were not mere fantasies) she retained even to the time she came to analysis, where she expressed her wish to be a man.

These deep disturbances, including states of panic and sleepwalking, started in childhood. At the period of adolescence when she had to sleep with other girls in one room at the boarding school, there were times when she could not fall asleep for at least half the night. The slightest noise in the room disturbed her sleep. A fear that there would be some noise, or anticipation that some of the girls might make noises, made her furious. Then the fury and the aggression kept her awake. At times she had fantasies that she would die in her sleep or that she might kill somebody while sleepwalking. These were the main reasons for her insomnia and fear of falling asleep.

When this young girl came to analysis at 19 she was considered by some of the members of her family to be promiscuous, and unable to discriminate between the young men with whom she was going out. Actually, she had so great a fear of sex and so much disgust, that promiscuity was impossible. She made it appear so, however, in order to be criticized and talked about. Despite her parents' and friends' opinions, she formed a friendship with a male

Negro college student. She wanted to challenge people, that is, to challenge the members of her family, in particular her mother and father.

Therapy in this case was very arduous. In the beginning there was much reluctance to relate her thoughts and feelings. She acted out in the analytical hour, being spiteful, defiant, and abusive. In the later phase this changed to greater compliance, but then, failing to get all the reassurance and protection which she expected, particularly at those times when her parents visited and interfered with her life, she again acted out continuously in the analytical hour. The hour was divided; the first half was spent in screaming, crying, and temper tantrums, and the other half in the analyst's relating that behavior to the behavior of early childhood and adolescence. Gradually, a very strong positive transference developed, making the analyst a father and mother ideal who was better and kinder to her, who would magically help her to adjust, and who cared for her more than her parents and siblings did. Naturally, this strong positive attachment and dependence carried with it the consequence that she was very easily hurt, and felt rejected because the analyst did not take her in as one of his family or even give her positive, definite instructions as to what to do in certain situations. On such occasions she felt a strong desire to torture the analyst, to shoot him, to kill him, all of which corresponded to her early desires and to her attempts at torturing her playmates, siblings, pets, animals of all sorts, etc. Only gradually did she begin to grow up in analysis, and to take a more adult, feminine attitude. While she still did not easily identify with the mother figure, she began at last to make a number of good friends of girls her own age.

The important problem in the therapy of this patient was for the therapist to gauge the patient's acting out and regression to childish ways of behaving in the analytical situation, and to know when to step in to curtail it.

DISCUSSION

The problems of the patients cited here are characteristic of all adolescents in varying degrees. The degree of acting out, which is a form of aggressive behavior, is of primary importance in determining therapeutic handling in analysis and in psychotherapy, because it indicates the strength of the influence of earlier conflicts on the adolescent. When the ego does not have the strength to meet the demands of reality, the tendency is to regress to a less disturbing period when the superego was not so harsh, or the young child could avoid the harshness by various forms of behavior which a child naturally does use at certain periods in his development.

Naturally, not all late adolescent cases are as amenable to analysis as the two cited above. Sometimes, even at this age, one starts analysis, and then the therapy must change to a different type. At times, the most that can be accomplished is to reconstruct, from the actual types of behavior, earlier forms of behavior, and induce the patient to give up and change this early behavior pattern.

References

1. AICHHORN, A. *Wayward Youth*. New York, The Viking Press, Inc., 1935.
2. BERNFELD, S. Types of adolescence. *Psychoanalyt. Quart. 7:* 243, 1938.
3. EISSLER, K. R. "Notes on The Problems of Technique in the Psychoanalytic Treatment of Adolescents," in *The Psychoanalytic Study of the Child*. New York, International Universities Press, Inc., 1957, vol. 13.
4. FRAIBERG, S. "Some Considerations in the Introduction to Therapy in Puberty," in *The Psychoanalytic Study of the Child*. New York, International Universities Press, Inc., 1955, vol. 10.
5. FREUD, A. *Psychoanalytic Treatment of Children*. London, Imago Publishing Company, 1927.
6. FREUD, A. *The Ego and the Mechanisms of Defense*. New York, International Universities Press, Inc., 1946.
7. FREUD, A. "Observations on Child Development," in *The Psychoanalytic Study of the Child*. New York, International Universities Press, Inc., 1951, vol. 6.
8. FREUD, A. "Adolescence," in *The Psychoanalytic Study of the Child*. New York, International Universities Press, Inc., 1957, vol. 13.
9. FREUD, S. *"Three Essays on the Theory of Sexuality,"* in *Standard Edition*. London, Hogarth Press, Ltd., 1953, vol. 7.
10. GELEERD, E. R. "Some Aspects of Psychoanalytic Technique in Adolescence," in *The Psychoanalytic Study of the Child*. New York, International Universities Press, Inc., 1957, vol. 13.
11. GITELSON, M. Character synthesis: the psychotherapeutic problems in adolescence. *Am. J. Orthopsychiat. 18:* 3, 1948.
12. GREENACRE, P. The Prepuberty Trauma in Girls. *Psychoanalyt. Quart. 19:* 3, 1950; and *The Yearbook of Psychoanalysis*. New York, International Universities Press, Inc., 1951.
13. HOFFER, W. "Diaries of Adolescent Schizophrenics," in *The Psychoanalytic Study of the Child*. New York, International Universities Press, Inc., 1946, vol. 2.
14. JONES, E. "Some problems of adolescence," in *Papers on Psycho-Analysis*. Baltimore, The Williams & Wilkins Co., 1948.

15. LORAND, S. Anorexia nervosa. *Psychosom. Med.* 5: 282, 1943.

16. LORAND, S. "The Psychoanalytic Contribution to the Treatment of Behavior Problems in Children," in *Clinical Studies in Psychoanalysis*. New York, International Universities Press, Inc., 1950.

17. SPIEGEL, L. A. "A Review of Contributions to a Psychoanalytic Theory of Adolescence," in *The Psychoanalytic Study of the Child*. New York, International Universities Press, Inc., 1951, vol. 6.

18. SPIEGEL, L. A. "Comments on the Psychoanalytic Psychology of Adolescence," in *The Psychoanalytic Study of the Child*. New York, International Universities Press, Inc., 1957, vol. 13.

chapter 13

Therapy of Learning Problems

RHODA L. LORAND

Psychoanalysts have given much attention to learning problems. Detailed discussions of theoretical formulations and of the various aspects of the problems are to be found in the articles by Blanchard,[3] Klein,[11] Pearson,[13] and Rosen.[14] These also contain extensive bibliographies.

Many problems arise for the first time in adolescence, when a struggle for mastery of the greatly strengthened instincts characteristic of this period of development results, in some cases, in inability to concentrate on schoolwork.

Masturbation conflicts can seriously interfere with ability to study. Children feel threatened by the unconscious sexual connotation of this solitary activity requiring manipulation and mastery of material, the successful accomplishment of which will make them more adult. Some adolescents become sexually aroused when they approach their work; others find themselves besieged by sexual fantasies when they attempt to concentrate on the printed page. Still others are so deeply concerned about their social relationships, appearance, popularity, etc., that very little energy remains for schoolwork, which, by comparison, is not meaningful but rather is an artificial task imposed upon them.

There are many bright children who have managed quite well in the primary grades where minimal effort produced adequate or above-average grades, but find in junior high or high school that the more difficult work requiring sustained effort is beyond them, and they begin to do poorly for the first time. Some, who are of the type whose narcissism has been fed throughout childhood by the realization that they are so bright they do not need to work, experience a great blow when this is no longer true and they must take a less exalted place amongst their peers who work in order to achieve.

Still other bright children have been brought up in mistakenly overpermissive environments in which they have never had to postpone or work for gratifications. They, too, have managed well in the lower grades, but suddenly, in the adolescent years, find that they must endure the tension of working *toward* mastery of knowledge and concepts, involving the ability to tolerate tension and frustration without becoming impatient, discouraged, or anxious. Not infrequently, these children give up and turn their attention to activities in which they can secure immediate gratification, pretending contempt for their fellow students who conscientiously keep up with the school requirements.

Other narcissistic children withdraw from competition because they cannot bear to have their performance compare unfavorably with someone else's. These are usually individuals who have suffered a narcissistic injury during the oedipal period, and the sense of hopeless inferiority which was aroused in them at that time is revived by any competitive situation such as exists in traditional schools. These children can learn without difficulty when tutored privately.[4]

Similarly, it is not infrequently found that a younger sibling of a successful older student in the school feels unable to compete with the older child who has always been the successful one in the family, and does poorly until the older one graduates, making a sudden spurt upward afterward. Teachers and parents are often at a loss to understand the dynamics of this change.

Some adolescent learning problems are the result of long-standing reading difficulties which have always slowed the child's progress but which become markedly apparent in the upper grades, when so much of the work depends on good reading ability, and when time becomes an important factor because of the amount of work involved. For example, the adolescent patient who has a reading inhibition may plod through assignments correctly, but use triple the amount of time these assignments would normally require. The inevitable result is that each night one or two subjects must be left undone, creating a backlog of work which periodically becomes overwhelming.

Adolescents whose early childhood curiosity was mishandled are prone to develop learning difficulties in special subjects. Subjects such as biology and science can be very threatening to the youngster who is struggling against allowing the emergence of repressed childhood curiosity about the creation of life and bodily functions in general. The same children can show proficiency in other subjects while failing these.

It has often been noted that some children are proficient only under certain teachers who show a special liking for and interest in them, doing poorly under indifferent or irritable teachers. Often, in this group, the children's need is for a good parent substitute to undo whatever damage the parental handling has caused in the attitude toward study or work.

The fact that a child can be so disturbed by traumatic occurrences at home as to be unable to concentrate seems almost too obvious to mention. No doubt this is true of most of the cases at county hospitals. Violent quarrels, alcoholism, physical brutality, lawlessness, desertion, illegitimacy, mental illness, lack of minimal privacy,* lack of minimal physical care, promiscuity on the part of either parent—all of these situations are deeply disturbing to the child. The child's security is shattered, anxiety is continuously evoked, and id impulses are stimulated. The energy required to combat normal aggressive and sexual impulses is exhausted in attempting to cope with the emotions aroused by the home situation; hence learning cannot take place.

In these situations the child has no motivation for study. Academic chores cannot arouse the child who has a tragic home life to adjust to daily. An algebra equation is a meaningless exercise to a young person who is struggling to understand the anguished relationships existing between his parents and himself, and who is striving to understand why these relationships are so different from what he has been able to observe or to surmise exist in other families. Often the child of such a home is stunted. Because his critical faculties have been too early awakened by the unfortunate circumstances in which he lives, the child attempts to avoid unbearable pain by trying not to know what is going on. The need to *not know* is a fundamental difficulty in many learning disabilities. To learn means to learn painful facts; therefore all learning is feared and avoided.

A further consequence to learning in this type of home is that it fails through affective ties to bind the child's aggression. These homes are the ones which breed delinquency, because the destructive urges remain isolated and manifest themselves independently instead of being fused with libidinal urges. In discussing pathological aggressiveness in children from broken homes, insti-

---

* Anna Freud[6] states that some children who have observed intercourse between their parents become involved in continual battles with the environment, since they are acting out sadistic fantasies associated with their observations.

tutions, and orphanages, Anna Freud[5] states: " . . . the pathological factor in these cases is not to be found in the aggressive tendencies themselves, but in a lack of fusion between them and libidinal (erotic) urges. . . . emotional development . . . has been held up through adverse external or internal conditions, such as absence of love objects, lack of emotional response from the adult environment, breaking of emotional ties as soon as they are formed. . . . Owing to the defects on the emotional side, the aggressive urges are not brought into fusion and thereby bound and partially neutralized, but remain free and seek expression in life in the form of pure, unadulterated, independent destructiveness." Implied in this is a lack of neutralization of aggression, which frequently results in learning difficulties.

Since these children are frequently addicted to acting out aggressive impulses, it is readily understandable that for them to remain passive recipients of the teachers' communications, or to have at their disposal a quantity of controlled aggression which can be diverted into schoolwork, is highly unlikely. There are no drive derivatives which can be sublimated into academic work.

Probably one of the most important causes of disturbance to the learning process produced by these delinquent (and other non-delinquent) homes is the sexual overstimulation which the child is unable to master and by which he feels threatened. Learning becomes too threatening because it is equated with sexual activity.

Some emotionally deprived children, who suddenly find themselves attractive in adolescence, derive so much gratification from dates, admiration, and physical contact, and from feeling lovable and attractive for the first time in their lives, that they cannot combine these experiences with any other, to the great detriment of their schoolwork.

Described in the foregoing are a number of types of learning difficulties encountered in childhood, with special reference to adolescence; the range is wide, and many can be handled environmentally. The most serious type is the learning inhibition, which is barely affected by changes in environment.

In *Inhibition, Symptoms and Anxiety*, Sigmund Freud[8] states: "An inhibition is the expression of a restriction of an Ego function. These restrictions have either been imposed as a measure of precaution or have been brought about as the result of an impoverishment of energy. The Ego renounces these functions in order to avoid coming into conflict with the Id." If a function has taken on either an unconscious libidinal significance or an unconscious, aggressive destructive meaning, then the need for inhibition may arise, and a person suffering from a neurotic inhibition is defending himself against the translation into action of some prohibited instinctual impulse.

As described by Anna Freud,[4] "The symptom [of inhibition] is not related to its real object but to a substitute in the present for some dominant interest in the past. For instance, when a child is inhibited in reckoning or thinking . . . the real activity avoided is not that of dealing mentally with ideas or numbers. . . . Such activities on the part of the Ego are in themselves harmless, but they have become related to past sexual activities, which the subject has warded off; these they now represent and, having thus become 'sexualized,' they are themselves the object of the Ego's defensive operations."

In *Three Contributions to the Theory of Sex*, Sigmund Freud[7] states: "About the same time when the sexual life of the child reaches its first rich development, from the age of three to the age of five, the beginnings of that activity ascribed to the impulse for knowledge and investigation set in. The desire for knowledge can neither be reckoned among the elementary instinctive components nor can it be altogether subsumed under sexuality. Its activity corresponds on the one hand to a sublimated form of acquisition and on the other hand the energy with which it works comes from the looking impulse."

The largest number of studies on learning inhibitions relate to reading disabilities. Common etiological factors have been found to be difficulty in handling aggression, with excessive guilt and anxiety over hostile, destructive, or sadistic impulses and fantasies, which frequently are oral in form. The much higher incidence of reading disability in boys has been attributed to the boys' greater difficulty in achieving normal repression of aggression.[3]

Trouble in learning to read has also been found to be an aspect of the disturbance of the exploratory function. The manifestation of curiosity as an aggressive activity provokes fear of loss of parental love and fear of castration. The child then defends himself against the exploratory drive by being unable to read. There is also much evidence in support of the theory that, if the exploratory function is overindulged, the child is unable to manage the undue quantities of stimulation.[15] Physical overstimulation of the child produces the same effect. The overexcited child is unable to sublimate the exploratory and aggressive drives. Reading thus becomes a forbidden activity because it represents past sexual activities.

The cases to be presented will illustrate various components of learning inhibitions and the corresponding variations in therapeutic approach.

CASE REPORT—RALPH

Ralph was the only boy and the youngest child in a family of three children. His two sisters were 3 and 5 years older than he. His mother gave a history of some feeding disturbance and prolonged toilet-training difficulties. Despite extreme anger and punishment on the mother's part, the child was still soiling at the age of 4. He was brought to treatment because of a variety of psychosomatic symptoms and anxieties.

The family custom was to walk around nude or seminude in their rooms, with doors always ajar. No privacy was required in the bathroom, regardless of the purpose for which it was being used. Bathing and toileting were shared family activities.

The father, a gentle, passive man, was in a line of business which required his being away from home several days each week. During his absences Ralph often shared his mother's bed. The mother, a rather aggressive former physical-education teacher, was given to explosive temper outbursts. Her anger was dramatically expressed in primitively colorful language which left no doubt in the child's mind as to the type of bodily damage she fantasied inflicting upon him.

The parents and their friends were unrestrained in the presence of the children, in making sexual remarks and jokes pertaining to the body and its functions, particularly excretory ones. The father kept a photograph collection of nude pin-ups in his dresser drawer, where the child often peeped at them.

Beautiful dress models who worked for the father, who was a dress manufacturer, were frequent guests at their home, where the handsome and seductive little boy was a ready prey for their exhibitionism and narcissistic flirtatiousness. He was danced with, teased, pressed close to half-nude bosoms, and altogether made a sexual plaything.

DISCUSSION

It is not surprising to find that, in such an environment, instinctual drives relating to oral, anal, and genital levels of development were unrepressed and that adequate sublimation into intellectual activities was difficult to achieve.

The normal aggression connected with the anal and oral periods of development could not be diverted into mastering skills and into attacking and incorporating knowledge because Ralph was still struggling with unresolved problems of those periods. The anal and oral problems further complicated his overcharged oedipal conflict. Full of anal sadism toward the frightening mother whom he, at the same time, desired to possess (dating from his toilet-training days when his conflict with his mother was openly shown), he also lived in great fear of paternal retaliation for his rivalrous wishes. Although the father was a passive, nonthreatening, rather colorless man, Ralph fantasied the most colorful and horrifying punishments at his hands. The violence and vividness of these fantasies came from two sources: first, the child's own sadistic wishes and drives which had been intensified by his experiences, and, second, from the type of threats his mother made.

The child was overwhelmed by the conflicting drives within him and struggled continuously to cope with them. So difficult was it for him to sublimate these drives that he was never able to play a game throughout the latency years. All of his play, in and outside of the therapeutic sessions, consisted of dramatizing the fantasy of being a detective in pursuit of a criminal—himself, of course.

Learning represented many things which were overwhelmingly threatening to him, and very little healthy aggression was at his disposal to be used in learning in school. Moreover, overwhelmed as he was by too much exposure at home, he defended himself by looking without seeing. He could not look purposefully at the outlines of letters without feeling threatened. Looking at letters symbolized looking at breasts, buttocks, genitals—activities which had aroused intense anxiety in the child because they had flooded him with excitement he could not master.

Mastery and manipulation of numbers unconsciously signified being the all-powerful male like the father. Such strength and omnipotence he feared, because it meant annihilation of his father and success with his mother.

During Ralph's latency years he was a great admirer of a popular comedian whose style was to present himself as mentally retarded. When Ralph reached the age of 12, the hitherto sophisticated and flirtatious boy became a replica of his admired comedian. He behaved very stupidly with girls and duplicated the comedian's half-witted innocence, which leaves all sexual pursuit, activity, and responsibility to the woman. The witty remarks with which Ralph once amused his teachers and his therapist gave way to buffoonery. The precocious child had become, to all appearances, a rather stupid young adolescent.

This change was brought about by the upsurge of instinctual drives reviving the oedipal conflict and necessitating renewed defenses against all the sadistic fantasies associated with it. By 12, he had lost his other symptoms and was able to do slightly better than average schoolwork, but still a far cry from his true ability. And, fortunately, he was not pleased with the social results of his playing the fool with girls.

It was necessary to work through the unconscious equation of learning in school with learning too much at home, and the equating of mastery of knowledge with mastery over the father, and possession of his mother in a sadistic sex act. His stupidity served not only to ward off castration by presenting himself as already castrated, but it also served to cover his murderous fantasies: "I could never hurt you. I'm just a harmless idiot." As he gained insight into the reasons behind his need to play the idiot, he was able to abandon the role; at the same time that the conflict was reduced, energy was released and utilized for school learning, which no longer represented danger.

Ilse Hellman's[10] studies of mothers of children with intellectual inhibition indicate that children with this type of difficulty have been given unusually great opportunities to see the mother's nude body and to share bathroom and toilet intimacies with her. Her findings also corroborate those of Margaret S. Mahler[12] that there is an unusually intimate bond between these patients and their mothers at a very early stage of the child's life. Ralph's case illustrates the effect of a sadistic seduction on intellectual functioning. His problem was more intense, needing a long and detailed analysis because of the fearful fantasies which were associated with his mother's sadistic approach to him. Only after many years of analysis did the learning inhibition subside; he did not begin to do really superior work until after analysis.

CASE REPORT—MARIA

A second case of learning inhibition, followed from latency to adolescence, took quite a different course. Maria had been in the slow-learners section of her class and gradually moved upward to the brightest group, although at no time did she work up to her full capacity. A core of difficulty remained, which was connected primarily with intense sexual fears partially caused by observation of parental coitus. During the relatively quiescent years of latency, however, she was able to repress and deny the fears and still keep up a fairly high level of work, since she was extremely bright. Unsublimated aggression deriving from oral and anal periods of development also contributed to her difficulty in working at her true level, but this was kept relatively under control.

With the onset of puberty, however, her work began to deteriorate markedly. Within a few months she slid down to a partially failing position in school, a situation she accepted (although with feelings of distress) and refused to do anything to improve. Therapy at this period was ineffective.

DISCUSSION

During latency, analysis of guilt and anxiety over masturbation, sexual curiosity, and aggression toward her parents had partially opened the way to sublimation and learning. But the revival of the problems in adolescence, through the upsurge of instinctual drives and preoccupation with vivid sadomasochistic sexual fantasies, proved overwhelming. Maria's heightened ability to learn in school had followed upon the gaining of mastery over overstimulated sexual drives in latency. Puberty threatened her with once again becoming uncontrolled in her sexual drives, and this she resisted in terror. The extreme degree and quality of her fear were determined by several factors, primarily, the recollection of her earlier state of helplessness in regard to sexual impulses. Second, latency masturbation fantasies had been of a frighteningly masochistic nature, and the upsurge of sexual desires in puberty had the effect of making the sexual fantasies seem in imminent danger of coming true. Third, her longing for sexual gratification in adolescence could find no other form of expression than the fantasy of being attacked. (In a symbolic way, her failure represented a realization of the fantasy, in that the bad marks which her teachers gave her constituted their attack upon her.) Consequently, she became entirely preoccupied with holding sexual fantasies in check, and all of her energy was utilized for that purpose.

As stated by Freud,[7] "When the ego is occupied with a psychic task of special difficulty, as by the necessity for holding constantly mounting sexual fantasies in check, it becomes so impoverished with respect to the energy available to it that it is driven to restrict its expenditure in many places at the same time."

Another determinant of Maria's adolescent learning problem seemed to be an activity-passivity conflict, a conflict over adopting a masculine or a feminine identification. (Sexualization of school subjects as being masculine or feminine was similar to the case reported in detail by Augusta Alpert.[1]) Accepting a teacher's instruction and knowledge and incorporating it unconsciously symbolized passive helplessness (her concept of femininity) and something being forced into her. Her rebellion against this position was also expressed in strong resentment and contempt for her teachers, male and female, for all kinds of offenses ranging from dandruff to indifference. Activity (on the teacher's part) meant masculinity—being the attacker, a role she wished to have as a defense against her desire for and fear of being attacked. The need to be the aggressor found some outlet in her tutoring of handicapped children in school. Her massive refusal to learn, however, in all probability unconsciously signified to her the preservation of body intactness.

In Maria's case, as in many latent learning difficulties which seem to appear for the first time in adolescence, there was a breakdown of sublimations owing to changes in the strength of the instinctual drives. The sequence of events clearly indicated that, unless prior sublimation has been well entrenched, so much energy is consumed during adolescence in combating instinctual drives that most of it is withdrawn from sublimatory activities, among which learning is paramount. Maria's learning difficulty had many facets and was overdetermined. It created a special therapeutic problem because it manifested itself with the greatest intensity in adolescence, at a time when the child was unable to cooperate in treatment. For 2 years (13 to 15) Maria did little but stay close to home and parents. She had no hobbies or interests other than the small amount of tutoring of the handicapped which was done in school and required as service, no heterosexual social life, and little contact with girls except occasionally to accompany one or two to the movies.

Supportive psychotherapy had to be substituted for analysis. Too frightened to examine her fantasies, she remained a prisoner of them until she quieted down sufficiently to be able to realize that they were spoiling her life. At that point she became motivated to attempt to work through them, and analysis became possible.

CASE REPORT—JIM

The following case is that of a boy who started treatment at 12, with an almost total learning block of 6 years' standing. When Jim was brought for treatment, his mother had just married for the third time, after several years of leading the life of a gay divorcee. He had been brought up mostly by nursemaids, and not too much information was available about his early development. He rarely saw his father, a man of violent temper, and, although he lived with his mother, did not see her more than a few times a week, because of her active social life. Jim's behavior at home and at school was described as provocative and mean.

DISCUSSION

This case seemed to illustrate (among other things) how the increased activity at adolescence, the greater flow of energy, can, under certain circumstances, be utilized to bring about improvement, even in as complicated a problem as a learning block.

Jim was a lonely boy, very much in need of a stable relationship with someone predictable and reliable. His one goal was to be able to do passing work in school, but he seemed to have made a pact with himself not to reveal to the therapist anything that went on at home, or that he had observed about his mother's and father's behavior in the past. He brought his schoolwork to his therapeutic sessions and asked the therapist's help in doing the assignments. This provided an opportunity to observe the manner in which he approached a learning situation. The therapist was able to point out that he apparently feared looking at the printed words and consequently made frantic guesses as to their identity. Immediately following this very superficial interpretation, there was noticeable though small improvement. Months later, when he almost absent-mindedly revealed a fear of insanity in connection with the bizarre behavior of his parents, whom he had observed in a drunken fight when he was about 5, the therapist was able to interpret his fear of finding out frightening things, of knowing painful facts about his parents and becoming aware of the very distressing feelings their behavior had aroused in him in the past. Again there was an improvement in schoolwork. While carefully guarded against talking about his parents, Jim began to ask many questions about the therapist and her husband. The questions provided an opportunity to interpret his confusion as to what married life was like in other families. Did other people live as his parents did? What made people love and marry, then hate and divorce? His interest in the therapist's private life was thus utilized to show him how much he actually was thinking about his parents' behavior, despite his disclaiming any interest.

Although the problems were by no means worked through, apparently even describing them for him within the framework of the one positive, consistent relationship the child had, that is, the therapeutic one, brought about sufficient diminution of anxiety and brooding to release energy for learning, which had become a slightly less frightening activity.

A most important factor in Jim's progress was his strong motivation to become at least a passing student. Therefore, the energy released by interpretations which enabled him to look at his painful reality and have some understanding of how it affected him was immediately channeled into learning. But it is likely that in a more quiescent period there would have been less of a change in intellectual functioning (partial though it was), in so short a time, because of the extremely traumatic background.

It is interesting to contrast Jim's fears resulting from a painful reality situation with Maria's fantasy fears. Superficial treatment was effective in a bad reality situation in which motivation was high. Being confronted with painful reality brought relief to Jim. Confronting the girl (who came from a stable home where the parents were devoted to each other) with her adolescent fantasies was disturbing to the point of being unendurable, additional evidence that fantasy fears are more frightening than reality, and more difficult to deal with in therapy. To confront the child with her own fantasies was confronting her with a part of her self. In adolescence this is more painful than perceiving what is wrong with the environment and the parents.

There was evidence in Jim's case that accidental or secret observations of the mother's activities, which the child had had to repress, led to impairment of memory and inhibition of looking. Clear evidence of oral disturbance in this case and in the preceding one was revealed in an insatiable greed for sweets and in general demandingness, pointing to a disturbed relationship with the mother in the earliest years. Jim, however, was able to "incorporate" the therapist's interpretations (along with pounds of sweets!) and use them well. He was a neglected child who was hungry for warmth and affection. Maria on the other hand, had an intense and complicated relationship with her mother from infancy. Vomiting was one of her symptoms. Although she ate greedily during her sessions, it was difficult for her to decide what she wanted, and she often felt nauseous afterward. Oral incorporation was obviously fraught with conflict. Ralph also suffered from nausea and vomiting at times. He, too, had an ambivalent relationship with his mother, but it was less severe; hence he was able eventually to incorporate and fully utilize interpretations. (The relationships between learning inhibition, orality, and sexual overstimulation are strikingly illustrated in the case presentation by Erna Furman[9] of a little girl whose treatment started at the age of 3 years and 8 months, the child having already experienced actual seduction by an adult male and having observed perverse sexual activities and coitus between her parents.)

In contrast to Maria, Jim was more responsive to treatment during adolescence when he could put his increased reservoir of energy at the disposal of learning. In Jim's case the principal difficulty was the traumatic situation at home. Because of the continued disturbed behavior of the parents, only modified analytical therapy was possible. Eventually, arrangements had to be made to send Jim to a boarding school to safeguard his further development.

In cases of severe learning difficulty which involve development of perceptual and motor mastery, it is most important to start treatment long before adolescence. The results of such all-encompassing inhibition make almost all learning impossible and can render the child tragically inadequate to meet reality demands. The following case of an almost total learning inhibition in latency is an example of a therapeutic approach which probably would not have been as effective in adolescence.

CASE REPORT—CRAIG

Craig was a 7½-year-old boy who was referred by his school for uncontrollably wild behavior in the classroom. Just by looking at him, one could see that he was a seriously disturbed little boy. His eyes had a peculiar unseeing expression. His speech was retarded and defective. He could hold a pencil only by grabbing it in a very awkward clutch. His writing was large, uncertain, and primitive. He could barely read or spell a word, and he was in almost continual motion. In fact, he was untestable. Defective reality testing and bizarre thinking were apparent. At the beginning of treatment he probably would have been diagnosed as schizophrenic.

He was the illegitimate son of a woman, the report of whose behavior was considered by hospital authorities who evaluated the case, to indicate schizophrenia. (The mother had died before the child was brought for treatment by his aunt.) The child had been placed in a substandard foundling home for the first 3 years of his life. At the time he was taken from the foundling home, Craig was completely toilet trained and had excellent table manners. At the age of 3 he was brought to the home of his mother's sister, with whom the mother was living. After being reunited with his mother he reverted to soiling and ate with greedy lack of control.

The mother died when the child was 5, and he remained in the care of his aunt and uncle, who had a daughter a little younger than Craig. The aunt (especially) and uncle were kindly and tolerant people who had become discouraged at Craig's continuing deficiencies and wild behavior, despite their best efforts to provide as good a home and upbringing for him as for their daughter.

Craig lived such a great distance from the therapist's office that it was not possible for him to be brought more than once a week. For the same reason, his aunt could not manage separate consultations for herself. It seemed a hopeless task to help a child as severely damaged as Craig on so limited a schedule. Therefore the weekly visits were supplemented by a lengthy telephone conversation one evening a week with Craig and his aunt, who will be referred to as Mrs. Z. Talking with the child had as its aim the maintenance and reinforcement of the contact established during the weekly sessions. As Mrs. Z. was unusually receptive, the talks with her gave the therapist an opportunity to effect changes in the emotional tone of the child's environment.

To begin with, Mrs. Z. was very much encouraged by the therapist's strong interest in the child and empathy with Mrs. Z. in her difficult situation. By comparing the child's psychological situation to a physical illness, it was made clear to her why her efforts did not produce the desired results. She readily understood that if Craig had been suddenly left in her care, at the age of 5, suffering from a severe case of tuberculosis, he would not have thrived on the daily regime of physical care which was entirely appropriate and adequate for her healthy daughter, but would have needed a highly specialized type of care aimed at correcting the illness. Insight and renewed optimism enabled her to relate with considerably more warmth to the child as time went on. She made spontaneous verbal reassurances of her affection and the permanence of their relationship: "You're never going to get rid of *me* . . . not even when you're grown-up and married . . . because then I'll be the baby sitter for your children when you and your wife go out to the movies."

In the therapeutic sessions the child was intuitively approached first on an oral level through being offered his fill of sweets. He would dig into the proffered box with a tense clawlike motion of both hands, which frustrated his attempts to get as much as possible. The therapist would help him to stow away a supply in his pockets, supposedly to last him until the next session. Thus an attempt was made by both aunt and therapist to reassure him of a continuing relationship.

Early in treatment he drew pictures of stick figures, showing his feelings of lack of relatedness to people and of warmth from them, and pictures of exploding bombs and planes, mirroring the uncontrolled explosive aggression within himself. Very gradually, as Craig became more related to the therapist, he began to refer angrily to unpleasant episodes at school. The teacher and the children were mean. Sympathy was expressed for the punishments he received, the hostility of the children, for the difficulty he experienced in being expected to be quiet like the other children, and above all, for how very hard it was for him to learn and how bad he must feel about it. The therapist promised that she would try to help him with all these problems. He eventually brought his schoolbooks (to try to convince the therapist that he *could* read). Actually, he looked without perceiving, making wild guesses. Spelling seemed overwhelmingly difficult. He became very confused in arithmetic, and his handwriting had a peculiar frenzied quality. Needless to say, he could hardly sit still while attempting to do the work.

Superficial interpretations of his difficulty in looking, and the tension and excitement that welled up within him when he attempted to learn, brought about some slight improvement. The teacher reported that he had become calmer and no longer wandered around the room *all* day, hitting the other children and taking their possessions. He had started treatment in February, and by June, when summer vacation time arrived, Craig had lost the unseeing look in his eyes. His ability to pronounce words correctly had improved. (At the beginning of treatment he could only say "tell-un" for television, and "preh-ehl" for pretzel, two of his favorite commodities.) He had begun to smile fleetingly for the first time in anyone's recollection and showed clear signs of positive feeling for the therapist. In fact, when the therapist was giving him his going-away-for-the-summer present, and assuring him that she would write to him and his aunt, and that his aunt would reply, so that the therapist would always know how he was until she would see him again when school started, he took both her hands, brought them together palms upward, and buried his face in them.

This is perhaps the most appropriate place to ponder the importance to the child's developing ability to relate, of his therapist's very strong positive feeling toward him. It probably penetrated his initial wall of detachment quickly because of its sustained intensity, and had a restitutive effect upon the child. Craig was also fully aware of the therapist's long telephone conversations with his aunt and showed that he knew beyond a doubt that they were for his benefit. For, contrary to his usual behavior, he never annoyed his aunt or attempted to interrupt when she was on the telephone with the therapist. Further, he followed the therapist's example of having a session à trois at times, by occasionally asking on his own initiative that his aunt be invited into the room. Usually, something important was brewing on such occasions. Craig had come to sense intuitively that understanding between his aunt and himself was sometimes greatly expedited by having her participate in his sessions, with the therapist serving as "moderator" of their discussions.

The handling of this case seems to have some points in common with the Corrective Object Relations studies reported by Augusta Alpert.[2] Craig seemed to be able to organize reality around two dependable objects, and the object relationships with aunt and therapist paved the way to positive identification processes. There was a beginning of a binding of aggression which had clearly derived from oral and anal levels of development, as indicated by his regressive behavior when reunited with his mother.

Shortly after his return to treatment the following fall, Craig mentioned that his class was studying history. His remarks indicated a simultaneous interest in the subject and an inability to learn it. He then began, and continued for two sessions, to subject the therapist to a guessing game in which the odds were hopelessly against her. (The game consisted of his holding up baseball cards and asking her to guess the number on the back, the range limits being one to several hundred.)

Assuming that the guessing game related to his own history, the therapist approached his aunt to see if she could persuade her to be frank with the boy about his past. Mrs. Z. was greatly upset at the thought of discussing his illegitimacy with him, stating that all the other members of the family would deeply resent her doing so. The therapist assured her that the boy knew of it anyway, because children hear conversations when they are thought to be asleep or not listening or not old enough to understand. (It was a much-discussed topic in the home in the evenings when the children were in bed.)

The therapist did not pursue it any further, but, during one of Craig's sessions when he had been verbalizing curiosity about the birth of children, he expressed disbelief of his aunt's knowing about the process. She was forthwith invited to participate in the remainder of the therapeutic session and confirmed the facts of conception and childbirth for him, concluding with the remark "and that's just how *you* were born." Then Craig startled her considerably by asking, after a long thoughtful silence during which he lay on the floor looking up at her, "But Janine [his mother] wasn't married, was she?"

Fortunately, the therapist had already discussed with Mrs. Z. how the situation might be presented to Craig in a constructive manner. His aunt explained to him that his mother and father had loved each other very much and had planned to marry as soon as his father could arrange to get a divorce, but that, alas, he had died before it could be realized.

Some time later, when the therapist touched on his earliest experiences, Craig expressed a desire to have his aunt again visit during his session. He then began to talk about his mother and the ride in the car with her when he left the foundling home. It was explained to him that his mother had been very ill when he was little and thought he would be better cared for at the foundling home than if she had kept him with her. He was assured of her love for him and was told that sometimes grownups do not understand how lonely and unhappy and unloved the little boy who is left there can feel. Both the therapist and his aunt assured him that if his mother or his aunt had understood how bad he felt to be away from them, they would never have let him remain there. They also had missed him very much. Craig then made several hostile references to the personnel of the foundling home. His remarks elicited from his two listeners warm expressions of sympathy for his experiences, reflecting their understanding of the confusion, loneliness, and anger engendered in the child by typical institutional upbringing.

After Craig had oriented himself in time, place, experience, and family relationships, his work in school, speech, manual dexterity, and general conduct showed definite improvement, but he was still considerably below the adequate students in his class.

One day, toward the middle of his third year of treatment, the therapist received a call from Mrs. Z. informing her that Craig was hospitalized with a broken leg, noting that visiting was permitted only twice a week. In her usual fashion, Mrs. Z. cooperated to the fullest with every suggestion made to prevent the child from feeling cut off from his family while shut away in the hospital. On the first visiting day the family brought him photographs of themselves to keep by his bed. (Mrs. Z. reported that he was visibly touched by the photographs; that they clearly meant a great deal to him.) He was supplied with toys and sweets. The nonvisiting days were brightened by mail from his family and his therapist.

When he was discharged from the hospital, he had, of course, fallen considerably behind in his schoolwork. Moreover, he was confined to his home for 3 additional weeks. Mrs. Z., who was by now beginning to derive real pleasure from Craig's general progress, decided to tutor him in his schoolwork. This self-imposed task she faithfully performed for several hours each day, with (to her surprise) a most cooperative pupil.

Suddenly, during the third week of home tutoring, Craig's reading became proficient, his handwriting controlled and even superior for his age; he no longer had trouble remembering how to spell and was able to master all of his school subjects in some passing degree. It seemed as though his hospitalization provided the opportunity to recall and abreact to an extent the feelings associated with his early institutional experiences. The nurses re-

ported that on the nonvisiting days he had been extremely restless, hopping about and onto high ledges and sills, one leg in a
cast, with such abandon that a horrified nursing sister suggested
baptism to exorcise the devil, by whom she was sure Craig was
possessed. When his family was present he was calm, but jealously
hoarded their attentions, showing distress if they paid attention to
another child, as his uncle once did, and forbidding them to do so.
His admonitions were respected by his uncle (who was, in general,
a passive observer rather than an active participant in the struggle
to help Craig find himself), and, of course, by his aunt who restricted herself merely to greeting the children near him.

His family's response to his hospitalization apparently had convinced him that he was dear to them, and this conviction was thoroughly reinforced through being the "only child" at home with his
aunt during the school hours when her little girl was away and
she devoted herself to him with true pleasure and interest.

It appears that these were corrective experiences which finally
undid traumatic fixations of the oral and anal periods and engendered a fully developed object relationship. Craig had become
able to organize reality, bind aggression, and sublimate aggressive
drives into learning activities. This had become possible also because his inner anxiety and tension had been reduced to the point
where he could tolerate the tension of working toward mastery,
replacing his former condition of needing immediate gratification.

Perhaps the effects of therapy, the change in environmental
handling, and the experience of hospitalization combined to "help
the child's arrested or otherwise disturbed libidinal impulses to
become more normal" so that fusion between erotic and destructive impulses followed automatically, and aggression was brought
under the beneficent influence of the erotic urges.[5]

SUMMARY

Learning difficulties, with particular reference to adolescence
were briefly surveyed. They were found to be caused by numerous
factors, including increased instinctual drives in adolescence; masturbation conflicts; narcissism; earlier learning problems manifest-
ing themselves; and parental handling and home environment. The
learning inhibition was found to differ from other learning difficulties in that it was not affected by environmental changes.

Four cases of learning inhibition were presented illustrating various components of the problem with corresponding variations in therapeutic approach and result. In the first case, the child was sexually overstimulated by both parents and terrified by the mother. A long analysis eventually eradicated the learning inhibition which had persisted from latency into adolescence.

In the second case, the learning difficulty was overdetermined and manifested itself markedly in adolescence, after having greatly improved during latency. Sexual experiences in childhood had given rise to sadistic fantasies, which in adolescence became overwhelmingly frightening to the child, rendering analytic therapy temporarily ineffective, and necessitating the substitution of supportive psychotherapy.

The home environment in the third case was so disturbed that only a modified form of analysis was possible. Because of the high degree of motivation, there was improvement in ability to learn as soon as interpretations relating to the traumatic environment were given. The energy at the disposal of treatment, however, was insufficient because of disturbed parental behavior, hence boarding-school placement was arranged to safeguard the child's development.

The latency child presented as the fourth case was treated by psychotherapy involving manipulation of the environment. The severely disturbed child gradually organized reality around two dependable objects—his mother-substitute and his therapist. This orientation, in combination with restitutive experiences, enabled sublimation and learning to take place.

Pseudo-stupidity served as a defense against castration fears and against sexual aggression in Ralph's and Maria's cases. The need to *not know* was of paramount importance in Jim's case. Observation of parental nudity and sexual activity resulted in impairment of memory and inhibition of looking in the three adolescent cases, whereas in Craig's situation, the family's refusal to allow him to learn about his past had the same effect.

In the first three cases, the phenomenon of adolescent upsurge of instinctual drives and the increased activity of that period played their part in the learning problem. Jim used it to make progress; Maria retreated in panic; Ralph required a renewed defense against sadistic sexual fantasies in order to maintain the progress made up to that point.

In all the cases oral greed and anal sadism were apparent; guilt and anxiety over sexuality were marked. The strength of the drives relating to oral, anal, and oedipal levels of development made sublimation difficult to achieve. There is evidence that, unless sublimations are well entrenched before the upsurge of pubertal instinctual drives takes place, they may break down as energy is withdrawn from them to cope with adolescent problems of adjustment.

It can be seen that all learning problems are by no means alike, and there can be no single therapeutic approach. Therapy will vary in accordance with the individual child's needs.

References

1. ALPERT, A. "Sublimation and Sexualization," in *The Psychoanalytic Study of the Child.* New York, International Universities Press, Inc., 1949, vol. 3–4.

2. ALPERT, A. "Reversibility of Pathological Fixations Associated with Maternal Deprivation in Infancy," in *The Psychoanalytic Study of the Child.* New York, International Universities Press, Inc., 1959, vol. 14.

3. BLANCHARD, P. "Psychoanalytic Contribution to the Problem of Reading Disabilities," in *The Psychoanalytic Study of the Child.* New York, International Universities Press, Inc., 1952, vol. 7.

4. FREUD, A. *The Ego and the Mechanisms of Defense.* New York, International Universities Press, Inc., 1946.

5. FREUD, A. "Aggression in Relation to Emotional Development: Normal and Pathological," in *The Psychoanalytic Study of the Child.* New York, International Universities Press, Inc., 1949, vol. 3.

6. FREUD, A. "Certain Types of Social Maladjustment," in *Searchlights on Delinquency,* ed. by Eissler, K. R. New York, International Universities Press, Inc., 1949.

7. FREUD, S. *Three Contributions to the Theory of Sex.* Nervous and Mental Disease Monographs. Baltimore, Williams & Wilkins, 1930.

8. FREUD, S. *Inhibition, Symptoms and Anxiety.* London, Hogarth Press, Ltd., 1936.

9. FURMAN, E. "An Ego Disturbance in a Young Child," in *The Psychoanalytic Study of the Child.* New York, International Universities Press, Inc., 1956, vol. 11.

10. HELLMAN, I. "Some Observations on Mothers of Children with Intellectual Inhibitions," in *The Psychoanalytic Study of the Child.* New York, International Universities Press, Inc., 1954, vol. 9.

11. KLEIN, E. "Psychoanalytic Aspects of School Problems," in *The Psychoanalytic Study of the Child.* New York, International Universities Press, Inc., 1949, vol. 3–4.

12. MAHLER, M. S. Pseudo-imbecility: a magic cap of invisibility. *Psychoanalyt. Quart. 11:* 149, 1942.

13. Pearson, G. H. "A Survey of Learning Difficulties in Children," in *The Psychoanalytic Study of the Child*. New York, International Universities Press, Inc., 1952, vol. 7.
14. Rosen, V. "Strephosymbolia: An Intrasystemic Disturbance of the Synthetic Function of the Ego," in *The Psychoanalytic Study of the Child*. New York, International Universities Press, Inc., 1955, vol. 10.
15. Sylvester, E., and Kunst, M. S. Psychodynamic aspects of the reading problem. *Am. J. Orthopsychiat. 12:* 69, 1943.

chapter 14 The Role of Parents

ANITA I. BELL

It is common knowledge that adolescence is one of the most turbulent periods in the entire lifetime of the individual. In a short span of time, physiological and psychological changes of tremendous magnitude take place. The effects of these changes on the adolescent himself have been well described by others. My purpose here is to deal with the implications of such changes for the parents. The experience on which this paper is based comes from interviews with parents living in large eastern cities. Primarily, this group is a sophisticated and educated one. Many of them have had contact with current psychological concepts. In some instances this has been a hazard rather than a help. Let me explain:

This is the very group that has been most exposed to the changes in psychology and education that have taken place over the past 25 years. During this period, psychological and educational attitudes have tended to influence parents and some educators to adopt a *laissez faire* policy toward their offspring. In fact, some of the principles with which therapists work and which really belong exclusively to the therapeutic situation have been taken over by parents and educators and applied to daily life. Perhaps we are partly to blame for not having made it very clear that the needs of the child in treatment are not the educational ideals of the average child. We have written a prescription of *laissez faire*, but we have left out the timing and the dosage. For example, one can walk into the home of young parents who are psychologically sophisticated and find that a child of 3, 4, or 5 years is still using a potty because he is afraid of the toilet; we also discover that the contents of the potty are not flushed away for many hours or even a day because Jimmy is afraid to lose his bowel movement. Or one finds that, because Jimmy is afraid of being rejected, he can come into the parental bed or bathroom whenever he pleases. If he wants to know about the genitals, mother shows herself or father does likewise, depending on the question. He does not have to wash his hands or face if he doesn't want to, even by the time he has reached the third grade. Although these are extreme examples, they are not infrequent, and they often represent attempts to be "good parents." Why do I bring them into a discussion about parents and the adolescent?

I think that early experiences of such overstimulation and permissiveness have a number of deleterious effects on both parents and offspring, the repercussions of which are often seen in adolescence. The child, in addition to being overstimulated, does not learn to tolerate frustration of any kind; nor is he well prepared to handle anxiety. There is an atmosphere of acting out of unconscious impulses. Boundaries and standards have not been set. Important ego functions such as reality testing, sublimation, mastery, and a sense of identity do not develop adequately. Normal superego development is likewise impeded.

When adolescence is reached, the poorly developed ego of such individuals is incapable of mobilizing adequate defenses to cope with the demands of the increased genital drive and the eruptions of pregenital impulses which normally occur at this time; hence an even greater degree of regression and general disturbance exists than under ordinary circumstances. A further complication is the tendency to act out unconscious impulses with which even the "normal" adolescent is hard pressed to cope.

What is the effect of all this on the parent?

Let us go back a little. Under the best of circumstances, the daily contact with the developing child has an effect on the parent. Even when unusual permissiveness is not the case, we find parents reacting to the developmental viscissitudes of their offspring. There are those parents who, although physically ready, are not psychologically ready to withstand the daily bombardment of the unrestrained acting out of early impulses. Coleman, Kris, and Provence[1] have pointed out that there are many parents who function exceedingly well as parents of infants but cannot manage when the child begins to become more independent and indicate needs of his own. For example, a parent may function well in many other areas yet not with anal problems; another may be well able to deal with anality but find himself unable to deal with questions referring to genital development, etc. It is in the daily relationship with the developing child that the parent, usually the mother, is inevitably confronted with situations touching on her own unconscious emotional difficulties. Some may have been solved adequately, others may have been repressed because of inadequate solutions. Certainly she, and the father as well, relives some part of her own childhood through these daily experiences. Defenses which have been adequate up to the state of parenthood may begin to break down under the daily bombardment of the young child's behavior. It is inevitable for the developing child to exhibit a freedom of expression and an acting out of pregenital and oedipal impulses. The as yet undeveloped superego attitudes, the numerous direct expressions of unconscious wishes on the part of the young child, are a constant threat to the defenses of the parent. This is particularly true when there has been excessive permissiveness.

Obviously, varying degrees of regression and anxiety, depending on his own psychic structure, will be stimulated in the parent by such freedom of expression in the child. Sometimes the regression is slow and insidious, sometimes transitory, sometimes it appears only in relation to a particular problem. If the parent of an adolescent has had the strength and good fortune to "survive" to some degree the early pregenital experiences and the oedipal phase of his or her offspring, latency brings a short breathing spell. The home temporarily becomes peaceful.

When puberty arrives, however, and bodily changes begin to make their appearance along with indications of the intensification of unconscious drives, the parent is again threatened. The threat to his authority, self-esteem, and psychological defenses increases with the vagaries of the developing adolescent. No longer is there the chatty youngster who comes home from school with news of his or her exploits. No longer does an eager listener accept advice or proffered help. Comments of any kind tend to be misinterpreted. Authoritative maneuvers in response to rebellious activity are of no avail; neither are protestations of interest or affection. As one parent remarked, "It's like constantly sitting on the edge of a volcano. You never know when there will be an eruption." The puzzled parent comes with the questions: "What is wrong with my child?" "What is wrong with me?" "Why can't we have the peaceful days of childhood back?"

What has happened to the relationship between parents and offspring? Some of the characteristic changes that occur during adolescence might offer an explanation for this change in the relationship.

Two main categories of change exist—the biological and the psychological. The physical or biological changes can be startling indeed. In a matter of months, sometimes within a year, a new individual makes an appearance, as it were. In place of a familiar child, there is a large, muscular, deep-voiced boy showing many signs of sexual maturity. Secondary sexual characteristics rapidly appear. If the offspring is a girl, bodily changes such as breasts, a waistline, hips, etc., become visible. The onset of menstruation climaxes these changes.

To the teen-ager such bodily changes threaten his sense of identity and his reality testing. His resultant anxiety is readily transmitted to the parent, who may or may not overtly react. This is but one facet of the larger problem. The physical changes of the teen-ager, although defended against by the parent, are a source of tremendous stimulation to him.

The psychological development of this period from the adolescent's point of view, has been discussed by many.[2,3,4] For purposes of orientation, I would like to mention a few characteristics which seem to provoke reactions of some magnitude in the parent.

We know that adolescence brings with it an eruption into consciousness of pregenital impulses. One aspect of this phenomenon is that of regressed behavior. Indeed, Geleerd[3] feels that most adolescents do experience a regression "to the undifferentiated phase" at this time. In addition to pregenital impulses, oedipal impulses likewise rise to the surface. The parent now becomes a dangerous object. The earlier libidinal tie must be broken. The threat of the parent as a love object in a genital sense cannot be tolerated. The combination of these eruptions with the increase of the genital drive upsets the entire structure that has been built up thus far. All possible defenses are mobilized, such as avoidance or withdrawal, displacement, reversal of affect, and a host of others.

How does the parent react? Almost overnight he is confronted with a careless, messy, unreasonable, sarcastic individual who is alternately hostile or affectionate, seemingly without provocation. Violent eruptions of anger burst forth in response to innocuous questions. To the parent, particularly the parent of today, who is inclined to do whatever possible to further "good public relations with his offspring," such a state of affairs can be disheartening indeed. Any attempts to reach the young person are met with further withdrawal. Many parents react with anger, guilt, or an increased attempt to tie the teen-ager closer to the family. But the very individual toward whom the parent was able to show overt signs of love during childhood has now become *a sexually stimulating and taboo object for the parent as well.* As a result the parent also must mobilize additional defenses to handle the anxiety provoked by his own incestuous fantasies. Unfortunately, the daily intimacies of family life help neither the parent nor the adolescent to ward off such stimulation. For example, a father was conducting a serious conversation with his wife and a visitor. Their 18-year-old daughter suddenly appeared in her nightgown to inquire about the family car. Although this father answered her very seriously and his outward manner was most proper, his glance fastened itself on her genital area. Actually, her pubic hair was distinctly visible through the transparent nightgown. The daughter left and the conversation went on, but certainly both father and daughter were momentarily stimulated.

The intensity of feeling and the tendency to act out may be further illustrated by Mary, age 14, who was Daddy's "best girl" when she was small. With puberty she developed breasts, wore bras, had grown pubic hair, and had begun to menstruate. She was quite excited about her mature state. She vacillated toward and away from her mother; sometimes there were confidences and at other times she turned to her father and complained about the way the mother treated her. Frequently, she fought with everyone in the house, including her father. He was hard put to understand her behavior, and even more threatened when half an hour later, in a burst of positive feeling, she made up to him. She would hug him and sit on his lap, causing him to feel a momentary sexual arousal. She frequently sat astride facing him, while on his lap, and chatted of unimportant happenings of the day. To his utter consternation he found himself having erections. This father accepted his daughter's overtures but seemingly denied whatever implications they may have had for him by viewing his daughter as still a child, a fantasy she abetted him in by behaving as a very young child at such moments. When 1 year later she began to go about with boys, however, he reacted with violent protestations. His righteous attitude toward his daughter was his defense against his own incestuous involvement. Actually, his daughter had withdrawn from him and was attempting to find another love object. It was the father who now needed help.

The father of a teen-age son complained because of the bickering that went on at home. He was in analysis, so we more readily got to his real complaint. His wife had a tendency to permit her son to ask her seemingly "very important" questions at a time when she was getting dressed in her room. Since everyone was in a rush in the morning, her rationalization was, "It only takes a minute, and I'm wearing a slip. We are talking about important things he has to settle before he goes to school. I don't know why it bothers you so!" This very observant father, however, had often seen the fleeting glances of his son as they fixed on the mother's bosom and quickly moved away. He had also noted the mild erections of his son at such times, which had infuriated him. The tension in this family mounted until the father was able to discuss this with the mother. The maturational development of their young son had been the source of considerable stimulation to his mother, who found herself with mounting irritation toward her husband and alternating mood swings toward her son. The son, in turn, indicated his involvement with her by engaging her in seemingly "important" conversations while she was dressing. It was only when this mother was able to have therapy that the situation improved. Such triangular situations frequently promote tension in all members of the family.

The above instances involved threats to the parent because of the fact that the adolescent had acted out an incestuous wish, and the parental defenses had threatened to become inadequate.

Another source of considerable anxiety to the parent is the tendency on the part of many adolescents to utilize flight as a means of avoiding the incestuous object. Such teen-agers join gangs, maintain intense heterosexual or homosexual friendships, and are extremely secretive about their comings and goings. The reaction in the parent, who feels shut out by this behavior, is a frequent cause of difficulty. The fear of loss of the offspring, which threatens the neurotic balance of forces within the family, often motivates the parental wish for help. This is particularly true in those cases where the child has been utilized to serve the projective mechanism of one or the other parent. The impending loss threatens the defensive structure of the parent involved. When the teen-ager allies himself, as he so often does, with a group which is ideologically diametrically opposed to the mores of his parents, the threat of dethronement, fear of exposure to the community, and helplessness against the combined force of a group are sources of tremendous anxiety to many parents. Again help is sought.

One of the defenses which Anna Freud[1] quotes as indicative of pathology in the adolescent is the defense of reversal of affect. In such instances the adolescent "turns love into hate," "dependence into revolt," and "respect and admiration into contempt and derision." These young people act out within the family. To the parent, such a state of affairs can be exceedingly distressing when the outbursts become excessive. In these instances, too, we have to help the parent to free the protesting adolescent, who is actually pathologically tied to the family. It goes without saying that such adolescents also require therapy.

A frequent cause of disturbance is the narcissistic parent who is in competition with the adolescent of the same sex. Should the daughter become more attractive than mother, and want to go out on dates, use lipstick, and wear sophisticated attire at an earlier age than did the mother, the latter, with well-rationalized jealousy, will want to "protect" her daughter by prohibiting these things. On the other hand, a mother may attempt to relive her own teen-age desires through her daughter. She may urge her to date and wear sophisticated clothing, etc. In each instance the relationship between parent and adolescent becomes disturbed.

I am reminded of a 14-year-old girl whose parents divorced and whose mother remarried. This mother saw in her daughter a rival whom she feared and hated as a potential threat to her new marriage. Yet, in her attempts to deny this, she bought all kinds of sophisticated clothing for her daughter and gave the girl too much freedom, with unfortunate results. The girl became delinquent.

I have very superficially tried to sketch a little of the heterosexual aspect of parental reactions to teen-agers. We must also touch on the homosexual problems. Illustrative of this was the history of X. This 12-year-old boy came to the clinic because of anxiety, stealing, and truancy. There had been considerable friction between the boy and his father. The fights occurred over such apparently reasonable things as keeping his room clean, but they really involved a triangular situation. This boy was intensely jealous of his next older brother, who was his father's favorite. He actually provoked many of the beatings that he received at the hands of his father. The father indicated that after such beatings the boy seemed more relaxed. Although, on the surface, this boy was hospitalized because of truancy, there had been a latent homosexual relationship between himself and his father, and possibly also some homosexual activity with his brother, 4 years older than he. During adolescence, when acting out was at its height, we found X.'s defenses breaking down, precipitating a severe state of anxiety.

Why was it that the family waited until X. had attained puberty to come for help? Although the history was one of continued disturbance between the parents as well as between father and son, it is quite likely that the homosexuality was the underlying cause of the friction. Whatever differences the parents had had, they apparently were able to contend with them to some degree until their son reached puberty. Adolescence, with its bodily changes, increased genital drives, and acting out of unconscious strivings threatened the existing defenses of the boy as well as his parents. Since X. had many problems about his identity (his mother had preferred a girl), his repressed unconscious wishes of submitting to his father now threatened to erupt. Only when the stimulus of the physical proximity with a sexually developed male became too much for the father did they seek help.

Not only did the homosexual desires play havoc with this family; there was an added factor. Both father and mother felt helpless to cope with the violent mood swings and the actual physical danger of this boy's aggressiveness during adolescence. This is not uncommon in families where physical expressions of anger had been exercised unduly by parents and siblings.

Summary

From the foregoing, it is apparent that a number of factors contribute to the parent-adolescent relationship as far as the parent is concerned. The foundation upon which the parent relates to the adolescent is laid during the pregenital and oedipal phase. We have seen that the free expression of the pregenital and oedipal urges serve as a daily bombardment of existing parental defenses. The result is often a weakening of these defenses and some degree of regression.

Where the atmosphere has been very permissive, the parental reaction is often more pathological. It is with such somewhat weakened defenses and heightened anxiety that the parent must now cope with the adolescent. The typical acting out and impulsiveness, so characteristic of this turbulent period, serve to intensify whatever difficulties the parent may have. Often the parent is seduced into violent scenes, despite his better judgment.

With the flowering of the adolescent's regressive phase, the parent reacts with prohibition, intolerance, and irritation, in an attempt to ward off his own unconscious urges.

The physical maturing of the adolescent poses one of the very difficult problems for the parent. The offspring now becomes a sexually stimulating but taboo object who, because of his predilection for acting out, threatens the already weakened defenses of the parent. Again, anxiety with renewed attempts to ward off incestuous wishes is the lot of the parent. He steers a course between Scylla and Charybdis, but founders on the rocks whichever way he goes. If he attempts to restrain his positive feeling, he is accused of neglecting his offspring. If he permits these feelings to come forth, he is guilty of incestuous stimulation.

Last, but not least, are the adolescent's attempts to withdraw from the family, thus threatening the parents in many ways. They experience a feeling of loss of prestige and a loss of *raison d'être*. Neurotic relationships that for years have been maintained on earlier levels are now threatened. Where sadomasochistic relationships have existed, the impending departure of the adolescent from the family circle leaves the involved parent without a partner. Where projective mechanisms have been established, again the offspring no longer furnishes the wherewithal for the projection.

We hear only too often about the depression of parents, the emptiness of the home, and the loss of goals, when the teen-ager finally leaves for college or to pursue his own life.

REFERENCES

1. COLEMAN, R. W., KRIS, E., and PROVENCE, S. "Study of Variations of Early Parental Attitudes," in *The Psychoanalytic Study of the Child*. New York, International Universities Press, Inc., 1953, vol. 8.
2. FREUD, A. "Adolescence," in *The Psychoanalytic Study of the Child*. New York, International Universities Press, Inc., 1958, vol. 13.
3. GELEERD, E. "Some Aspects of Ego Viscissitudes in Adolescence." 1958 Fall Meeting, American Psychoanalytic Association, Panel: Ego Development in Adolescence.
4. SPIEGEL, L. A. "A Review of Contributions to a Psychoanalytic Theory of Adolescence," in *The Psychoanalytic Study of the Child*. New York, International Universities Press, Inc., 1951, vol. 6.

chapter 15   Institutional Treatment

SIMON KWALWASSER AND SIDNEY L. GREEN

The needs of emotionally disturbed adolescents have been a matter of concern since antiquity. It has been only in modern times, however, that the possibilities of a systematized, scientific, sustained approach have been explored. With the development and growth of psychoanalytic theory and practice, an important new dimension was added. The early work of Aichhorn with adolescent delinquents in Vienna is probably the first intensive application of psychoanalysis to the psychopathology of adolescence. With this stimulus, the interest has never waned and is at an all-time high at present.

This chapter will not encompass all forms of institutional treatment for emotionally disturbed adolescents; rather, the discussion will be limited to the consideration, in the light of psychoanalytic dynamics, of the characteristics of a particular group of emotionally disturbed adolescents. To begin with, they are unable to sustain themselves either in a family setting or in group settings which require a considerable capacity for the assumption of responsibility geared to the realities of social life. These are adolescents who are going through an acute period of crisis which requires separation from home and placement in a highly structured and intensively supportive therapeutic program. Their ego resources are such that they would be capable of responding to this treatment program within a period of 1 to 1½ years, and then continue in treatment on an outpatient basis.[5] Our discussion will be presented in the light of experience with such a program at the Israel Strauss Pavilion for Adolescent Girls (ages 13 to 17 years), which was set up at the Hillside Hospital as a pilot demonstration project in 1954.[7,10]

It was originally anticipated that the patients at the unit would be girls with relatively intact ego structures who are temporarily severely incapacitated. Our actual experience with the candidates who were referred for admission, however, revealed that there were hardly any girls who met these ego qualifications. It therefore became our task to attempt to identify those girls who, in spite of more serious ego defects than we had originally anticipated accepting, would not require a period of institutional treatment in our program beyond 1½ years. Furthermore, our treatment goals had to be modified to include the preparation of some of our patients for a more "open" type of institutional treatment rather than for extramural psychotherapy (Linden Hill; Pleasantville Cottage School).

The clinical conditions that these girls presented were mostly overt or borderline psychoses, usually schizophrenic. The behavior patterns covered a broad range and included sexual promiscuity, compulsive stealing, incapacitating rituals, tormenting obsessions, phobias, marked irritability and severe rages, pathologic religiosity, unreasoning rebelliousness and negativism, suicidal tendencies (overt and covert), and reactions of a manic, depressive, or catatonic type.

To evaluate properly the current and potential ego resources of the adolescents presenting such problems, we had to scrutinize more closely their personalities and their life histories. The more detailed examination of the personality structures of these adolescents revealed that they had a particularly limited tolerance to frustration and were easily given to impulse gratification. They might express remorse or guilt over their actions, but their concern was never substantial enough to result in any meaningful degree of self-restraint upon their objectionable behavior patterns. The meaning of everyday reality was distorted to a marked extent owing to their tendency to considerable narcissistic preoccupation, which was usually of long standing. In keeping with this, object relations were tenuous and were established primarily for narcissistic gratification linked in largest measure to infantile aims.

Although considerable shifting of identification is noted in most adolescents, it is part of a continuous maturational process in those with adequate ego resources and is characterized by an accretion of impressions which leads to a reasonably mature concept of self and toward goals which will enable them to become more effective adults. This is not the case with the group under discussion. Their self-image has never been clearly established in a healthy way and is often confused with regard to sexual identity. Their life goals are determined more by infantile fantasies and fears than by identification with the constructive life goals and ego-integrative aims of parent figures. They are governed little by the desire to establish a warm empathy with others or by an interest in learning to cope with troublesome life situations. Instead, they are dedicated to devising means of avoiding having to meet the everyday problems of life and the feelings such problems engender; to being constantly on the lookout for every real and fancied source of danger which they then deal with by either flight or assault. The source of pathological danger to their egos may be from their instinctual drives or from the exaggerated penalizing demands of neurotically hypertrophied superego elements. We speak of superego elements in these adolescents because the superego aims are variably developed and, often, inconsistent with each other—an outgrowth of unstable identification and defective self-image formation usually present since early childhood.

The dynamic processes operating in these severely handicapped adolescents may be those associated with efforts to deal with primarily poor ego integration, with internalized conflict between ego and superego, or with dangers and inadequate emotional supports in the external environment. Individual members of this group may present elements of all three factors. The picture of lifelong inability to establish a cohesive, mutually supportive integration among the functions of the ego, however, regularly emerges from their histories.

Closely related to this is the frequently revealed inability of the parent figures to provide adequately warm and supportive relationships in the period of infancy and early childhood. In some instances the early-childhood needs and demands were too great to have been reasonably met by any parent. A considerable number of the parents of these adolescents, however, were too involved with their own narcissistic needs to be able to provide an unthreatening, predictably supportive object for the infant and toddler to relate to. These handicapped parents usually had no real awareness of their children's emotional needs. Some were seductively indulgent or violently rejecting and disapproving—sometimes alternating between these extremes. Others had been involved in relationships with these adolescents, from the time they were very young children, which were obviously intended primarily for mutual frankly erotic gratification.

Although the foregoing presentation has not been an exhaustive statement of every detail of the dynamic forces which determined the psychopathology of these adolescent girls, enough has been presented to delineate the kinds of problems we had to meet, and on which the program structure and goals had to be based.

One other problem encountered in the adolescent girls' Pavilion is that of sexual preoccupation. For some of the girls it is a continuation of an overt pattern already present prior to their admission; in others, it makes itself manifest for the first time following admission. Qualitatively, the phenomenon is not limited to the unit, having been a familiar one to all mental hospitals. The differences from the pattern in the older age groups lies in the intensity of the preoccupation and the fact that the girls not so preoccupied are the exceptions rather than the rule.

As might be expected, the manner of expression of the sexuality varies according to circumstances and patient personality. The forms taken include obsessional rumination about sex, overt and latent homosexual attachments, attempts to seduce male attendants and patients, compulsive drive to engage in petting with beaus among the male patients at every opportunity, and compulsive masturbation. At times, pent-up sexualized aggression has been responsible for explosive outbursts from one or a group of the girls, but this has not been frequent. Staff attitudes, especially those of the therapists, nurses, and aides, can be critical factors in determining the levels of sexualized tension which may be created in the unit.

Frequently, the preoccupation with some form of sexualized activity appears to be an attempt to cope with an underlying depression by means of denial of affect and displacement of object. In many instances there is a marked contrast between the apathy with which some girls approach activities which can provide relatively little opportunity for erotization (school, occupational therapy, self-government meetings, auditorium presentations of plays or concerts) and the vigor with which they pursue activities which lend themselves readily to it (clandestine coitus, petting, dancing, elopements, tantrums, group rebellions). Obviously, there is nothing remarkable about the preference for erotized over more sublimated forms of gratification in this type of patient. What makes it noteworthy is the greater intensity and frankness of the expression of this preference after admission, even for girls not given to considerable sexual promiscuity previously.

There are numerous and variable factors which we believe are responsible for the phenomenon. The tendency to regression is favored by the relative diminution in the demands for social adaptation after admission, compared to those made by the family and community outside the hospital. There is also experienced a need to provide for a means of escape from the increased anxieties mobilized in the face of the "danger" of confrontation with the unconscious elements of their conflicts as a result of therapeutic probing and uncovering. Another potent contributing factor is the combined anxiety and stimulation which results from living in sustained, close contact with other girls, and the resulting constant exposure to their unrelenting, quite frank, expression of instinctual needs.

The total structure of the program attempts to provide an approach to the answers to these as well as the other problems presented by these girls. Although limits and restrictions are necessary, they must be established to the minimal degree which is still consistent with adequate ego support, and they must be exercised with great care to avoid creating an increase in sexual and aggressive tensions. Staff members must be aware of their responsibility in avoiding those behavior patterns and attitudes which may be sexually stimulating or may provoke sexualized aggression from the girls. Stated positively, in accordance with this principle, every staff member in contact with the girls must contribute to an atmosphere of warmth and stability which favors interest in developing those ego functions and skills that permit the discovery of the more substantial satisfactions to be derived from the use of neutralized energy in the pursuit of more sublimated aims in relation to more mature object choices.

The following brief digest of four cases will illustrate different aspects of the problems discussed above.

CASE REPORT—BETTY

This girl is presented as an example of "delayed therapeutic effect" resulting in considerable ego strengthening following her discharge from the unit, even though seeming worse, in some ways, on discharge than on admission.

Betty was admitted to the Adolescent Pavilion at the age of 15½ and was discharged 14 months later. Three months previously she had been found in a coma after taking 27 Nembutal capsules, a usually lethal dose. She was seen by a psychiatrist who, presumably, advised no specific treatment. Subsequently, she was given a psychological examination and seen in consultation by a child psychiatrist because she was tense, would be found crying quietly in her room, and stated that she seemed to hear her name called on the street. Immediate hospitalization was arranged when she was found to have intensive destructive drives, primarily toward herself, and a severe schizoid type of pathology.

Betty was an unwanted child with a 4-years-younger brother with whom she was very rivalrous. The family was financially comfortable. The parents had always been given to frequent outbursts of anger and violence toward each other.

Betty was an intellectually gifted girl who had studied ballet at her own request, played the flute well, and had done well in school.

We learned that Betty had frequently had thoughts of killing herself and had taken the Nembutal with that purpose after seeing a TV show in which a child had been allowed to die because of parental ignorance. She had been in the habit, from early childhood, of conversing with people she knew of and imagined present. Her family had known of but ignored the habit.

Immediately after admission, Betty was pleasant and cooperative, although clearly unhappy. In a short time her attitude changed to defiance of those in authority. She became easily angered and would become violently destructive and assaultive in her rages. She dressed in leather jacket and jeans and got a boyish haircut. She led the group against authority and conformity of any kind. She formed a close "motherhood" relationship with A., who was also paranoid, impulsively hostile, and intellectually very inferior to Betty. They indulged in much horseplay and, eventually, engaged in overt homosexual activity with each other. After A. left, Betty formed a similar relationship with another girl who was on her intellectual level and who, in spite of healthier capacities than A., formed a powerful unit with Betty, constantly stimulating the other girls to act out their aggressive and sexual impulses. Betty saw herself as helping the girls to emancipate themselves.

Betty accepted the opportunities given to expend some of her energies along constructive lines and, finally, she obtained employment and did extremely well as a part-time switchboard operator on a job for which she had to leave the hospital daily. Her employer was very pleased with her, but, as soon as she returned to the Pavilion, the pattern of behavior described above was resumed. In her therapy sessions Betty related well, but she consistently expressed feelings of worthlessness. Her imaginary conversations, however, ceased soon after admission.

Betty was discharged rather suddenly when the generally violent behavior of the other girls, in response to her instigation, reached unacceptable proportions. For a few months she was part of a motorcycle gang and continued her homosexual friendship. She then terminated these relationships, moved away from home, and resumed treatment with her Pavilion therapist who had since gone into private practice.

She worked hard in therapy, married an apparently wholesome young man, took good care of her home, and worked full time as a telephone operator.

Her therapist reported that Betty has a real interest in living and in people, which grew directly out of the firm but kind understanding she had received while a patient in the Pavilion. A crucial factor, to her, was the fact that she had been unable to manipulate, seduce, or bribe her therapist either during or after discharge.

CASE REPORT—CAROL

In this instance a deceptive impression of considerable ego adequacy resulted in the Pavilion staff making a sustained but ineffectual therapeutic effort to rehabilitate the girl.

Carol was admitted to the Adolescent Pavilion at the age of 16 and was discharged 14 months later. She had one sibling, a younger brother 4 years her junior. She came from a middle-class family.

She was described as having been an excellent student, who was a fussy eater. Although at times willful, up to the age of 13 she had been shy, quiet, and rather prim. At the age of 13 she underwent a marked change. She became unhappy and had difficulty doing her schoolwork. Her parents reacted with anger when she complained of her unhappy feelings. She improved under treatment at a mental hygiene clinic, but she worsened when her mother removed her, after 6 months, in the face of pressure on the mother to become more involved in the treatment.

Carol became uncontrollably rebellious at home; ran away after quarrels with her parents, sometimes remaining away for days; and became engaged to an apparently delinquent boy not of her religion. After her admission, we learned that she had been picking up men and having sex relations with them. Her parents finally brought her to court as a wayward minor. She was remanded to "X" State Hospital for observation. The clinic and state-hospital reports described Carol as a girl of very superior intelligence with creative abilities, a good range of interests, and good comprehension, who had a marked tendency to active fantasy life. It was felt that the girl was reacting largely to her parents, who kicked her, slapped her, and called her abusive names for her misbehavior.

In the Pavilion it was found that Carol was completely unable to involve herself in schoolwork, could not sustain any effort, and could finish few of the things she started. She displayed sudden outbursts of violence, especially as a culmination to horseplay with the other girls. It soon became clear that she was unable to handle her sexual or aggressive feelings and frequently tried to run away when she felt threatened by them.

Carol saw the hospital only as a refuge from her punitive parents. In the Pavilion she could not accept the fact that she also had serious emotional problems. She often became involved in overt homosexual activities. At times, she would lie in bed for days, curled up like an infant. On other occasions she would report to her therapist, like a child, that she felt like running away and wanted help to control herself. A number of times, she tried to seduce her male therapist by disrobing when in his office; she was surprised when she failed.

Carol was transferred to a state hospital on a voluntary commitment, since she seemed to accept her need for a longer period of living in a well-structured environment. She signed herself out at the age of 18, however, and has been living in various places in and out of New York City in accordance with her preadmission pattern. It should be noted that Carol comes to our aftercare clinic when she is in New York and communicates with us by mail.

In retrospect, it is likely that much developmental information was withheld from us by the parents which probably would have highlighted Carol's poor tolerance to frustration, her highly erotized concept of her interpersonal relationships, and her limited capacity for identifying with relatively stable figures.

CASE REPORT—NANCY

This patient, admitted as a regressed, withdrawn, ritualistic, 14½-year-old girl, is presented to point out the need, at times, for a vigorous and active program of ego support to restore therapeutic accessibility.

This patient had been transferred from Linden Hill (a relatively "open" residential treatment center) where she had been for over 2 years. She had shown an acute picture of severe rituals and impulses after the death of her father when she was 12. She would wash her hands and face for from 1 to 4 hours, until her skin was excoriated from scrubbing. This ritual was frequently accompanied by repetitive counting and humming. She would redo her homework for the slightest mistake, underlining all words, continuously check the contents of her schoolbag, and keep cleaning her plate after eating. Because of the severity of her rituals, she became homebound. An enuretic picture developed. There had been some easing of the rituals during her stay at Linden Hill. In the spring of 1956, however, her condition took a turn for the worse. She refused to see her therapist, became mute and inaccessible, and would lie in her urine and stare blankly into space. It was at this juncture that Nancy was transferred to the Hillside Hospital Adolescent Pavilion.

On admission to Hillside Hospital, she seemed obviously much sicker than most of the other patients in the adolescent unit, appeared markedly regressed and withdrawn, would wet and soil, and resisted vigorously when efforts were made to clean her. She had a ritual of beating her chest with clenched fists, throwing her head violently back and forth so that her hair would cover her face, and swinging her arms. At a staff conference it was decided that a firm and vigorous supportive program would have to be instituted to compensate for her temporarily inadequate ego resources. By the use of an adequate number of people, we changed this girl's soiled clothes and bathed her. In addition, we explained to Nancy that we did this because we were interested in her and that we could not let her reduce herself to this animal type of existence. With this very firm and positive attitude, after a few days, Nancy accepted this "interference," and she was easily bathed and kept clean and helped toward participation in activities.

Soon Nancy had good days as well as bad days. On her good days she had charm and was verbal, warm, affectionate, and appealing. In spite of all the difficulties she caused the staff and the patients, she was well liked by everyone. Her therapist was gentle, sympathetic, and positive in his approach. Treatment was supportive, and only conscious material was dealt with. In a short time Nancy talked readily of her father and his death. She was able to relate her positive feelings toward her father. One of her rituals consisted of a rotating, dancelike movement when passing through a door, this way always looking back to see what she had left behind. She could understand here the connection with her loss of her father and the conscious fear of people and things disappearing. Nancy's father had died suddenly of coronary disease. Now, we learned that the worsening of Nancy's condition at Linden Hill had begun with the interpretation of her hostile feelings toward her therapist and her father. The more the hostility had been discussed, the more she had become ritualistic and withdrawn. At the Pavilion, Nancy was geared toward doing things. She was graceful and loved to dance and do things with people. These assets were utilized in the activities program in the Pavilion. She participated actively in the athletic and swimming program, and was praised for her extreme gracefulness in swimming. School was very difficult for Nancy, since she was very much behind. Her limitations were accepted. Womanhood and female identification were difficult for her to accept. From the history it was learned that Nancy was eagerly expected as a boy and at birth—"a ritual circumcision"—had been planned. Many of the patient's rituals pointed toward an identification with her father. He would also count to 5 when washing, and had had many other rituals. He also had had a long history of enuresis. Her hand washing was connected with the idea of washing germs away, being afraid they might kill her as they did her father. Nancy menstruated at 16 for the first time, while in the Pavilion. She was the first one to notice the pregnancy of one of the nurses, and this led to a flood of material about womanhood. Nancy had a male therapist for the first year and was assigned a female therapist at the end of that time, deliberately to help with further feminine identification.

Although the prognosis originally was quite pessimistic, this patient seemed in very good state when she left the Pavilion. Schooling was to be continued on a home-instruction basis, special arrangements were made for dancing instruction, and she continued to be carried in the aftercare program. The turning point in this patient's handling was the decision at the staff conference to show actively, vigorously, and forcibly, if necessary, enough interest in this girl to keep her neat, clean, tidy, and fed. As soon as she became verbally accessible, not only did she not resent this treatment but expressed great appreciation for everything that had been done for her.

CASE REPORT—JILL

This girl is presented to indicate the progress in a 14½-year-old girl who, from her history and her early uncontrolled, impulsive, hostile, destructive behavior in the hospital, seemed to have little ability to develop control and an adequate capacity for sublimation. This patient was admitted when the unit was first opened and, although she did not fit our criteria for admission, she was deemed suitable for trial.

Jill was the adopted daughter of a college professor, had lived in foster homes until the age of 6, and was described as a problem child from infancy. She was described as having been a destructive baby, having had a feeding problem as she grew older, having played with her feces up to the age of 6. In the foster homes she was described as unmanageable, impulsive, aggressive, destructive, and unpredictable. After adoption, she developed affection for her parents, but she remained ambivalent, destructive, and assaultive. The adoptive father and mother had successfully raised a son who was, at that time, of college age. Jill developed a close relationship with her brother. They went hunting and fishing, and played ball together. Her assaultive episodes at home were frequently in relation to her mother. She once threw a knife at her parents and, at another time, set fire to the home. The episode which precipitated her hospitalization was the threat to shoot her parents with a shotgun. She developed a close relationship with her dog, whom she treated sadistically at the beginning, but at other times could be very affectionate with him.

She was hospitalized at 10, for behavior problems, at a Boston hospital for 5 weeks. At 11, she was hospitalized in a state hospital where she remained for 9 months, and from there was transferred to the Adolescent Pavilion. On admission, she was anxious, hostile, suspicious, and disheveled. She had little to say except that she had come to the hospital to get well. She wore boots, jeans, and leather jacket, and she was always ready to fight people off. Although the staff was frightened by her, they were able eventually to accept her. In the occupational-therapy shop she was very productive. She liked to show her strength and her ability to handle these tasks, and she helped the other girls. She became an assistant, cleaned up, and did many of the chores the other girls did not like to do. School was difficult for her, and little was demanded of her. For months she revealed very little of herself to the therapist (a man). Eventually, she developed more positive feelings and could discuss some of the present living situations and her past situations. She seemed to appreciate that not too much was demanded of her intellectually, having grown up in an intellectual environment (college campus) where her feelings of inadequacy were enormously increased. She gained in group status and became the leader of a small group of girls. Her need to work had helped her to rid herself of some of her aggressive impulses, and at the same time to prove that she could be useful. She still was difficult to manage owing to her extreme sensitivity, which made her feel rejected on minimal provocations. This led to intense outbursts of verbal and physical violence.

As she eventually became more comfortable in the Pavilion, she would indulge in horseplay with the other patients, and she developed friendships with her horseplay as the principal form of shared activity. She would constantly take masculine roles but was eventually able to accept, with encouragement, a more feminine role. She then developed a relationship, with one of the girls, in which she was definitely a female partner. She changed her appearance, began to dress in girls' clothes instead of boots and jeans, began to wear make-up, and spoke in a much more feminine way. Although she did enjoy her feminine role, she was not by any means ready to give up her masculine role. In her over-all functioning this girl was considerably better at the end of 13 months, but she was still extremely fragile. Her hostility could easily be aroused when she felt rejected.

We were fortunate in being able to plan for her to live with a couple who owned a kennel and trained dogs. Jill accepted a position to train the dogs and act as assistant to the owner. The place was in the country about an hour from her own home. This arrangement worked out extremely well. Jill became very much involved with the dogs. She would frequently visit her family and got along infinitely better with them than she had before. She developed a very good relationship with the people she was working with.

In view of the long chronic history of violent, destructive, impulsive, uncontrolled behavior in a child with extremely low frustration tolerance, this case appeared to have an extremely poor prognosis. The unit was able, however, to accept her and her behavior for a sufficiently long time, so that she was able to develop some substantial feelings of adequacy and acceptance in this new environment, a much better picture of herself, and a greater measure of self-esteem. It may have been fortuitous that one was able to find for her a couple who could accept her when she left the hospital, as well as a kennel of dogs whom she could relate to more easily than to people. Here again, she had a feeling of some achievement and of some personal worth.

Hillside Adolescent Pavilion

The Hillside Adolescent Pavilion program was designed as an intensive, individualized, psychoanalytically oriented treatment program which takes into account the importance of the total living experience and of the interpersonal relationships between the patients and staff.[7] Although the ability to involve themselves in conventional psychotherapy is a goal of this institutional treatment program, these adolescents do not have the capacity, emotionally, to do so to any meaningful extent initially. Highly disturbed adolescents, however, are in great need of those experiences and relationships which help to remove the particularly stubborn barriers that interfere seriously with psychotherapeutic accessibility in the early period of hospitalization. Conventional psychotherapy comes to be meaningful very slowly to these girls, only as certain fundamental physical and emotional needs are properly and adequately provided for in the course of the established pattern of the daily life in the Pavilion. Well-crystallized and consistent transference relationships are nonexistent for quite some time in the sense that they are found in the treatment of neurotic personality disorders. These girls are groping aimlessly and only tentatively for identification. Therefore, it is necessary for all the members of our institutional treatment team to be consistent in the conception and implementation of the purpose of the program and the role each one plays. Each member of the staff must vividly see his own contribution in relation to that of all the other members of the staff.

The psychiatrist must accept the fact that the patient unconsciously considers herself to be once again in the family scene and that the psychiatrist occupies the most important position in it. For some time then, the psychiatrist who is conducting her therapy acts as the coordinator of the program, which involves the patient in multiple relationships, and as the person who interprets the purpose of the program, in terms of its realities, to the patient and to the staff. The psychiatrist also gradually helps the patient to recognize her own distortions of reality, her denials, and her projections, as they are revealed in the pattern of both her group living in the Pavilion and her productions during her sessions with her therapist.

Lately, we have been fortunate indeed to find a new type of personnel, called "counselors," with whom we have replaced some of our less skilled psychiatric aides. These are college graduates who have had special experience in working with children, in addition to possessing special skills. Not only have they been able to add new interests for the girls, but they are also much more acceptable ideals for the girls to emulate. This has been a valuable addition since, in any psychiatric hospital setting, patients are in an active process of growth and change and are very sensitive to the attitudes and relationships about them. This is even more true in an adolescent unit, where the patients are so much in need of using all the adults around them as objects for identification.

It should be recalled, from the earlier discussion, that the greater number of these girls have been unable to find any meaningful object for identification in their parents or in the other important adults in their environment. Therefore, it is of cardinal importance to provide the warmest and most stable personnel for these girls in every staff category. The principle categories include the departments of Nursing, Social Service, Psychology, Occupational Therapy, Group-Work Activities, Academic Education, and such volunteer services as may augment and strengthen the core program.

The Department of Education is staffed by two teachers from the "600 School Program" (for emotionally disturbed children) of the New York City Board of Education.[4] Early attempts to have some of our girls attend schools in the local community proved impractical. The two classrooms on the hospital grounds, at some distance from the Pavilion, have, however, given the patients the feeling of "going to school." Having all the patients attend the "600 School Program" on the hospital grounds has enabled the establishment of a close liaison between the patients, doctors, and teachers. Through their regular attendance at clinical conferences and informal conferences with members of the staff, the teachers have been able to become familiar with the particular needs of each girl and to contribute valuable observations of their own. The schoolwork is geared to each girl's academic and emotional capacities. The atmosphere of the classroom is as informal as can be consistent with effective and productive effort.

At Hillside Hospital the school program and the occupational-therapy program alternate with each other, so that the girls who go to school in the morning go to the occupational-therapy program in the afternoon, and vice versa. Emphasis in occupational therapy is on the personal relationship with the occupational therapist, who is fully cognizant of the therapeutic goal envisaged for each individual patient and tries to provide, through occupational therapy, an opportunity for the patient to achieve this goal through appropriate need satisfactions.[3]

The Group-Work Activities Department provides activities such as music, dancing, physical education, sports, cooking, hairdressing, and homemaking. The members of this department also assist the girls in the self-government program which is encouraged. As with all other activities, these are utilized in accordance with the over-all therapeutic program which has been carefully conceived and planned for her by each patient's doctor.[1]

The Social Service Department plays a vital role in the team approach. It provides casework services to the parents of the patient and helps in planning for the mobilization of all community facilities in behalf of the patient and her family. Experience has shown that, because of their immaturity, these patients continue to be closely bound to and deeply affected by their parents, even after admission to the Pavilion. For this reason, the casework treatment with at least one and, if possible, both of the parents, is an essential part of the activities of this department.[9]

A psychologist is included as part of the therapeutic team. A battery of tests is administered to all patients when they are first admitted to the hospital. These may be repeated during the course of hospitalization and again prior to the patient's discharge. Where vocational guidance and rehabilitation are necessary, the Psychology Department takes a very active part in the testing, planning, and referral to the appropriate agencies in cooperation with the Social Service Department.[6]

The Nursing Department has the most intimate contact with the patients, and many of the programs initiated by the departments of Occupational Therapy or Group-Work Activities depend on the assistance received from nursing personnel. The Nursing Department consists of nurses, psychiatric aides, and the previously mentioned counselors. Because they spend more time in the company of these women than in that of any other adult on the staff, the girls turn more to them than to anyone else as substitute parental objects. Because of their limited knowledge, training, and skill, the average aides currently available are particularly handicapped in their ability to grasp the fundamental emotional needs of these girls and thus to function in stable, consistent, and appropriately supportive ways. They are particularly prone to develop intense anxiety in response to the behavior of the girls, and it is not unusual for them to respond with immature, provocative, and retaliatory behavior. We have already noted what a marked improvement there was in the contribution made by the Nursing Department when the more mature, stable, trained child worker was added.[2]

When the Hillside Adolescent Pavilion was opened, it was at first thought of as a highly specialized, intensive treatment unit that would function as independently of the remainder of the institution as possible. The original feeling was that the unit should have its own specialized personnel who would be carefully screened and indoctrinated with the program and treatment goals of the Adolescent Pavilion. The unit was to be provided with its own activities and recreational program divorced from those provided for the adult portion of the hospital.

Our experience with the philosophy of an independent self-contained unit, where all the facilities mentioned above would be provided within the unit, turned out to have unexpectedly negative results. Both the patients and the employees developed a feeling of isolation from the remainder of the hospital. Although the facilities provided at the Adolescent Pavilion were often much better and more elaborate than those in the adult portion of the hospital, the Pavilion patients felt that they were being excluded from the life of the hospital and were constantly striving to take part in it. The girls now do participate in a good deal of the recreational activities of the remainder of the hospital. Although this has created some problems of its own, its benefits far outweigh the negative effects. It has also been necessary to explain more fully to the personnel of the entire hospital the function and aspirations of the Adolescent Pavilion and to arouse some interest in these people so that there would be more tolerance and understanding for the problems created by the adolescents during their excursions into the adult portion of the hospital. It is now much more possible to have our employees from the adult portion cover the Pavilion in time of need, without the overwhelming anxiety and fear that characterized the response to such a request in the early days.

As the use of the facilities of the entire hospital was explored, it was occasionally found advantageous to transfer temporarily an acutely disturbed girl to the closed adult female ward. This measure was resorted to only under the most stringent circumstances, since we found that we had to guard against the tendency of the personnel to fail to make the fullest possible effort to help the girl so that she could remain at the Pavilion during her period of acute disturbance. More recently, temporary transfers have been less frequently required, and those transfers which have been made have increasingly been cases in which the girl's therapeutic needs are best served by continuing the remainder of her hospital treatment while living with the adult female patients.

Some mention must be made of the balance which has to be set up between necessary limits and constructive permissiveness in an institutional program for girls like these. All these patients have proved, by their behavior on the outside of the hospital, that they could not impose proper limitations on themselves. Since they have been unable to conceptualize healthy goals and set reasonable limitations, the program must set the necessary limits for as long as is necessary. At the same time it must afford an adequate opportunity for the expression of the *healthy* physical and emotional needs and capacities of the girls. The failure to provide limitations on the behavior of the patients in the unit would invite objectionable and even dangerous acting out, to which we would thus be giving our implicit consent from the point of view of our patients. Through "hygienic programing" we have tried to provide acceptable activities which can serve as growth-promoting outlets for drives which would otherwise have been expressed in undesirable behavior. Through this means we have sought to keep the number and kind of limitations which must be imposed to a minimum, consistent with the proper implementation of the over-all therapeutic program.[8]

We consider this social unit in which the patient is being treated as the therapeutic instrument of prime importance. The patient's hospitalization is structured, in so far as is possible, to provide the patient with a continuously therapeutic experience. Recreation or occupational therapy, drug therapy, social-service help, the daily routine of hospital experience, such as getting up, going to school, mealtime experiences, going to bed at definite times, pass, telephone and visiting privileges, in fact all the things that happen around the clock, must be regarded as essential components of the therapeutic process.

One of the vitual functions in the proper operation of such a unit is staff intercommunication, and this requires the existence of proper techniques for the collection and exchange of information so that the correct decisions can be made to provide those therapeutic interventions which will constitute the corrective emotional experiences necessary for individual patients. Patients at the unit are all very well aware that there is a free flow of information between their doctor and all departments, for their common good. In the case of Betty, described above, one of the conditions she made was that she would not talk to her psychiatrist unless he agreed not to discuss anything she said with any other Pavilion staff member. This the therapist said he could not do. He explained that all data form the basis of our understanding in each case, and plans are then made in terms of individualized, specific, therapeutic goals for each girl. Since we function as an integrated unitary team, the more that each member of the team knew, the better she could be helped to achieve the chosen therapeutic goal. Betty, reluctantly, finally accepted this decision and, as we pointed out in our presentation of her case, it was our feeling that the crucial factor in this case was that Betty had not been able to manipulate, seduce, bribe, or threaten the therapist, either during hospitalization or after discharge.

The purpose of the Pavilion is to create a realistically unified, harmonious, hygienic atmosphere, dedicated to the emotional maturation of the patient. This can be done only by the careful evaluation of all data on each patient and the formulation of an individualized plan in terms of a specific therapeutic goal based on a scientific theory of behavior. As we noted in the opening of our paper, the psychoanalytic point of view is the one by which we have been guided at the hospital.

References

1. BRADLOW, F. K. Contribution of social group work to the treatment milieu of the adolescent pavilion Hillside Hospital. *Journal of the Hillside Hospital.* 9: 1, 1960.
2. CLIGGETT, K. Nursing staff functions in a treatment setting. *Ibid.* p. 88.
3. ENGEL, R. Occupational therapy at the adolescent pavilion. *Ibid.* p. 80.

4. GALE, M., and SHATZKY, B. P.S. 611—Queens Annex: a school in a psychiatric hospital. *Ibid.* p. 94.
5. GLYNN, E. An after-care program for adolescents. *Ibid.* p. 61.
6. KAVAZANJIAN, T. The role of the clinical psychologist in the adolescent pavilion of the Hillside Hospital. *Ibid.* p. 66.
7. KWALWASSER, S., and GREEN, S. L. Treatment program at the Israel Strauss Pavilion for adolescent girls. *Ibid.* p. 14.
8. LINNELL, Z. M. Authority as a treatment modality with adolescents in a psychiatric hospital. *Ibid.* p. 48.
9. RIBACK, S. The parent as part of the team in treatment of hospitalized adolescents. *Ibid.* p. 72.
10. STAHL, A. S. The first five years of the Israel Strauss Adolescent Pavilion program. *Ibid.* p. 5.

chapter 16 Diagnostic and Prognostic Considerations in Psychological Tests

SOLOMON MACHOVER

As we know, the problems of diagnosis and prognosis in adolescence are infinitely complicated by virtue of the fact that this is a period of extraordinary stress. The occurrence of sexual maturation, one might say the sexual explosion; the reactivation of the Oedipus complex; the advent or intensification of masturbatory activities; the need to organize a satisfactory sex role; the need to crystallize an acceptable, integrated, autonomous, differentiated identity on the road to adulthood all constitute sources of such stress to the ego as, in many cases, to make very real the major differential diagnostic question: When are we dealing with a transient exaggeration of adolescent behavior which remains within normal limits, when with an uncovering of a psychotic process, and, finally, when with a psychoticlike exaggeration of normal adolescence?

The problem of distinguishing between acute reactions and early manifestations of a chronic process particularly confronts the psychologist for, quite understandably, it is the uncertain borderline case that is most often referred to him for examination. Often, the adolescent who presents confusing diagnostic problems to the psychiatrist does exactly the same to the psychologist. On the other hand, it not infrequently happens that the patient who, on clinical psychiatric evaluation, appears psychotic, showing a morbid pathological process, on the psychological appears to be in a reactive state, showing acute panic features and presenting the picture of adolescent crisis. Sometimes the opposite obtains; that is, the patient who, on psychiatric evaluation, appears to show simply an acute manifestation of adolescent problems, presents evidence on the psychological tests to suggest that some more morbid process is involved.

The projection into test protocols of disturbing adolescent problems, by itself, is not necessarily indicative of a pathological process. To illustrate some of the forms that adolescent problems take in projection on psychological tests, let us consider a drawing of phallic preoccupation made by a 10-year-old prepuberal boy. In this drawing (see Figure 1A) the child's rather extreme phallic preoccupation shows up in symbolic form. Of course, the drawing is a complex product and does not confine itself to the particular point at issue. In this instance the projection of castration anxiety is as eloquent as the projection of phallic preoccupation. What is relevant to the present context is this child's virtually compulsive concentration on projections of all kinds. Even the finger comes up; the hat has a spike coming up; the brim of the hat comes over in an exaggerated projection; the big cigar in the mouth and even the back of the chair have suggestive phallic appearances. The very considerable preoccupation with projections is obvious. At the same time, notice that one arm is cut off, so that some concern with castration seems also to be evident. If this drawing is kept in mind, it will appear later how it correlates with similar implications shown in the Rorschach. In the drawing of the female (Figure 1B) one can detect a preoccupation with fertility. Curiously enough, this child was most eloquent in the expression of his aversion to the idea that his mother might have another child.

Oedipal problems frequently emerge in fantasies generated in response to TAT 6 BM. A story not infrequently offered by the adolescent sees the young man as a detective, or some friend of the family, who has come to report to the mother of the child, not visualized in the picture, that her husband has been killed in an accident. This is a not-infrequent expression of the desire to dispose of the competitive parent. Similarly, on Rorschach Card I, the same child who at 10 made the drawings in Figures 1A and 1B said of this card that this was two men, one on each side, attacking the woman in the middle. Again, it doesn't take too much imagination to assume that this has something to do with the feeling of the adolescent boy in his competitive attitude toward the male parent in relation to the mother.

This same card is very often seen as a mask, the white spaces representing the eyes and mouth. I think it is fair to assume that this has some reference to the feeling of dissociation between outer self-presentation and inner feelings. It seems to express a need to conceal from others what is going on inside. It is an expression also of the extreme sensitivity and self-consciousness of the adolescent who knows only too keenly, and feels only too keenly, the evil he associates with his surging inner impulses and related fantasies. In the same vein, this plate is often seen as the face of a leering animal or of a man. Card III, held upside down, is also often seen as a weird face. In the forced quality of this response may be appreciated the lengths to which adolescents sometimes go in projecting the paranoid or, perhaps, phobic anticipations arising out of the guilt feelings with which they are oppressed. The percept seems to involve an intuitive projection, an elaboration of barely suggested elements in the card which touch off a vivid and active preoccupation.

Expressions of adolescent sexual tension, and of the pressure to act out in a none too organized fashion, are frequently seen in the Rorschach. Thus, Rorschach Card II is very often seen as an explosion, a volcano erupting, or a bullet which has been fired by a gun below. Card IX, upside down, in much the same way, is also often seen as a volcano, or as the explosion of an atomic bomb with a mushroom cloud at the top. The upper part of Card VI is sometimes seen as a sparking electrode. The interpretive implications of these examples seem quite evident and require no further elaboration.

Preoccupation with masturbation and castration anxiety is frequently evident on projective tests. On TAT Card I, for example, a 16-year-old boy gave a story which may be paraphrased somewhat as follows: "This boy has been given this strange object as a gift on his birthday. He doesn't know what it is. As he regards it, as he plays around with it, he picks up a stick which is part of it. And, while fooling around with it, the stick happens to touch the string and, lo and behold, a sound emerges. He tries it again—more sounds. It's music. He decides to ask his parents to give him lessons on how to play it. And, after much practice he finally learns how to do it, and he looks at it, and he says, 'Isn't it remarkable, just a box and a stick, and a few strings, and such wonderful music emerges.'"

Castration anxiety is implied in some of the Rorschach responses of frightening faces, cited above. In addition may be mentioned the perception of Card IV as a threatening giant or monster, as well as the frequently encountered preoccupation with projections of various kinds.

The adolescent's somatic anxiety, his anxious preoccupation with his own body, often finds expression in anatomical percepts offered in response to Cards VIII and IX. Often there is no clear conception of any particular part of the anatomy. There is only the general feeling that the insides of the body are represented in these affect-laden, colorful cards.

The adolescent's ambivalence with regard to organizing a persistent and appropriate sex role often finds expression in an inability to reconcile conflicting indicators of sexual identity in the human figures perceived on Card III. The people perceived on this card are often seen as half men and half women.

Self-concept ambivalences are sometimes projected on Card VIII, where the animals at the side are perceived first, perhaps, as rats and then again as lions or tigers.

The emotional capacities of the adolescent under stress are reflected in the contrast between his handling of the vivid red blots on Cards II and III on the one hand, and his handling of the pastel shades on Cards VIII, IX, and X. The former may be instantly perceived as representing blood and fire, at the same time that the latter elicit no color-determined responses at all. What this seems to imply is that the intense primitive affects associated with the tensions of sexual maturation and with the anxieties generated in the course of the adolescent's frustrations in his striving for an appropriate self-concept readily emerge under stress. By contrast there would seem to be relatively little development of, or confidence in, his capacity for the more refined and socialized forms of affective expression implicit in the pastel shades of Cards VIII, IX, and X.

Difficult to evaluate and yet eloquently and poignantly characteristic of the adolescent's struggle are the projections of his ambivalence between the desire to progress and the desire to regress. An 11-year-old boy offered, in response to Card VI, what seemed rather a dramatic although symbolic example of the extremes to which the adolescent often goes in his fantasies as he experiences the conflict between the drive to grow and the regressive weight of his own dependency. The upper half of the card, side view, was seen first as a sunken ship with the uppermost projection as its mast, then as a submarine with the same projection serving as its conning tower, and finally as a sailing vessel on the surface. Noteworthy here is the fact that the submarine and the sunken ship were more clearly seen than the sailing vessel on the surface. This patient's next response was of an airplane perceived in the blot as a whole. Of particular interest is the fact that these responses run

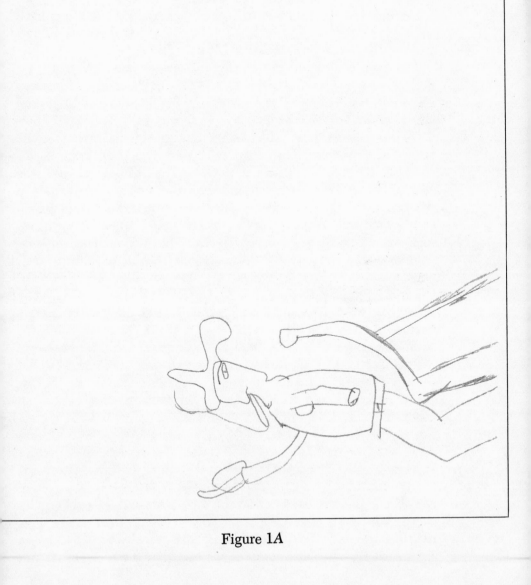

Figure 1A

Figure 1*B*

Figure 2A

Figure 2*B*

Figure 3A

Figure 3*B*

Figure 4A

Figure 4B

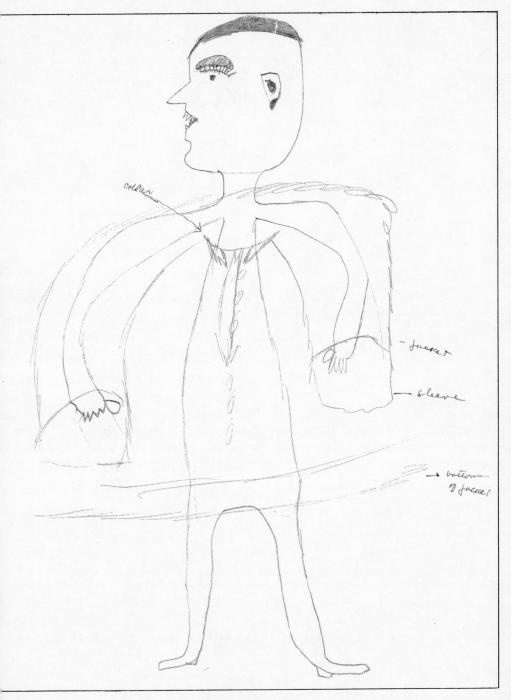

Figure 5A

Figure 5B

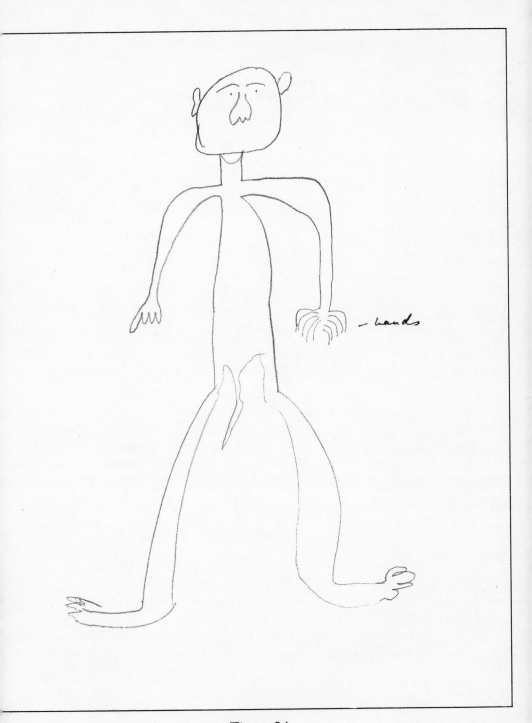

hands

Figure 6A

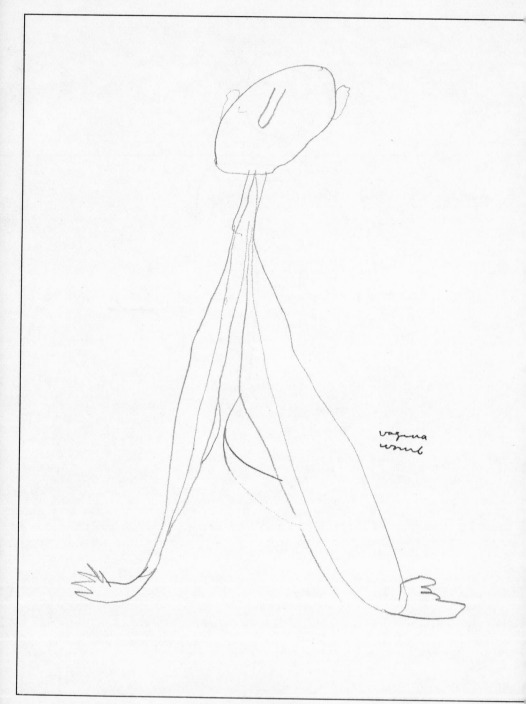

vagina
womb

Figure 6*B*

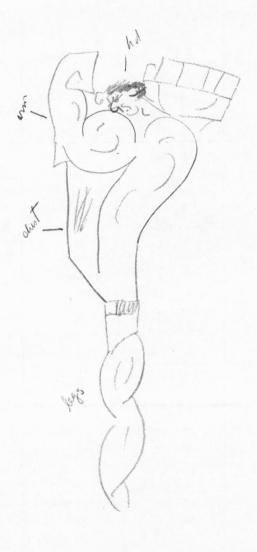

Figure 7

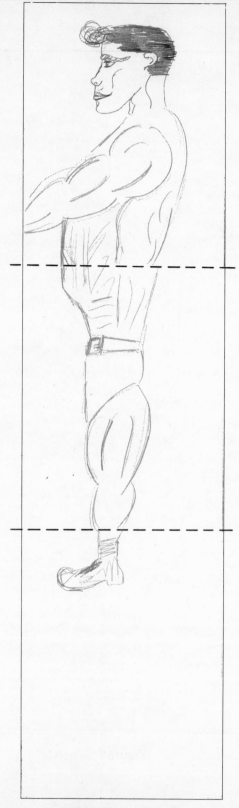

Figure 8A, 8B, 8C

(Three sheets of paper were used for this drawing.)

Figure 9A

Figure 9*B*

a gamut of levels from undersea to surface to upper space. This casting about for a level on which to frame and stabilize a sense of his own being is reminiscent of another adolescent boy who projected a similar problem in discussing his vocational preferences. When asked what kind of vocational activity he might find attractive, he said, "Well, I would like to be a frogman."

"If you can't be a frogman, what would you like to be?"

"An astronaut—to explore outer space."

"What about something on the surface?"

"Well, I never did like the appearance of water on the surface. I hate that. It frightens me."

Very clearly, what are projected here are the conflicts, the extreme difficulties in making a realistic here-and-now object-oriented, object-related adjustment. On the one hand, there is the desire to regress, expressed, I think, in the interest in undersea life, and, on the other hand, there are fantasies of progression which know no bounds. Feelings of extreme inadequacy and extreme insufficiency alternate with fantasies of omnipotence, of unbounded greatness; and lost somewhere between is the matter of adjustment in the world of reality, the world in which the problems of adaptation are experienced with such acuteness.

The foregoing examples can be scarcely more than suggestive of the richly diversified ways in which the adolescent expresses his essentially normal problems on projective tests. Perhaps they convey something of the artlessness which often breaks through his defenses to confer a startling clarity and poignancy on the symbols he chooses to represent his problems. The examples described above were intended to indicate where *not* to look for pathology. It must be acknowledged, however, that the last response cited, with its hint of escape into unreality, may well be open to question as to its pathological import. The diagnostic significance of perceived or fantasied content which is concerned with regressive and autistic ideas, but which is nevertheless clearly perceived or logically and articulately structured, will be considered later.

DIFFERENTIAL DIAGNOSIS

Now, where are we to look for criteria? What kinds of criteria may be formulated, in our effort to distinguish between what looks like evidence of a morbid process on the one hand, and what, on the other hand, may merely be a psychoticlike, acute exaggeration of normal adolescent problems? In the first place, let me disavow any deep conviction as to our ability inevitably to do this. It is a difficult task, and I don't think there are any really hard-and-fast rules which will always reliably guide us in making this kind of differential diagnosis. Let me remark, parenthetically, that I feel that one of the most important areas for research should be oriented precisely around this question. What is needed is a long-term follow-up study of the many adolescents whom we have seen on the wards, over the past decade or two, who were in critical states, in the sense that they were in a panic, showing at least transient disorganization and raising serious questions as to the essential morbidity of the underlying process. Such a follow-up study should help us to get a clearer picture of the implications of the acute manifestations at adolescence.

As to the differential-diagnostic guidelines, actually I do not have many. I really have only one. What I should like to suggest is the following: The more severe the disturbance of the basic structure of thought, that is, of the cognitive processes, the greater is the likelihood of pathological process. Peculiar thought content, and I have illustrated some, may alert us to possible deviations in process, but it is essentially the nature of the process by which the content was arrived at that I feel is significant for the question of pathology in the sense of ego disorganization. I need only to call attention to the peculiar content of some artistic productions. It is not so much the artistic content which raises the question of pathology but, rather, the process by means of which it was determined. Does the apparently deviant content occur in a context of clear control? Is it within the organized perception of the artist? Does it serve his purposes which ultimately are oriented toward reality?

Similar questions might be raised concerning the Plains Indians who cultivate the ability to hallucinate. The hallucinations may be considered as constituting a kind of content, but what is the nature of the process which produces them? Are they an autonomous, independent, and spontaneous expression of a person's struggle to adjust to reality? Or do they represent something which is coordinate with his own intentions, with his own purposes, which themselves are coordinate with the reality within which he lives? These would be some of the essential questions in distinguishing between content and its determining process of production.

As an auxiliary principle, it may be stated that the clearer the state of consciousness, the greater the freedom from anxiety in which the cognitive distortion is offered, the more serious and more nearly pathognomonic is the given deviation in cognitive process. These are statements which obviously require specification and definition, but I am going to avoid that in the hope that as I go over a number of cases, what they mean will become clearer in concrete contexts.

CASE REPORT

First, let us consider a 16-year-old boy who was admitted to the adolescent service at Kings County Hospital some years ago. This is one instance where the psychiatric judgment, on initial examination, was that this was a case of schizophrenia, and the intent was to certify the patient as such to a state hospital; the psychological examination, however, suggested that the picture was actually an acute one. The psychologist felt that the boy was reacting in a state of panic, that he might actually be a good case for treatment, and that he should be given some time before final disposition was made. I quote from the psychiatric summary:

"This is the case of a 16-year-old boy brought here because of periods of sudden excitability in which he yelled, screamed, smashed windows, complained of feelings of unreality, could not concentrate, had visual and auditory hallucinations, and some paranoid ideation. His personal history is that at the age of 1 month he turned blue, and at 2 months had his first convulsion. At 6½ he had two convulsions, one right after the other, with foaming at the mouth and twitching of the extremities. Following the convulsions, he had severe headaches and was hospitalized for 5 days, but, according to the mother, was never placed on medication. Convulsions continued with a frequency of once a month and always during the night. They gradually decreased and finally stopped, however, when he was 10. He has had none since.

"As a child he was very quiet, tense, nervous, and sickly, suffered from nightmares, was afraid of darkness and of sleeping alone, and had screaming spells. His mother had always been greatly concerned over his sickly and nervous condition, and took him to numerous doctors and clinics. The boy was not allowed to play with other boys and was overprotected by his mother, with whom he spent most of his time. He was hospitalized for 10 days at the P—— Hospital. The electroencephalogram done there was quoted as probably abnormal. On the ward he was apprehensive, anxious, and preoccupied with religion. The patient states that he has slept with his mother for a number of years, the father sleeping in another room. The boy was quoted as saying that his mother knew two men, his father and himself.

"During the last 5 years he has shown all kinds of nervous mannerisms, eyeblinking, abortive movements of his hands, and, in the past 6 months, a tic of his head. For the past 6 months he has become withdrawn and afraid that other people laugh at him because of his tic. He took part in social activities and became very excited and restless following a party which girls attended. He did fairly well in school. He was on the staff of the school paper. But it was noted that in the last 6 months his work has begun to deteriorate. The patient is extremely religious, and for 4 years served as an altar boy. During his stay at the hospital, the patient revealed that he was intensely preoccupied with sexual feelings, guilt about masturbation, and fears of dying. In several interviews he was able to bring these ideas into the open with great feelings of relief."

On the Wechsler-Bellevue this boy had an I.Q. of 106 on the verbal scale, 109 on the performance scale, and 109 for the scale as a whole. I think the first thing to note here is that there is little discrepancy between the verbal and performance I.Q.'s, suggesting that he is rather more object oriented than some of the history suggested and than was felt in the psychiatric examination. Following is his Rorschach protocol:

Card I: "Looks like a bee. Some kind of insect, with wings here and the body in the center."

Card II: "Some kind of insect also. Does it have to be something? Isn't it just an ordinary ink blot?"

One gets a feeling here of defensive perseveration and of evasiveness. This kind of defensiveness suggests some measure of insight, a felt need to defend himself against the emergence of guilt-engendering thoughts.

Card III, upside down: "Some kind of monster, with eyes, nose, his mouth is down here and his neck is bleeding."

The content and the sheer boldness of the perceptual organization of this response suggest considerable disturbance. The blunt reaction to the red as blood points to marked emotional instability, even though some effort to rationalize and to integrate the affective impact of the color is evident. The bleeding neck is reminiscent of the patient's history of choking sensations which seem to have no organic cause and might easily have constituted a conversion of fellatio fantasies. The content of the response suggests castration anxiety. Nevertheless, what is essential, for diagnostic purposes, is an evaluation of the cognitive process which led to the perceptual response. To what extent does the percept reflect a passive release in response to inner needs which, stimulated by some aspect of the blot, led the patient uncritically to impose on the blot, as a whole, an interpretation coordinate with his needs but insupportable by the objective structure of the blot itself? In other words, to what extent is the percept so dominated by need as to constitute an autistic distortion of reality? To what extent does the percept reflect an inability to inhibit a tendency to respond to transient stimuli, as they impinge? This response is clearly need dominated, and it reflects a rather arbitrary and insufficiently self-critical organization of the total stimulus field. Nevertheless, the response is not without some warrant in the objective structure of the blot. Furthermore, the pathological implications of such arbitrariness, as the response reflects, are somewhat mitigated by the acute intensity of the needs attacking the cognitive process.

Card IV: "It seems like some man. Seems like an X ray."

Here we are alerted to the boy's concern with what is going on inside of his own body.

Card V: "A moth."

This is a popular response.

Card VI: "The skin of a wolf. This is the nose here at the top."
Card VII, upside down: "Shadow of two girls blinded by something bright."

The girls were visualized in the lower two thirds of the blot in the upside-down position, and the blinding object was seen in the mid-line of the upper third of the blot. On inquiry, the upper third became a huge, hairy monster from which the girls were trying to escape and which they were afraid to look at because it was too ugly.

The content of this response is of interest because of certain items in the boy's history. He remembered having walked, at the age of 4, into his mother's bedroom where he was frightened by a piece of fur lying on the bed. He thought the fur was actually an animal. In Sodium Amytal interview, it developed that he thought he had actually seen his mother's genitals. The associative complex involving furry animals, monsters, and guilty voyeurism directed at female genitals seems significantly involved in the way this patient structured Rorschach Card VII. It may be noted that his drawings of female figures (Figures 2B, 3B, 4A) also reflect a preoccupation with fur pieces. It was noted in the history that his choking sensations were, in part, related to anxiety generated in sleeping on a pillow identified as a fur piece.

Card VIII: "This looks like nothing to me."
Card IX: "The face of some kind of animal without the skin or head."

The content of this response is of interest in reflecting at least two significant trends. On the one hand, the response seems to express the familiar referential ideation arising out of the adolescent's guilt, his self-consciousness, and his need to keep the secrets of his inner life concealed. On the other hand, the absence of skin and head suggests that our patient has the feeling that his defensive measures are of limited avail. He confronts the outer world with a raw sensitivity. On the structural side this response is at best borderline, as far as the integrity of the cognitive processes involved is concerned. The seriousness implied in this sample of questionable reality testing, however, is mitigated by the intensity of the card's affective stimulation and of the conflicted needs aroused.

So much for the Rorschach, which I think we can characterize as generally disturbed and as giving us some pause as to the possibility that a morbid ego-disintegrating process is going on in this case. On the other hand, we must remember that on the Wechsler-Bellevue there were no indications whatsoever of deviant thinking. There was every good indication of object relatedness. There was only an indication of rather poor attention, as shown by relatively low digit retention, yet there was some capacity for concentration, as shown in the fact that his arithmetic reasoning held up quite well.

His TAT stories, some of which follow, further indicate how his preoccupations determine the kind of content which emerges on projective tests.

3 BM: "Is this a lady or a man?" (Of course, one might say this is a realistic conflict, considering the ambiguity of the picture. But then again, it may be a projection of his own uncertainty, and there is

much in the history to indicate that he was quite uncertain. In fact, at the age of 13, he was very much preoccupied with the fear that he was really a girl.) "Well, it's a lady. She has just committed suicide because she was in debt. She was financially embarrassed. Her husband ran away and left her. So she committed suicide." (The fantasy of getting rid of the husband is suggestive of oedipal conflict.)

V: "Lady opens the door. She is the landlord, trying to collect money for the rent. She sees this ma—, lady." (The person referred to in the story is not visible in the picture, but here again is the ambivalence noted before.) "She sees this lady crying on the bed, couch rather, comes in, and she goes over to her and asks her what's the matter? She says, 'My husband left me. That's why I'm crying.'" (More preoccupation with disruption of the family and reminiscent of the fact that the boy slept with his mother, while his father occupied a bed in another room.) "The lady, who is good natured, let her extend the rent a month later."

6 BM: "This is the picture of a man telling the mother that, breaking the news to her, that her son was killed in an accident. She loved her son very dearly. He was her only son." (This is an example of the adolescent's oedipal dilemma projected in tragic terms. On the one hand, expressed in the responses to the six previous cards, is the wish to dispose of the father; on the other hand are the guilt feelings which require our patient to dispose of himself as the son.)

12 M: "This is a picture of a boy who was injured in an accident. The man in the picture is a priest. He is giving the last rites." (This is not too often the kind of story which is projected here. Here again is fantasy in tragic terms. One gets the feeling of a boy whose disturbed emotional involvements lead him to think in rather extreme terms. There are depression, thoughts of doing away with himself, and fantasies of disrupting the family, of displacing his father, etc.)

13 MF: "This is a picture of a man killing his wife. He didn't like her because she was in love with another man." (Here is more disharmony within the family, expressed this time explicitly in terms of infidelity. It may have been his own feeling that it was infidelity in his mother which made possible so intimate a relationship to her as was represented in his sleeping with her.)

18 BM: "This is a man who committed a series of crimes. He's taken into jail by the police. He murdered his mother." (More of the same.)

14: "This is a picture of a man getting ready to commit suicide. He didn't like his wife because she was going out with another man." (More of the same.)

One point seems important about these fantasies. The content seems unmistakable in so far as it indicates the problems which preoccupy the patient, yet as far as the formal structure of thought, the formal structure of the fantasies, there is really nothing deviant. I think we must hold on to that fact in our effort to distinguish between a chronic disorganizing process, one in which an attack on the cognitive process is intrinsic, and the projection of acute and troubled concern with problems the adolescent is not yet quite able to handle.

I have cited the TAT fantasies in some detail because we shall have an opportunity later to compare them with the patient's responses to the same TAT pictures some 4½ months later. First, however, it may be useful to consider some of the patient's drawings. We have available a sequence of drawings made by him over the entire 4½-month period.

The distinction between disturbed content and reasonably integrated structure noted in connection with this patient's TAT fantasies holds equally well with respect to his drawings.

The patient's first drawings obtained during the initial week of his stay at the hospital are shown as Figures 2A and 2B. Inspection of these drawings scarcely encourages the interpretation that a disorganizing process, in the sense of impaired cognitive capacity and reality testing, is reflected. What seems clear from the drawings is that the boy who made them was at the same time depressed and excited, suffering from low self-esteem, plagued with guilt feelings, and anxiously convinced of his own castration. This interpretation derives from such characteristics of the drawings as the small size of the male, who is nevertheless depicted as quite active; the shortness, particularly of the right arm, which terminates in a scarcely visible, barely indicated hand; and the manifest uncertainty and conflict with which the legs were drawn. The female figure drawing presents a number of interesting details. The puffy furriness of the woman's jacket is immediately reminiscent, in its sensuous sexual implications, of the patient's response to Rorschach Card VII, and of his recall in Sodium Amytal interview of his confused reaction, at the age of 4, on seeing a piece of fur on his mother's bed, interpreted by him first as an animal and then as his mother's genitals. At the same time that the drawing suggests a sensuous, sexual arousal, the profile presentation of the figure suggests that the patient defends himself against the responsibilities of gratification by presenting the female as disinterested and unobtainable. In the same way, the woman's dress is both an object of excited attention and, in its forbidding length, a defense against voyeuristic impulses. The greater size of the female figure in relation to the size of the male figure suggests the patient's self-view as subordinate in relation to women and his sexual attitudes as still very much within an oedipal context. There seems no doubt, then, that the drawings project intense adolescent problems, perhaps more acute than in the average adolescent. Nevertheless, the organization of the drawings, in the sense of their formal structure, is essentially intact. It is this concurrence of structural intactness with evidence of fluid, conflicted, and emotionally volatile intrapsychic activity that encourages the belief that the clinical disturbance which the patient shows so far remains within the limits of a benign process.

The drawings shown as Figures 3A and 3B were done 12 days after the initial ones.

These drawings are a good deal larger, and their general outline is much more characteristic of the adolescent. Of particular interest is the presentation of the male figure leaning up against a wall. As it happens, for the first month on the ward, the patient never exposed his back, sidling around with his back to the wall. On clinical interview he expressed fears of being attacked from behind. Here, again, the boy's problems are richly projected, but the organization of the total field is quite realistic. There are no bizarre elements.

A male figure drawing made a month after admission, not shown here, includes an exaggeratedly large, conspicuous tie, a revolver in a holster, and a heavily shaded cartridge belt with a prominent buckle. However anxiously and immaturely rendered, these are, at least, fairly representative projections of the adolescent's interest in growth to mature masculinity.

The next set of drawings (Figures 4A and 4B) was made after 4 months of psychotherapy.

At this time the boy had been encouraged, through his treatment, to confront much more directly his masculine aspirations and attendant misgivings, and, although a good deal of his anxiety had been alleviated, the miniature hand and the absence of the feet suggest that he has by no means resolved his castration anxiety. It is of interest, too, that at this time he was showing the female in much smaller size relative to the male, and he was able to confront her. No longer is the female figure in profile. These drawings are fairly characteristic of the adolescent. The rendition of the hair is signalized by the familiar exhibitionistic phallic pompadour. The preoccupation with physical power is manifest in the way the chest and the shoulders are rendered.

Altogether, the progressive trend in the drawings over the period of his treatment seems to reinforce the original diagnostic impression of the psychologist. Such cognitive disorder as seemed to characterize the Rorschach occurred in the context of active problems which were producing a good deal of anxiety. At the same time, the retention of a quite satisfactory level of organization in the less ambiguous and more familiar projective test materials suggest that this boy was not really suffering from a schizophrenic process, despite the grave psychopathological implications of the clinical picture.

The patient's TAT fantasies offered after 4½ months' treatment are of interest in reflecting something of the nature of his progress. Only a few examples can be given here:

3 BM: "Man's crying, woman's crying, rather." (Again the ambivalence. He has not quite made up his mind. Incidentally, in the last of his figure drawings he drew the female figure first, so that he is very far from having solved his problems of sex-role organization. But there is a good deal of diminution of the anxiety with which he came.) "She is crying about the family situation at home. Her husband died in an automobile crash. She gets up, wipes off her tears, goes into the world, finds another husband, and lives happily ever after." (A very different kind of outcome from the one he offered before, although he is still preoccupied with the same kind of problem.)

V: "Lady opens up the door and peeps in and sees a man [not a woman, as before] here sitting at the table. She stares at him and later realizes it's her long-lost husband. So she runs over to him and kisses him and they live together ever more and have no more quarrels." (Here is a remarkable reconstitution of the family with some apparent abatement of his own oedipal problems.)

14: "This is a man getting ready to commit suicide. He doesn't like anybody because he thinks everybody hates him. He jumps out the window but, lucky for him, a tree breaks his fall, and he only breaks a leg and he finds out a lot of people like him and he is happy once more." (He projects here a very neat resolution of his own problems. Masochistically, he accepts some measure of castration, in line with the fact that fears of femininity have always threatened his masculine strivings. But making this kind of concession has finally made it possible for him to reintegrate his family and to go on living without constantly thinking of himself as the center of censuring eyes.)

The following is a summary of the psychiatric opinion at discharge:

"At present, the patient has no further feelings of unreality, and no hallucinations. He is gaining weight, his appearance has improved, he walks with his head erect, and his shoulders back instead of stooped, and he seems to feel that he can face his problems more efficiently. He is much more outgoing with girls, approaching them and introducing himself. He is, in addition, less fearful with his fellow patients. He is more self-assertive, no longer has feelings of unreality after a stay at home, and says that his friends have told him that he has changed. For a while, he had many feelings of doubt and consequently asked if what he was doing was correct. It was felt that this doubt had relevance to the correctness of his sexual feelings. He has not mentioned this doubt for some time now. The patient was discharged in the custody of his mother. His mental condition was improved. He is coming back to the hospital for psychotherapy.

"With reference to the diagnosis, there were many elements suggestive of schizophrenia. It is this examiner's opinion, however, that the condition could best be described as anxiety hysteria with a depersonalization syndrome in a constitutionally inadequate individual."

Discussion

Here is a boy who appeared at first to be schizophrenic, on clinical psychiatric examination and on examination of his history. On psychological examination he showed many of the problems of the adolescent in a very exaggerated form. His Rorschach protocol contained borderline examples of the kind of cognitive disorder we would ordinarily regard as constituting a very grave sign. But because the structural deviations occurred in a context of understandable, acute, panicky anxiety, it was felt that the boy was not essentially psychotic and that he would be quite responsive to treatment, which proved to be the case.

Case Report

The next case is of a 17-year-old boy who was regarded as psychotic on psychiatric examination, and who appeared more so, infinitely more so, on the psychological examination. This case is worthy of attention because, in comparison with the previous one, it shows in a very vivid way the contrast between the projection of exaggerated adolescent problems in a context of retained cognitive organization on the one hand, with the projection of similar problems in a context of cognitive disorganization, of deterioration.

Following is the intake note prepared by the psychiatric social worker:

"The patient is the oldest of five children. His parents are strictly orthodox Jews. He attended a parochial school and then transferred to high school. He was a member of the Arista, the Chess Club, and the Math Club. He had participated in many group activities and socials. The school psychologist reported that the patient had had an I.Q. of 132 on a group test some years before. Later testing has since confirmed this score, but his work in the classroom is considerably below his potentialities. The patient claimed that he had run a 92 average in high school, but the school psychologist reported that his average was actually about 74. He is now a part-time student at college.

"The patient graduated from high school, and, a week before graduation, he came into the psychologist in an agitated, upset state concerning philosophical problems. He was referred for psychiatric treatment. Each time he presented bizarre behavior and became involved in Talmudic discussions. He was going to solve all the problems of the world after studying all the philosophers in a 2-week period. The school psychologist, however, said that the patient had rationalized his ideas quite well. The patient admitted a serious withdrawal into reading and study."

The first thing that strikes us, on viewing this patient's psychological test results, is a discrepancy of 37 points between the verbal and the performance scales of the Wechsler-Bellevue. His verbal I.Q. is 136, whereas his performance I.Q. is only 99.

This discrepancy, in marked contrast with the intelligence-test findings in the previous case, already suggests the probability that this patient is a hyperideational, withdrawn personality with questionable relatedness to concrete objects. This inference gains support from a consideration of some of his actual responses. In response to the comprehension subtest question, "What should you do if, while sitting in the movies, you were the first person to see smoke and fire?" he stated, "My action would depend on how large the fire was. If it was a small blaze I'd extinguish it with a can of sand. If it was a large one, I'd tell the closest individual to put in an alarm and tell another person to go up and tell the man who is running the projection booth to stop the film. Then I would go up on stage myself and explain to people slowly that there was a small fire, and calm them, etc., etc." This response reflects, besides a hint of the fantasy of omnipotence, an ideational, obsessional approach that is more concerned with idea and with words than with the practical situation. The suggestion of felt need to exert a perfectionistic control over self and over others is sufficiently marked to generate the suspicion that the boy is under pressure to try to cope with inner chaos. However high his I.Q., there is good reason for concern about the effectiveness of his judgment.

When asked "Why does the state require people to get a license in order to be married?" he said, "To prevent deformed children from being born. It wants to have a good crop of children. Because people would marry against their advantage." The relatively unique quality of this response identifies it as a projection of a personal problem. The boy's wish is for control or avoidance of some felt inner deficiency, a guilt-engendered (masturbatory?) deformation of self-image. The anxiety resulting from the feeling of deficiency must be so great and the ego integration available for coping with it so weak that there results a distortion of the impersonal cognitive process required to deal effectively with the objective situation.

In both instances the implication of psychopathology is not in the nature of the content, in the indication of omnipotence fantasies, or in the guilt and anxiety associated with hypothetical distortions of body image. These are suggestive. What is decisive is their domination of cognitive process, their disruption of perceptual and logical processes oriented in their intention to the management of some aspect of reality.

The prominence of cognitive disorder is evident at a glance in the bizarreness of his figure drawings (Figures 5A and 5B). The page-filling size of the male figure suggests that fantasies of omnipotence have penetrated irrealistically into his actual beliefs concerning the relationship of himself to reality. The unintegrated and discontinuous, erratic intrusion of obsessional concern with such details as the ear of the male, the eyes of the female, the teeth, eyebrows, and lashes of both the male and female attests to the patient's susceptibility to the unpredictable and disordering, if anxiety-alleviating, invasion of his reality perceptions by needs for expression and defense he can no longer logically contain. Equally pathognomonic of a suspension of standards of reality are the instances of transparency, as in the sleeves of the male figure, the dress of the female figure, and the bottom of the male figure's jacket. The disproportionate, disarticulated, essentially symbolic rendition of the latter has similar import. The anxious accentuations of the ear of the male, in the context of the loose organization of the figure as a whole, suggests the possibility of auditory hallucinations.

The figure drawings are not without their indications of typical adolescent conflicts. The buttons on the male figure express the patient's dependency, and the "scooped-out" quality of the crotch points to feelings of sexual inadequacy. In opposition to these signs of felt weakness are the swollen thumbs of the male, the oversized little fingers of the female, and the tie of the male, all displaced phallic compensations in symbolic form. What is most serious is not the presence of this conflict but the absence of any sign of awareness of a need to reconcile the contradictions. The latter is most evident in the superimposition of the tie on the buttons, with no effort to deal with the resulting transparency. Worth noting, too, is the rendition of the bottom of the female's dress as an open ellipse, a confession of voyeuristic interest. The indications of voyeuristic interest and of displaced compensatory phallic striving are of interest in foreshadowing their more unabashed expression in drawings made by the patient some 4 years later in a more regressed phase of his psychosis (Figures 6A and 6B).

The uneven character of this boy's functioning is most dramatically illustrated in the contrast between the autonomously retained abilities implicit in his verbal I.Q. of 136 and the bizarre primitivity of much of the figure drawings. Uneven levels of abstraction and conceptualization characterize, to a lesser degree, his interpretation of proverbs. Here are some of his proverb interpretations:

"To fiddle while Rome burns" means "To amuse oneself with nonsense while something significant happens." This is an interpretation which clearly meets a satisfactory standard of abstraction.

"The proof of the pudding is in the eating" means "One can know exactly how good something is when one has experimented in the respect in which it is supposed to be good." Here the interpretation is a trifle obsessional, but still satisfactory in the sense that it reflects pertinent conceptualization.

The concreteness of his interpretations of other proverbs stands in radical contrast to these evidences of intrinsic capacity for abstraction. He interpreted "When the cat's away the mice will play" to mean "The mice have more freedom when the cat's away." "Don't cry over spilt milk" means "Nothing you can do about spilt milk so crying is needless." "It never rains but it pours" means "Whenever it is raining it is pouring." At times, he is capable of abstract generalization; at other times he cannot extract himself from a primitive, concrete, and literal repetition.

The word-association test offers further evidence of disordered cognitive functioning. Eleven out of twenty-five of his word associations were individual in the sense that they are not given, in response to the respective stimulus words, by a single person in a thousand. This uniqueness of associative pattern is itself suggestive of schizoid isolation and autistic thinking. His actual associations, however, are more definitively instructive: dream—sweet, sweet—girls, soft—girls, sleep—girls, dark—girls, quiet—bat, hungry—man, anger—knife, beautiful—girl, man—fool, land—clock, long—coat, blue—me, slow—me, working—me, child—my sister, heavy—load, etc. The associations are characterized by perseveration, overpersonalization, occasional irrelevance, but more often excessive and concrete closeness, in relation to the stimulus words. Serious ego deficiency is indicated, for the integrated, properly functioning ego would quite automatically cast up associations adaptively balancing the pressure to impulsive, affective self-expression and the opportunities for meeting the demands of the task in an impersonal, logical, socially communicative, essentially syntactical way. Here again, pathology consists less in the nature of the conflicts and complexes implicit in the content of the associations, and more in the indications of impairment of cognitive process.

This patient's Rorschach protocol is replete with examples of distorted perception and association, only a few of which need be described here.

Card III: "This looks like two men facing each other as if in a scientific drawing where we can see their stomachs [It is a scientific drawing.] because they show stomach and esophagus."

The content of this percept is not particularly significant beyond indicating an effort to rationalize anxiety somatized or otherwise centered in the alimentary canal. The process by means of which the content was developed, however, will bear examination from the standpoint of possible cognitive pathology. The details of the blot seen as men do, indeed, look like men, and they are often so perceived. The lower center details seen as stomachs might well resemble drawings of one and are not too infrequently perceived as such. What immediately appears strange to the point of bizarreness, however, is the fact that the details representing the stomachs are completely outside, in fact at some distance removed from, the areas within which the whole figures of men are delineated. The form of the details connecting the "men" details with the "stomach" details becomes almost altogether irrelevant, and their identity as esophagi becomes predicatively determined by the gratuitous assumption that the "stomachs" belong to, and must therefore be functionally related to, the "men."

The intact ego, normally and efficiently performing its function of automatically, even unconsciously, screening impinging stimuli and the perceptual hypotheses which might confer on them meaningful and realistic structure would have rejected as irreconcilable any connection between the "stomachs" and the "men." It would have led to any one of a number of realistically feasible perceptions. The details seen as stomachs could have been so interpreted, but as completely independent of the "men." On the other hand, they could have been easily integrated with the percept of men by seeing them as bowling balls being launched by the men, or as hats being swept in an extravagant gesture of courtesy by Alphonse and Gaston. The permeability of logical boundaries in our patient, however, allowed him, perhaps under some pressure from anxious preoccupation with oral conflict, uninhibitedly and uncritically to agglutinate disparate details into a confabulated pseudo integration. The resulting deviance from reality, evidently perceived, however faintly, by our patient, generated the need for a rationalizing concept which would explain away all discrepancies. Our patient met this need with his percept of the whole as "a scientific drawing." This global concept, however, fails in its intended purpose, for it leaves unreconciled much that is contradictory. Thus, because of a passive concession to an initial illogical and irrealistic hypothesis, the patient became involved in a widening series of syncretisms increasingly attenuating his contact with reality. It is in this passive loosening of cognitive operations, insufficiently accounted for by acute stress, that the morbidity, the chronic, deteriorative character of the patient's illness may be discerned.

The patient offers in one of his responses to Rorschach Card IX a typical example of primary-process thinking, with passive, unrationalized interpretation of logically disparate ideas producing an absurd condensation. With the plate in the upside-down position, he sees the whole of it as "a bird or an animal that had a technical framework." The variegated hues of the blot undoubtedly suggested technicolor. Perhaps the color variations, perhaps the deviance of the blot form from a literal representation of a real bird or animal skeleton, certainly the prefix of the word, technicolor, suggested the idea of some kind of diagrammatic or "technical" illustration. In any case, these vaguely, physiognomically related ideas coalesced into the contaminated concept of a bird or animal with a "technical framework."

The full sequence of the patient's responses to Card VII is worth citing, perhaps less as an illustration of disordered cognitive structure and more as an eloquent expression, in symbolic form, of some of the problems with which he is attempting to cope. All six of his responses to this card involved the blot as a whole:

1. May be some sort of basket.
2. May be a water receptacle.
3. May be a urine receptacle.
4. An ashtray, if it had any depth.
5. Looks like part of a skeleton of a hand.
6. A slicing device comes to mind.

The sequence of ideas, as symbolic representations, is of interest irrespective of the accuracy or inaccuracy with which they identify the blot structure. The blot is seen first as a receptacle suitable for food and water. The idea of water suggests that the same blot area could be a receptacle for "water" expelled from the penis. There is hinted here a close and confusing association between oral dependency and phallic activity. The latter becomes, still symbolically, yet more explicitly sexual in the next response which sees the same blot area as a receptacle for ashes, the product of a burning, consuming process in a long cylindrical object which, appropriately enough, is held in the hand and sucked at by the mouth. Masturbatory guilt, and an attendant feeling of libidinal and somatic erosion, which, in the light of the oral dependency, are probably incestuously centered, are suggested in the concept of ashes and in the immediately following concept of "a part of a skeleton of a hand." The final percept of a slicing device, evidently a two-handled meat cleaver, suggests the fantasy of self-castration as a final solution to his oral-sexual conflicts. Interpreted on a symbolic level, this sequence of responses is seen to have a kind of internal unity which our patient has managed to forge through his own rigorous, if schizophrenic, logic. Of particular interest is the foreshadowing of the oral-sexual conflict in the representation, in the male figure drawing (Figure 5A), of a transparent "phallic" tie so that the buttons below, symbolizing dependency, show through.

The chronicity and the deterioration forecast on initial examination of this boy are clearly manifest in figure drawings made by him some 4 years later (Figures 6A and 6B). What was represented before in symbolic form, with defenses battered but not disintegrated, is here presented in an unabashed, undefended, concrete manner. The tie in the male figure, seen before as a symbolic phallic displacement, has here descended to its point of origin. In the drawing of the female the skirt, with its voyeuristically implicated opening at the bottom, is now altogether omitted, revealing the "vagina" and the "womb" as the objects of original interest.

The structure of the drawings is now more simplified. They are devoid of the obsessional defensive efforts which characterized the earlier drawings, albeit in somewhat decompensated ways. The defensive effort has given way to the clear emergence of the underlying preoccupation.

Discussion

This patient presents a clear instance of the adolescent precipitation, emergence, or aggravation of a psychotic process. Its chronic, deteriorative character is manifest, in the psychological-test protocol, in an intrinsic disturbance of cognitive structure as illustrated in concreteness, syncretic, and contaminating interpenetration of disparate ideas, concept domination of perceptual processes, and autistic paralogic, all offered with uncritical conviction and free from anxiety, and all implying a suspension of actively directive ego function. The pathology in the psychological-test protocol is so obvious that we may well question whether the tests contributed anything to differential diagnosis. The boy was recognized as schizophrenic on psychiatric examination. It is doubtful, however, that the severity and chronicity of his illness were recognized, for the boy was accepted for outpatient psychotherapy.

Case Report

The next illustration is of a 16-year-old boy originally diagnosed, on psychiatric examination, as a sociopathic personality. The psychological-test diagnosis of schizophrenia, based in part on the boy's figure drawings, was finally accepted. Figure 7 shows the boy's drawing of a man. The obvious preoccupation with power, familiar enough in the normal adolescent, is not pathological as such. Here, the pathological indications are in the confusion between realistic and symbolic representation. The preoccupation with power has acquired a kind of detached or dissociated abstractness which dominates his serious effort to draw a male figure. This boy's drawing of himself, as shown in the three parts of Figure 8 (originally taking up three pages) is more realistically structured. His inability to confine himself to a single page, or even to two, however, suggests that compensatory fantasies of power have decompensated into a conviction of omnipotence.

CASE REPORT

The final illustrative example, presents a problem in the evaluation of an adolescent's viability, his potentiality for the mobilization of growth-oriented forces. On psychiatric examination at 16, the adolescent in question was thought to be not psychotic. The psychologist who examined him at that time could not be sure that a morbid process was not under way. Psychological-test evidence of cognitive disorder was minimal so that, seemingly, the presence of a psychotic process should have been fairly safely ruled out. It was stated above that the content of test production, without reference to the cognitive processes that produce it, can never be decisive as a guide in appraising the morbidity of psychopathological manifestations. As will be seen, the content in this case is of a special sort, concerned less with circumscribed adolescent problems and more with a comprehensive self-image of such character as to suggest a kind of existential collapse, an inability to see the self as organized or organizing, as purposing, directing, managing, or even caring. The immediate picture is not one of acute psychosis, yet it raises a serious question in prognosis. How long can existential surrender, with its passive and tenuous relationship to objects, endure without invading the integrity of cognitive processes?

Our patient was first examined when he was 10 years of age. His mother complained at that time that he hated her, insisted on sleeping in the same room with her, demanded that she dress him, and frequently "beat up" and generally persecuted his younger brother. His father, apparently a dependent and inadequate man who had never provided sufficient support, abandoned the family when the patient was 3. His mother, expressing a sadomasochistic penchant for inadequate men, married a gambler some 5 years later. Contributing nothing to the financial support of the household, the stepfather found it convenient to absent himself from the house, as much as his shaky finances permitted, rather than face his wife's censorious complaints. The mother continued working throughout the years of her marriage and assumed virtually full control of the family finances. Fortified with a pseudoemancipation derived from a misreading of modern dynamic psychology, she succeeded in being quite seductive in her relationship with the boy.

It would seem that the familial circumstances within which the boy developed could only fan the flames of the oedipal fire while obstructing the flow of the cool waters of latency which might quench them. The resulting sexual stress under which the boy labored is clearly manifest in the psychological-test protocol obtained when he was 10. It will be worth reviewing the figure drawings and the Rorschach protocol he offered at that time, for they furnish a remarkable background contrast to the picture of drive burned out, of emptiness and defeat which his test protocol at 16 presents.

The boy's drawings at 10 years are those shown in Figures 1A and 1B. They were discussed earlier as essentially normal examples of phallic preoccupation at puberty. Actually, this boy was at the time prepuberal, so that the intensity of phallic push which the drawings portray is clearly excessive.

The Rorschach protocol, taken at the same time, follows:

Card I: "Looks like two men fighting over a lady. She's holding her hands over her head and yelling."

Card II: "Two men fighting. They're bleeding very bad. They are tired and out of breath. Red in the faces. Bleeding down the back and legs."

Card III: "Two men picking up something that's very heavy. They cut themselves and they are bleeding. They were picking up a heavy rock and they dropped it. It scratched their chin and it started to bleed."

Card IV: "Looks like a monster going after somebody. The bottom [lower center projection] looks like the body of the thing he's going after. It's a human being in the 15th century."

Card V: "A bird flying in the air. It looks like an eagle. The wings are rough, like the bird went through a bush."

Card VI: "Looks like the skin of a lion with something laying over his neck. On top is something put there for bravery."

Card VII: "Looks like bones of some kind of creature. The whole picture is bones. It's one solid bone maybe from a beast. It could be a headless, armless, and one-foot-missing person. You can see the body. It's probably a woman because of the breast."

Card VIII: "Looks like some kind of a house with two mice climbing up to go on to the roof."

Card IX: "Looks like a monster from over three thousand centuries ago. All colors."

Card X: "Looks like a monster of five million centuries ago, from a different world. All different colors. Little creatures jumping on it, like little mice."

This Rorschach protocol is no sample of relatively placid, object-oriented latency. It is, instead, a highly dynamic portrayal of virtually ceaseless fantasy, intense in its instinctual involvement, yet almost stereotyped in its compulsive reiteration of interrelated themes. The latter reflect strivings for power and an aggressive competitiveness whose oedipal context is revealed in the very first response of the protocol. Voyeuristic overtones are suggested in his percept of mice climbing on the house. Preoccupation with fears of retaliative castration are suggested in several places. The men in combat are bleeding; the monster of Card IV pursues someone visualized in the blot's phalliclike lower-center projection; the powerful eagle of Card V has had its wings frayed in penetrating a bush. Perhaps both the instinctual origin of the sexual wish and an urgent effort to neutralize it overdetermine his perception of the monsters on Cards IX and X as archaic, hence unreal, creatures. The castration implications of the boy's perception of Card VII have a special connotation. He sees the blot first as bones, presumably hard, ungiving, and unyielding. The same area is then seen as a woman deprived of several projecting members. It may be recalled that the mother, for all her seductiveness, nevertheless played a paternal role in the family, being its sole source of stable financial support even to the point of doling out a daily allowance to the boy's stepfather. The castrative wish projected in the percept of Card VII would seem, then, directed at the mother who would thus become a less ambiguous, more manageable object.

The figure drawings this boy made at 16 years of age are shown as Figures 9A and 9B. The drawings are reasonably well integrated and show no evidence of cognitive disorder. The content of the drawings, however, is of interest in contrasting his present status with his status at 10. The female (Figure 9B) is reduced to a virtual nonentity. She is in full face, and without hands, and her breasts are timidly, barely limned. She is now accessible enough, but she has the status of a renounced object no longer invested with the power to offer fulfillment. The male (Figure 9A) has been inflated into a puffy softness, with legs tapering down to insubstantial feet, and the curvature at the bottom back of the jacket betraying a gratuitous consciousness of the buttocks. In even greater contrast with the evidences of sexual turmoil at 10 are his associations to the present male figure drawing. He says: "This is Jack Cohn. He is the man who has no ambition in life. He walks around with a chip on his shoulder. He does not care how he looked at any time and is very self-reliant. He wants everyone to think he is somebody." The discouragement is plain, but the interest in effect, though enmeshed in ambivalence, is promising.

The boy's Rorschach protocol at 16 is as expressive as the one given at 10, but with dynamic implications of a very different sort. For convenience, interpretative comments are given parenthetically after each response, where pertinent, in the protocol which follows.

Card I: 1. "Looks like two animal heads, dogs with wings and with feathers sticking out connected to some sort of insect or frog." (This is an ominous beginning, for the implicated cognitive process is passive, unselective, agglutinative rather than integrative. An intact ego, maintaining an implicit orientation in reality, would automatically screen out percepts and associations whose inclusion would lead to an uncritical violation of reality's boundaries.)

2. "Looks like two birds of some sort asking for food." (This confession of oral dependency, consistent with the puffiness of the male figure drawing, contrasts with the size of the drawing, with the wish to give the impression that he is somebody, and with the striving for power projected, at 10, in his percept of the eagle with frayed wings.)

Card II: "Like animals fighting. Both hurt severely. They are swirling all over, trying to get away. Twisting, trying to hold on to prey, but trying to keep from being hurt." (Here, indeed, is a tragic view of the problem of existence. If he is to go on living, he must, in desperation, hold on, with incorporative intent, to the very object that threatens his own incorporative annihilation. The stakes are no longer a mere matter of castration; they have regressed to the more primitive level of existence.)

Card III: "Two ballplayers, both doing the same thing, friendly, like there's no competition involved. They are dribbling basketballs calmly, without worry about anything else." (The wish to be out of the struggle, to live effortlessly, perhaps in homosexual renunciation of sexual maturity, is in marked contrast with the competitive strivings for power expressed in his Rorschach protocol at 10. The way to avoid active castration is to accept it passively.)

Card IV: "The whole thing looks like an amoeba just moving along. It has no particular form, floating along the ground like a liquid." (As a projection of self-concept this percept can hardly be exceeded for its passivity. This blot is often seen as a powerful figure, interpretable as a father surrogate. It will be recalled that at 10 the boy saw the same blot as a monster in pursuit of somebody. What he seems to be saying now is that identification with a fluid and formless father leaves him no recourse but to adopt an identity equally fluid and formless. His early view of his father has not stood the test of his own growth.)

Card V: 1. "Looks like a bat flying in air. It is ungraceful. Because of the nonsmoothness of its supposedly wings." (The language here is disturbing in light of the boy's I.Q. of 119. This is the second, but still not decisive, example in the protocol of possible disorder in cognitive organization. What was before an eagle with frayed wings is now an ungraceful bat. The progression is from damaged or castrated power to a feeling of over-all bodily oddity.)

2. "Looks like two flamingoes." (The transformation, as though completing the process of castration, is into a form of feminine grace.)

Card VI: 1. "At the top, two insects looking for prey."
2. "Looks like a bear rug. A ruliness to it. The fur is smooth. It's been patted to each side of the animal's body."
(An oral-phallic concept is followed by a manifest wish for the regulation of sensuality.)

Card VII: "Looks like nothing. Just one bigness of nothing suspended in space, doing nothing, absorbing nothing. It has no meaning, no specific value. It's just there." (It will be recalled that our patient saw this blot before as a woman without head or arms, and with only one leg. The castrated mother is now a formless nothing, a shift which is reminiscent of the contrast between the female figure drawing he made at 10 and the one he offered at 16. Like the amoeba he saw on Card IV, the "bigness of nothing" on Card VII projects a tragic conception of personal identity. He seems to see his mother, like his father, as offering no substantial model for identification.)

Card VIII: 1. "Two rats."
2. "A pair of birds, skeletons of birds, birds starting to decay, and it's not finished. The tip is like a head, as though reaching out for life, I guess. The lower part of the back is decayed."
3. "Everything seems related, connected in some way. Each color fades away slowly but surely into the other, giving it a sort of unity."

(Here, indeed, is content, however clearly perceived, which projects a concept of self in process of disintegration. The "reaching out for life," the wish to resist the process of disintegration is offered sadly and wistfully, and gives way to the capitulation to the nirvana of an undifferentiated unity. The notion of decay, referred to the bird as a whole, is centered in the sexual area. The terrible sexual stress that this boy has endured without surcease, even during the period normally given over to latency, has finally abated, but at the cost of meaningful, integrated existence.)

Card IX: 1. "Two wolf heads."
           2. "Looks like two heads of two camels, I guess."
           3. "Some effect of a sunset." (This last response, clearly enough seen, confirms the depressive surrender implied in the patient's percepts of the previous card.)

Card X: "Looks like bugs crawling all over the place, trying to cling to something as if there isn't any gravity." (Like the amoeba and the "bigness of nothing" before, this percept projects a self-concept that is rootless, passive, unorganized, capable of no purpose other than the defensive one of reaching out for a nonexistent stabilizing support.)

DISCUSSION

It seems clear, from the psychological-test protocols presented by this boy, that his ego is devastatingly passive in certain ways. The passivity is shown in the nature of the boy's evident concept of himself as formless and fluid, as purposeless and drifting, as the victim of a process of disintegration. Yet this passivity of ego seems not, with a few relatively minor exceptions, to have invaded the integrity of cognitive structure. His drawings are well enough, and realistically enough, organized. His Rorschach form level is, on the whole, good. His performance on the Wechsler-Bellevue is intact and yields him an I.Q. of 119 which contrasts with a Stanford-Binet I.Q. of 104 obtained when he was 9 years old.

It is because of the relative intactness of cognitive structure that a definite diagnosis of a psychotic process may be premature at this time, even though the evidence on the tests is much more suggestive than the psychiatrist found on clinical examination. Yet the picture is undoubtedly a grave one. It may well be that the boy's implicit image of himself foreshadows a process which, in time, will be more clearly recognizable as schizophrenic. The psychological-test protocol presented by this boy poses a crucial problem in prognosis which, perhaps, cannot be solved without taking account of the stressful and therapeutic experiences to which he will be henceforth exposed.

This case was presented as a near exception to the general rule that the decisive criterion for the diagnosis of a pathological process, as differentiated from a benign adolescent reaction, is the presence of impairment of cognitive process. In this case the content is highly suggestive of pathology, while the cognitive structure remains relatively intact. But the suggestive content is of a special character. It points not simply to circumscribed areas of adolescent conflict but to a kind of existential surrender. This case clearly and poignantly raises the question: How long can existential surrender, passivity in the molar processes of living, endure without giving way to disintegration on the molecular level of cognitive organization? This question (and the case that raises it) underscores the importance of follow-up research. What very much needs doing is the follow-up, after 5 and 10 years, of patients thoroughly examined, in the fever heat of adolescence, with extensive batteries of psychological tests and with clinical psychiatric methods. The results of such a study should help us in differentiating what must be ascribed to an inexorable inner process from what will respond to growth, to stress, and to therapeutic experience.

chapter 17 The Adolescent in Society

WARNER MUENSTERBERGER

I apologized like a madman, because the band was starting a fast one. She started jitterbugging with me—but just very nice and easy, not corny. She was really good. All you had to do was touch her. And when she turned around, her pretty little butt twitched so nice and all. She knocked me out. I mean it. I was about half in love with her by the time we sat down. That's the thing about girls. Every time they do something pretty, even if they're not much to look at, or even if they're sort of stupid, you fall half in love with them, and then you never know *where* the hell you are.[22]

Here, Salinger has revealed, as have few other writers, the turmoil of teen-agers, their jumpiness, excitement, doubts, and despair—attributes which are common to adolescents everywhere. Theirs is a problem which has always existed; it belongs inextricably to the life cycle, and, because it does, it impinges upon the consciousness of the adult community—the dynamic quest and uncertainty which seek resolution in the culturally evolved forms.

To be sure, some societies would decidedly frown upon young people of the opposite sex dancing together or holding hands or necking in the back seat of an automobile, in the same way that other cultures take prenuptial sexual license for granted, while still others actually provide institutionalized dormitories where their adolescent youth can go and enjoy the freest possible sexual exploration and adventure.

Since the average girl attains full genital development when she is about 13 and the average boy approximately 2 years later, we can witness the emotional pull of forces within the preadult age group, a disturbance which is set in motion by internal biological and psychological forces as well as by external social and economic pressures.

346

Adolescence, the time of transition from childhood to maturity, is a human process which can also be observed among mammals. Yet man's development is more involved than this comparison indicates. The evolution of *Homo sapiens,* from the moment of birth as a helpless and absolutely dependent parasitic creature with seemingly simple, innate reflexes to the more and more complex, highly differentiated and as yet only partially comprehensible individuality, has been observed and studied from many angles—an endeavor which can be called the study of man.

Each human individual is born into a social environment, but we are concerned here with those socializing forces which operate particularly during the stormy years of puberty and adolescence. Out of all the external factors instrumenting the process of growth, the particular set of environmental conditions—the social organism —constitutes a perpetual influence over the unique and subtle unfolding of the self-reliant, adult, human individual. In the same way that the human embryo passes through characteristic phases which resemble mature forms of simpler organisms, man, in his extrauterine development, proceeds through more or less definite stages which mark the transition from birth to infancy, childhood to adolescence, and adult status to death.

Adolescence has received comparatively less attention than have other phases of the life of the individual in his society. The modes of human existence under various external conditions, the types of human behavior, the patterns of human cohesion, and the adult as a representative of his society have been observed and understood, and, indeed, provided the first insights into the specific phenomena of man's cultural milieu. Portrayals of this kind, however, dealt with the adult's world rather than that of the child or the adolescent.

An inventory of the rules and customs manifested among a great variety of peoples soon reveals the differences and similarities in their ways of life. Behavior patterns, laws, and attitudes show a considerable degree of plasticity. Yet all human societies permit certain interrelationships and disallow others, and thereby demand that the individual conform to specific habits, societal roles, and requirements. The rule of avoidance placed on brother and sister as soon as they reach adolescence would be one example of this social control. Paleontological and anthropological research has disclosed that even the Aurignacian and Cro-Magnon cave dwellers, in their famous rock shelters, had evolved cultural patterns and magic rites which were centered on the mutual need to subsist and to stay alive. These customs were potentially not far removed from those of our contemporary Australian aborigines.

Mankind was forced to evolve modes of living, to find norms and ways of conducting his life in a more or less circumscribed fashion. This, then, can become a measure with which to observe social systems as well as those patterns of interaction that are related to sanctions and beliefs, economic developments, and ideological concepts. Since every milieu is characterized by a great variety of cultural elements, each person living within his particular society can adjust his behavior according to the range of distinctive traits which belong on the spectrum of his particular cultural environment. Thus the social structure provides a graduated series of rules and values. The individual modulates his aims and needs on the accepted scale—controls his impulses and modifies his gratifications on it.

The Lynds, doing research in Middletown during the 1920's, show a changing scale in the following remark by a young mother: "My daughter of fourteen thinks I am cruel if I don't let her stay at a dance until after eleven. I tell her that when I was her age I had to be in at nine, and she says, 'Yes, mother, but that was fifty years ago,'" while mothers of boys observed: "Girls are far more aggressive today. They call the boys up and try to make dates with them as they never would have done when I was a girl."[14]

Compare this to the controlling attitude which a young girl is forced to observe in the village of Bontoramba in the Goa area of the South Celebes: From the onset of puberty, she is commonly known as a *ammantammi ri ballá*, which means: "She must stay at home." The expression indicates that she now belongs to the women's group. She will sometimes be called *badjú edja* which means "red jacket," a bright crimson garment which custom forces her to wear. She can rarely leave the woman's compound and would be severely frowned on if she went unchaperoned. Tradition, however, asks her to conform to the general practice set down for her sex: Women in Bontoramba stay at home while the men enjoy a much greater independence. " . . . in July 1949 visitors on market day, in the same area were counted: There were 62 women against 904 men" (p. 145).[4]

The comparison between the teen-ager in Middletown and the adolescent of the South Celebes was made to highlight a relevant point: Regardless of the impressive variety of culturally defined regulations concerning human needs and human desires, these codes are determined by basic biopsychologically inspired principles which are common to all mankind. Murdock has pointed to a numerically large variety of modes within the social machinery which appear fundamental and universal, and thus border on zoology, biology, and physiology in addition to anthropology and psychology. Among other observable elements, all human groups show a variation in the behavioral rules governing the way in which individuals must treat one another. All have some basically structured social institutions centered on age groups, government, and ideas about justice. Certain methods of education are also common features; so too are the restrictions concerning interpersonal relationships and the imposition of barriers among group members.[18]

One need not pursue this point further: Cross-cultural similarities appear to have originated not as the result of a specific cultural prerogative or condition but simply out of the fact of our being human. There is a biologically and physiologically determined need for the type of structure which, relying on integration and regulation, permits human coexistence in a functioning, self-perpetuating society. Our biological uniqueness forces us to depend heavily upon one another in more or less tightly knit groups operating associatively. The smallest and most intimate of these is called the *nuclear family*, which consists of father, mother, and offspring. This does not imply that we are unaware of subhuman associative societies—even children know of those resourceful communities of ants and bees. But the similarities between these and human social organizations, though illustrative, are functional and only show resemblances rather than explanations.

In examining adolescence from a cultural point of view, we must not neglect those biological and physiological preconditions which underlie and precede the cultural responses to the reproductive maturational process. In this sense, we can speak of distinctly human characteristics.

An essential differentiation between the individual's physiological and emotional development in puberty and adolescence should be noted. Puberty is preceded by the production of gonadotrophic hormones which eventually lead to the production of mature germ cells—eggs and sperm. With the growth of the reproductive glands, physical and behavioral effects can be observed; social and cultural traditions also stress this new stage in the life of the young generation. As her mammary glands increase with the onset of puberty, the girl's breasts begin to take on adult shape and size;

her pelvis and hips become broader and thus ready for reproduction. Around the time of her first menstruation, society most often takes cognizance of the physiological and sociological consequences: The young woman now enters the phase of reproductive ability which prepares her for a new status in society. With her coming of age, society emphasizes the fact that her biological destiny is, as Hooton put it, now in line with her instincts.[10] The subsequent process—the rupture of ripe follicles with the release of the ovum—does not, however, start simultaneously with menstruation and ovulation. This has a certain bearing on the fairly common premarital sexual freedom allowed among many primitive peoples. Since the first menstruations are generally unovulatory, adolescent "sterility" is a well-known fact; this explains the comparatively rare premarital impregnation of the adolescent girl, who cannot become procreative before she is about 15, at which time she is often married.

The biological process for the pubescent boy is not quite parallel, although genital stimulation and the erection of the penis do occur long before the seminal vesicles and prostate glands can function adequately.

Other secondary signs herald the advent of sexual maturity, drawing the boundary line between childhood and adult status. A most outstanding signal is the growth of body hair in the pubic and axillary areas of the male and female body. But the male youth, in addition, develops facial and body hair on the chest, arms, abdomen, and legs; conspicuous too is the change of voice. There are societies which recognize these secondary manifestations, whose socioreligious rituals and regulations are connected with initiation ceremonies, fertility rites, and magic beliefs.

A wealth of evidence suggests that the advent of these physiological changes carries with it behavioral and emotional alterations in the adolescent personality, which the environment must deal with in one or another way. These behavioral effects are partly determined by society; they vary according to the individual drive endowment and the environmentally condoned behavioral patterns and conditions. The process of maturation is a ubiquitous human phenomenon, and the psychological phenomena accompanying the physiological changes are, to a certain extent, administered by environmental expectations. This highly charged, biopsychological period of transition arouses in the teen-ager elementary emotions basically aimed at finding solutions, that is, adapting himself to the environmental conditions and conforming in his interindividual relations by gradually increasing his ego autonomy.

The phenomena just dwelt upon from a causative viewpoint lead us to more concrete observations of their reflections in different environmental settings. Taking the underlying maturational process into account, we must ask and eventually show how so culturally divergent societies as those of the Australian natives and the highly civilized Chinese deal or dealt with physiologically similar impulses. Since adolescent behavior is basically self-preservative in nature, we must discover the pathways provided for expression of the adolescents' demands and efforts. The prevailing nuances—be they ethnic, national, historical, or determined according to class or caste—suggest that, within a conceptual framework, a combination of institutionalized and noninstitutionalized response patterns can be seen.

A majority of human societies acknowledge this period of transition with rituals and customs, and the many-faceted regulations governing learning, examination procedures, fertility rites, apprenticeships, and coming-out or sweet-sixteen parties, mark this time also. The term *rites de passage* refers to the tendency to divide life into definite phases (birth, puberty, marriage, death, and rebirth) and, at the same time, to accept the interconnection between one life chapter and the next.

As Western man tries all possible ways of prolonging life, he also attempts to prolong the process of growing up by keeping the younger generation dependent and subject to parental aid and control for a considerably longer time than the adolescents' biophysiological constitution calls for. We find certain variations in the treatment of young boys and girls in Western society. There is a difference between peasant and city communities, between higher- and lower-income brackets, between ethnic and religious backgrounds. Many societies treat the transition from childhood to adult status in a more ritualized fashion, ceremoniously marking the connection between psychobiological and sociological requirements.

INITIATION RITUALS

Initiation rituals are aimed at helping the new generation attain adult status and prerogatives; in other words, these rites stress the social side of the psychosexual development in young men and women and deal, in a culturally prescribed manner, with both the oedipal rebellion of the adolescents and the ambivalent response of the older generation. Puberty rites, then, certify that a certain phase has been reached in the life of the individual, that a new physiological and social status has been attained. In those closely knit homogeneous societies which we are in the habit of calling "primitive," these ceremonies concern not the initiand and his family alone but the entire community. The average age of the neophyte may vary; generally, however, initiation does not begin until the ninth year and rarely ends later than the sixteenth or seventeenth.

These rites generally take a definite course which can be summarized as follows:

1. When a youth comes of age, he must observe certain food restrictions.

2. He is taken from his "family of origin" (LaBarre) and put into seclusion, either in the ceremonial men's house or somewhere outside of the community proper.

3. During the period of seclusion, which may last from a day to several years, the neophyte is indoctrinated with certain tribal traditions, customs, mythology, secret ceremonies, and beliefs. In learning to prepare his own nourishment, he becomes independent of parental care. Sexual rites, frequently painful, including circumcision, flagellations, tooth extraction, and examination, help the novice identify with adults. In numerous societies he also learns that the masked ghosts or ancestors, who appeared as threatening creatures, are nothing more than the elders of the tribe; he can also wear a mask from then on and, in that way, *become* the ancestor represented by the mask. This is a primitive form of identification.

4. In a ritual meal (communion, totem feast) previous restrictions are canceled, thereby stressing the young adult's final separation from parental sponsors. Now he is independent and responsible for his deeds.

5. He re-enters the community as a self-reliant adult.[23]

There are a great variety of similar but modified puberty rites in civilized societies. Doubtlessly, the motivation is the same: Antagonism and rivalry with the parent of the same sex must be replaced by identification. Following are some examples of the way this process takes place in primitive societies:

The pubescent boy, among the Gusii of Nyanza Province in Kenya, is expected to volunteer the information that he would like to be initiated. He does this by disassociating himself from work and play with younger children and by seeking the company of older boys who have previously been given full tribal membership. A father may try to convince his son that he is still too young for the ordeal. The average age for circumcision is about 11 or 12; the older people nevertheless insist that when they were initiated the proper age was about 16. One informant remarked that initiation used to take place "when we had grown hair" but "nowadays the novices are only children; can they, when they come out of seclusion, stop a 'bull' (that is, enemy)?"[15]

A simple one-room hut for one or more boys is erected before the actual ceremonies begin. Traditionally, the hut stands at the outskirts of the village so that the boys can go in and out without being seen, especially by the boys' mothers. Circumcision takes place in the early morning, usually in the hut of the local circumciser. Unshaven, naked, and unfed, the boys set out at dawn, having previously washed their entire bodies and especially the foreskin. Older, initiated men escourt the novices to the circumciser. On the way, their "sponsors" tease, poke, or hurt them with sticks and clubs, exclaiming: "You are all cowards! You are a cheeky lot. You have insulted me. Just wait and see what happens today! You'll see how those who cry out are punished!"

The castration threat is even more evident in the following observation by Mayer: "When Monari was showing me his knife, for instance, he gave a sudden menacing lunge towards a nearby small boy, who giggled nervously and retreated a step" (p. 14).*

During the operation the novice stands with his back to a tree holding onto the trunk; he gazes straight ahead, having been instructed that the circumcision will not hurt if he does not look. If the boy cries, the circumciser does not operate but strikes the initiand sharply with the handle of the knife, saying: "You have spoilt my tree," or "Your wife will die. Your children will die." After the removal of the prepuce the boy receives a bunch of *ekerundu* grass, a symbol of fertility. Once the surgery is done on a group of boys, the circumciser and the novices' escorts sing songs. The following, perhaps, is quite telling:

---

* Róheim, who had seen the operation performed among the Pitjentara in Central Australia, used to tell of a joking remark made by the initiator while subincising a neophyte: "Better cut it off all together," the man exclaimed laughingly.

Uncircumcised little boys have had pain!
The circumciser has taken our penis:
He has made you a spear and a hard shield.
Fight the Kipsigis, fight the Kipsigis!
Fight the Abasuba, fight the Abasuba!
Uncircumcised little boys have had pain!
Mother's clitoris, mother's clitoris;
Mother's pubic hair, mother's pubic hair.
Uncircumcised little boys, copulate with mother!
Uncircumcised little boys have had pain!

In the afternoon, the neophyte returns to the seclusion of his enclosure where a most important act takes place—the kindling of a ritual fire with a "male" stick of hardwood which is twirled in a "female" stick of softer wood. The fire and the grass are believed to be magically connected with the young man's well-being and potency. During the next phase of seclusion, "mysteries" take place. In reality, the adolescents are subjected to various kinds of torture which reveal the aggression of older men toward their younger rivals.

A man will catch the novice's just-circumcised penis and put some substance on the wound which causes a great deal of pain. Then the initiands are forced to eat unpleasant foods; one is called "the breast," which turns out to be a purgative but, in larger quantities, is a poison. Another, called "fresh eleusine grass," is actually a berry which burns the mouth and stomach. If only blistered swollen lips and a painful mouth are the result, the neophyte is lucky. Similar to so many other societies, bull-roarers, which are often described as the voice of the devouring creatures, appear. The Gusii know of the *enyabububu*, the big beast of the outside.

In the final phase hot pegs are stuck in the ground, one for each novice. He is supposed to pull it out with his teeth, and in so doing he gets his face scorched. If he hesitates, he is beaten until he succeeds. Next, a string is twisted around his finger. The string bites painfully into his flesh. Finally, the initiand closes his eyes while his body is whipped all over with a stinging plant. This ceremony is called the beast that bites.

The girls, too, participate in the tortures: When the wounds on the penis have not yet healed, the girls come to the seclusion huts in order to perform *ogosonia*, that is, "arousing desire." They dance naked and provocatively around the adolescent boys: "You boy, you said you would become an *omomura* (initiated young man) and have intercourse; now, are you ready, Here it is—what you wanted. Come and copulate!" "The girls have their triumph if a resulting erection causes the partly-healed wound to burst open, with acute pain to the novice" (p. 22 F).[15]

Significantly, among a number of people—the Kiwai of the Papuan Gulf in New Guinea, the Iatmul in the Sepik area of New Guinea, and the natives of Arnhem Land in Australia—preinitiation seclusion is called the "womb," the word thereby conceptualizing the process; emergence is marked by a feast for young and old, food and beer having been prepared to celebrate this day of coming out. The neophyte is then supposed to show himself to all his people, avoiding only his mother until he has presented her with a small gazelle which he has hunted.

In studying the environmental implications of puberty and adolescence, we can see how particular social settings deal with the pressures of conformity: In an effort to help young people accept the traditional rules and mores, the older generation brings about a forcible separation of the youth from the mother. The tortures which so often are part of the rites not only check the neophytes' aggression but help the older men express, and partially satisfy, their hostile impulses. Finally, for the young men, the pain of initiation rites—the remembered pain of childhood—is also a tempering process, as though this pain conditions them for future suffering.

The separation from the mother is particularly well dramatized in the *horiomu* ceremony of the Kiwai mentioned above. Here, the initiand is carried by some female relatives from his mother's side to the beach where his parents wash him thoroughly and, as the Kiwai put it in pidgin English, "take away smell belong woman." He is then returned to the parental hut where his mother lies down at the entrance and the boy walks over her, placing one foot on her abdomen. The meaning of this act is explained by the Kiwai: "What place boy he come from that time he born, he finish now along that place."[12]

Günter Wagner describes initiation rites among the Vugusu, a subtribe of the Bantu Kavirondo in Kenya. Here too, a clearly defined passage from one phase to the next is equally well featured. The boys spend several months in seclusion, where they are circumcised. When the elders decide to let them out, the girls are allowed to join the lads, and the couples pass the night together making love. The following afternoon, the novices go to the nearest stream to bathe. They then exchange their old skins (or clothes), which they have worn until now, for new ones. These have been prepared by their fathers for this day. Washed and dressed in new skins, the youth are now called *vátembete,* the "new and soft ones." Meanwhile, at their fathers' huts, friends and relatives have gathered to celebrate the occasion by drinking the "beer of getting out."

After the meal, the fathers or elders perform the significant ritual of handing the *vátembete* shields, clubs, and spears, thereby initiating the boy as a warrior: " 'My son," the father says, "you have left behind "the mother's cloth" (that is, the prepuce), but now you are given the father's cloth. . . . Now you are a man. Do not join the women when they sit together and talk about their own things. If you go there you will hear foolish things and become a fool yourself. Go where the old men are sitting and join them!' "[25]

The emphasis is placed on the disruption of the (oral) unity with the mother: The physical detachment from her is first symbolized with the entrance into the seclusion hut (that is, "womb"); here, his "female" part, the prepuce, is cut off, thus reflecting the transition from pregenital to genital interests.[20] Finally, rebirth is brought about when, after emergence from seclusion and after bathing, the boy accepts the father's cloth, accepting also his identity with the father and the group recognition of his developing virility.

More closely observed, these various transitional rites, or the different manifestations of the ways in which sexual freedom and identification with the father are ultimately achieved, yield an even greater harvest of insights: The seclusion of novices, the detachment from the mother, and the grouping together of initiates into age groups or age grades, in addition to being a sociological reflection of a psychological tendency, is also a characteristic attempt to sublimate the aggressive as well as the homosexual drives which emerge during the years of adolescence.

In our society the well-known adolescent gang finds its counterpart for example in the more structured Scout group, but more particularly in the age grades among primitive—or can I say, less civilized—peoples. The contemporary need for gang or group identification, as a way of resolving latent aggressive and homosexual drives, can be shown most graphically in the following case history. Here, however, we find that the resolution is reversed and becomes a neurotic problem.

CASE REPORT

Robert, a tall, good-looking young man in his early 20's, had already achieved some success in his chosen profession when he entered analysis with the presenting symptom of excessive masturbation.

The patient was the eldest child of a middle- to upper-middle-class second-generation Jewish couple. He grew up in a small urban community in which the father played a prominent role. When a younger sister was born, Robert felt rejected, particularly by his father who is best characterized as a little Napoleon. The boy grew up thinking of the younger sister as a rival and feeling that his father showed her much greater affection.

For many years the patient suffered because he was physically the smallest boy in his class, and he constantly compared his bodily size and strength with the other boys. The father rubbed salt into the wounds by reproaching his son about his height. "You will never amount to anything," the older man would say over and over again. "You are a nobody. You have no character; no backbone." As the boy approached puberty, the father, considering Robert deficient because he had no pubic hair took him to several physicians to see whether the hair could be made to grow; in other words, stressing over and over again that his adolescent son would never grow up and become a rival.

Robert was prepared for *bar mizvah* at the usual age and was given the usual instruction. He anticipated the event with great anxiety, as though he were to pass through an inexplicable ordeal. Possibly because of his alienation from his father and also from schoolboys of his own age, Robert sensed most keenly the aloneness of the day when he was to become a man.

On the morning of his *bar mizvah,* he awoke with a backache which became increasingly more painful until Robert finally lay on the floor, unable to move. A doctor was summoned and found nothing organically wrong with the boy; he was, nevertheless, unable to stand erect and did not become *bar mizvahed* then or later. Robert had, to put it symbolically, proved his father correct: The boy had no backbone.

At 15, he left high school, against his father's wishes, and ran away from home to earn his own living. He became a bus boy in a summer resort, searching for the type of group security such communities afford. He had gotten the job through his charm; however, it turned out that he could not hold the position, and he was dismissed. At the earliest possible moment, he joined the Army, hoping to find in that boisterously virile environment not only group security but also a kind of identification with the father which his own father's neurosis impaired.

Robert was saved from homosexuality because the father's intolerance was counterbalanced by the considerateness of the grandfather who gave him the unfulfilled paternal love his father did not show him.

DISCUSSION

If the father's aggression toward Robert mirrors, in many respects, the teasing and physical assault made on youngsters in primitive societies by the elders, a certain distinction should be noted: We have been dealing with a *neurotic* case where there is a kind of homosexual submission to the father and a deviation into a delinquent or semidelinquent gang; we have been dealing with an atypical situation in *our* society. It cannot be compared with a typical institution in a preliterate community. Primitive fathers institutionalize their aggressions and, in that way, normalize them; the affect does not produce socially misfitted youngsters.

OTHER PRIMITIVE TRIBAL CUSTOMS

What must be considered abnormal in our communities can be found socially acceptable in a different social setting. Indeed, we find that a number of tribes provide an active outlet for the passive homosexual aims of adolescent youth. The Big Nambas of the Malekula Island in the New Hebrides group demand that a boy, prior to circumcision, spend some time as the passive homosexual partner of an older initiated man. The latter has complete sexual rights over the boy, and their association is a very intimate one indeed.

"Thus, if the *mugh vel* (boy lover) were to have sexual intercourse with any other man, without the consent of his *nilagh sen* (man lover, literally sister's husband), the latter would be very angry. Further, the *nilagh sen* can 'sell' his rights over the boy to another man. When this is done it is customary for the second man to copulate with the boy. . . . Boys are 'sold' in this way only for short periods of time; after a few days they always return to their real 'husbands,' who have use of them as before. The bond between *mugh vel* and *nilagh sen* is, however, not only a sexual one. The boy accompanies his 'husband' everywhere; works in his garden, and if one or other of the two should die, the survivor will mourn him deeply."[5]

Further examples of the way in which primitive societies institutionalize the characteristic active and passive instinctual aims, and in that way resolve the adolescent's homosexual instinct by weaving it into the social fabric, can be given: Before subincision, the boys among the Nambutji of Central Australia are used as "boy-wives" by their future fathers-in-law. Among some mountain tribes in Morocco, homosexual intercourse takes place between the student of the Koran and his teacher. The latter is supposed to possess *baraka*, a beneficial magic power. These people believe that the boy cannot learn properly unless he is used by a teacher for pederastic intercourse.[17] Here, the rectum is thought of as a receptive orifice. The neophyte, in order to identify with the male, the father, must first regress and accept his submission and passivity, becoming a "boy-wife," and in such a manner control his aggressive impulses toward the father.

Still other tribes turn to different ways of distributing libidinal and aggressive energies during adolescence. The Kayan and Kenyah of Borneo let them take part in warfare. Except for the transverse perforation of the glans penis, with the insertion of a short hardwood rod, there are no overt homosexual initiation practices. Rather, these people perform a ceremony which appears to be a remnant of the days when head-hunting was their customary practice.

Some 50 years ago, Hose and McDougall[10a] observed one such a rite, which gave the lad full-fledged membership in the community. It began with a "master of ceremonies" killing a fowl and giving part to the initiands. Then the older man mixed the fowl's blood with water and smeared the liquid on the boys' wrists. Subsequently (after ritual washing), each boy had to strike a captured head with a sword. In the feasting which followed this short ceremony, a ban was lifted: previously, the neophytes seemed to have been under some sort of food restriction, being permitted to eat only twice a day. No adolescent could join in a war party until he had undergone this initiation. Some older field reporters mention that the girls, before agreeing to a lover's wishes, demanded the head of a slain enemy.[6] Obviously, the girl wanted her man to be a successful warrior. On the other hand, a counterphobic de-

vice can be seen in the strategy of the older men, that of demanding
from the adolescent youth that he bring home the head of a
stranger, instead of turning his aggression against his own people.[6]
Here, masculinity is still largely identified with the power to kill;
in it we find an unconscious understanding of the intrinsic disposition: These people institutionalized murder in a modified form,
that of slaying a stranger. (We should not overlook the fact that,
to the infant, the father is the original stranger who stands between
him and his mother.) We have here a telling example of how the
environment in a psychoeconomic way regulates and administers
the emotional distress which is paramount during the decisive
years of maturation. One might surmise that, as superego barriers
fail, parricidal impulses are collectively channelized against those
who do not belong to the tribe. Thus, cultural habits provide outlets for aggression and self-assertion. Yet the natives of Mentawai,
on the Indonesian border, had or still have another valve: Only the
young, unmarried men were permitted to touch a dead person's
body and take care of funeral procedures. It is they who carried a
dead chief to his boat and, on reaching the burial ground, cut the
corpse's fingers, thighs, and toes to the bone. The Mentawain believe that this measure prevents the dead man—or, as they say,
his ghost—from returning to the village. In this way they express
hostile feelings through a religiously rationalized vehicle provided
by the culture.[16]

Biologically, adolescence in the girl is more clearly indicated
than in the boy. As tumescence is already observable in infants,
the menarche is the physiological characteristic of the onset of
sexual maturity in the female. This fact is widely recognized in
most societies, and some show remarkable ways of acknowledging
the event.

R. Parkinson, doing field work in a group of small islands west
of the Admiralty group in Melanesia, reported how the girl, when
she first menstruates, becomes *tabún* (*tabúni* means sacred, forbidden) and is isolated in a specially reserved hut.[21] She remains
in seclusion for some 18 to 24 months, at the termination of which
time she is brought back into society, and a feast is arranged for
her by her parents. The celebration is, in other words, her coming-
out party which bestows on her adult status within her environment.

We observe here a specialized form which this society uses to
emphasize this phase of the young girl's transition from childhood

to womanhood. Before the girl became *tabún* her ears were pierced in a ceremony which excluded men. In the house of the women (probably the menstruation hut), the mother held her daughter in her lap. Other women pulled the ear lobe tightly, while an experienced "surgeon," using a splinter of obsidian, cut the ear from the *fossa innominata* to the *antitragus* and then again to the *fossa triangularis auriculae*. After this operation, the woman washed the wound with salt water. The opening is considered a beautifying adornment in the same way that removed or filed incisors are among many other people. From an ethnopsychological point of view, however, the aspect of aggression against the young competitor cannot be overlooked.

Temporary seclusion of the adolescent girl is rather common in many societies. In prerevolutionary China these girls were not supposed to leave the compound without proper company. In Cambodia the girl would "enter the shadow," as the saying goes. Her retreat would be announced to the ancestors: "Our daughter has reached marriageable age. We let her enter the shadow. Give her your blessings." No strange man was supposed to look at her. She could eat only between sunrise and noon, and her diet had to be free of fish and meat. Lastly, her bathing, too, was limited to nighttime, to those hours when no one could see her.

Interestingly enough, these patterns of the treatment of adolescents had a polyvalent meaning: The use of aggression by the older generation was seen as a way of protecting the younger member from the hostile stranger. Concomitantly, separation from the parental hut symbolizes the recognition of factual events, namely the awareness that the girl is about "to become" a rival whose evil impulses must be curbed.

Older women act out their hostile impulses toward the young girl in other primitive communities. Some field observations of these rites are quite illuminating. The Nandi, for instance, a Bantu tribe in equatorial Africa, separate the adolescent girls from the community, but not before certain ceremonies are performed. Theirs begins with the ritual exchange of attire: At the start, male youths adorn themselves with female ornaments while girls put on decorations otherwise reserved for men. (This ceremonial exchange seems to hint at the inherent emotional confusion of youth and is customary in a number of primitive societies.) The following day, the first part of a long-drawn-out initiation takes place. Since the virginity of the girl novice is important, an old and experienced woman examines her; if the youngster is proved a *virgo intacta,* the older women will kiss and hug her, and her father will celebrate the day by slaughtering a cow.

For the girl, however, the event is less joyous. A *materyot,* a woman initiator, asks her to spread her legs and then applies a stinging nettle to her clitoris. This causes immediate pain which the girl can in no way protest. The operation creates a considerable swelling. The following morning, however, a *materyot* actually removes the clitoris with the application of a red-hot coal. The girl must take this, too, without a whimper. But the women of the tribe, perhaps remembering their own initiation suffering, experience momentary elation.

At this point, carefully guarded by an old aunt, the girl goes into seclusion which lasts about 4 months. Permitted only the company of small children, the girl is expected to live quietly and to abstain from work in order to become round and voluptuous and more desirable when she is married.[3]

Manipulation of the genitalia is frequently reported and ought to be understood, within the specific tribal matrix, as an expression of aggressive and oppressive acts against the adolescent. Excision of the clitoris belongs to the more drastic actions; artificial elongation of the clitoris and the labia has often been described. Thus in the island of Ponape in Micronesia, impotent old men are given the task of constantly pulling on the *labia internae* of small girls, with their teeth as well as their hands—a not-too-surprising assignment in a culture where cunnilinction is an expected component of sexual congress.[7]

The phenomena just described are intended to survey briefly the entire range of problems related to the adolescent's maturation and developmental adaptation to his environment—a process which must be seen in juxtaposition with the reaction of adults to the physiological and psychological transformation which takes place during those significant years.

The specific activity of old men on Ponape has more than one interesting aspect. I am under the impression that it is a variation of an institutionalized practice met with in many areas: the *jus primae noctis* which also reflects a specific societal attitude toward the maturing girl.

Among the Bánard of the Sepik region in New Guinea, a psychologically meaningful system has been developed with rather illustrative semi-incestuous implications. With the advent of the menarche, the young girl is required to live for 9 months in a closed cell attached to the parental hut (here the idea of rebirth is quite evident), and she can eat only a thin sago porridge. After she has served her term, the women "liberate" her by chasing her out of the enclosure, playing games, and adorning her with new ornaments and finery. It is a great day for the girl: she will meet her *mundú* that night. Who is the *mundú*? He is her future father-in-law's best friend, and, according to Bánaro tradition, it is he who has the right first to possess her sexually and to continue to do so until the girl shows signs of pregnancy. In return, the girl's father-in-law can now become the *mundú* of his friend's daughter-in-law. The young husband can start having sexual relations with his wife only when she is with child. Once born, this infant is called the child of a ghost, and the mother will ask her baby: "Who is your father? Who had relations with me?" Her husband answers: "I am not his father, he is ghost's child." The bridegroom's father pretends that he himself deflorated his son's wife and that he is now "ashamed" of his action.[24]

The defloration of the nubile girl by a father substitute is a custom known in many corners of the globe and reflected in various forms, such as the well-established *droit du seigneur* in Europe. Among the Tamil of Tanjore, India, the Brahman priest's task, in performing the wedding ceremony, also includes the defloration of the bride. Among the Vellalas of Coimbatore a boy marries a grown-up girl; the boy's father, however, actually consummates the marriage and continues relations with his daughter-in-law until his son has reached a marriageable age.

These few examples point to a general tendency equally relevant in matrilineal and patrilineal societies—that of unconsciously identifying the nubile girl with the forbidden object. The young girl becomes the incestuous symbol, but this is veiled by the etiquette of societal rules such as seclusion, avoidance, and the *jus primae noctis*.

Here we can readily observe that the societal measures have the essential goal of channelizing the libidinal and aggressive drives which are developing in—and also projected on—the new generation. In the same way that each older man was once in rivalry with his father for his mother's love, he now experiences unconscious guilt which tells him that his son is in the same position. In the wake of the oedipal constellation, earlier memory traces are revived. The danger that remains behind the mask of consciousness is principally the same as before—the loss or separation from the first love object. This must be handled through projection.

The regulations and cultural paths mapped out for the discharge of instinctual energy may vary to a considerable degree, yet the phenomena, in their very essence, are obviously determined by the biological and psychological processes of adolescence.

At this point we can consider still another aspect of the many channels which man has created for directing the instinctual drives of the teen-ager—that of work. In peasant communities, pre-adolescent boys and girls gradually assume a share of the family's labor and thus contribute to its livelihood. Children help in the fields or tend the garden, take care of the cattle, or watch over the younger members—an institution which has evolved, in modern cities into baby sitting. In small towns, boys will earn their allowance by starting a newspaper route, thus identifying themselves with the breadwinner. Among the Kwoma of the Sepik area in New Guinea, adolescents are supposed to take over those economic tasks for which they are physically equipped. During their childhood they could rely on their parents, who would provide all the sago for the household, "but now both sexes must share in the labor of collecting and preparing this staple."[26] A boy and a girl, therefore, work as a team, he cutting down the palm tree and removing a section of bark while she crushes the pith. Thus we observe a well-defined division of labor which has already been established for young adolescents. They are told at an early age that if a woman does a share of the men's work, especially washing and squeezing pith, the flour will be inedible (Ref. 26, p. 69).

Adolescent girls are allowed to cook and, in this way, made to feel like responsible members of the family. Boys keep themselves busy by joining a team of adults who take care of the gardens. A principle task for these boys, however, is that of helping to clear land sites by climbing trees, an activity which was forbidden during their childhood, as were other chores. Yet, significantly enough, although he lends a helping hand preparing the yam hills and planting tobacco, he is not allowed to put the seed yams into the ground until he becomes a full-fledged member of the adult society.

We can see, in the above examples, the ways which the Kwoma have developed to let the physiological, psychological, and socio-economic gears mesh rather consistently. Other opportunities are provided which help the youngsters to find their rôle in society and also to shrug off some parental control and supervision. Here, the young boy's childhood ideal, especially, comes closer to realization: They are permitted to participate in cult ceremonies which are intimately connected with fertility rites. Membership in these "clubs" adds considerably to one's status in the Kwoma society.

Work, then, seems to be one of the socially tolerated ways of integrating young people into the adult fold. No doubt, in their struggle for recognition and acceptance, that is, their wish to identify fully with the adult generation, participation in adult tasks is most meaningful. Nash[19] observed an Indian community in the western mountains of Guatemala where children of 5 or 6 already assume certain household tasks, such as taking care of chickens or fetching water. A young girl will own a miniature water jug, a small broom, and a tiny grinding stone for maize. A boy of 8 or 9, carrying a small hoe and a small net bag, will accompany his father to the field and, in that way, take part in the family's labor.

One might say that many societies give their children and adolescents such economic tasks as their physiological abilities allow. Honigman commented on this in his observations among the Kaska Indians, a formerly primitive society, now in a state of transition owing to the influence of Americanization: "Around puberty the boy's education begins as an independent trapper and hunter. Unlike the earlier trips with his father, this is more serious work. If he is acting as the protégé of an older man, his winters are occupied in hauling and cutting large supplies of winter wood, hunting rabbits and chickens for daily food, and guiding the toboggan. . . . If, however, a youth shows a tendency to lie in bed on cold mornings and is slow in executing his expected tasks, his life is plagued and made miserable. Father, uncle, and brothers lecture him about his laziness and may even plant practical jokes on him. Thus late one morning, while Donald Suza was sitting up in his sleeping place sipping coffee and eating late breakfast, Old Man planted a thin stick behind the youth's back. When Donald lay down again after his repast the stick snapped, but not before it had sharply jabbed into his back. If the boy is afraid of the bush (in other words, if he has not unlearned the socially patterned attitudes of childhood), he is 'talked to' and cajoled. . . . It is apparent that adolescents often have to 'unlearn' fear of the forest when they begin to travel alone, but this seems to have been successfully accomplished in most men and even in many women."[9]

Thus, integration into adult society is reinforced by adults who build and cement this sense of identification by imposing on the adolescents tasks which were hitherto reserved for grownups. Participation in adult work can then be seen as a sublimated approach to full maleness.

SUMMARY

Our study of adolescent affects and behavior and the reaction of adults to youth's approaching equality has shown the inherent biological, psychological, and sociological elements which belong to this time of turbulence. We have also been able to consider the way in which these aspects are modified by pressures which find their origin in the social habitat. The fundamental condition is evident: Observations show the wide variety of elements, that, even in their specificity, demonstrate the universal aspect of unconscious tendencies which, as they are released, encounter environmental qualifications and controls. It is here that psychoanalytic theory— leading us beyond the different aspects molded by religion, etiquettes, laws, or traditions—affords a clearer view of adaptation and of social events, such as puberty rites and related symbolic actions.

Adolescence can only be understood as a universal phase in the development of the human libido, one which makes its appearance in many deviant ways: Whether it be a Brooklyn mother of Eastern European Jewish background who strikes her daughter's cheek upon hearing that the girl is menstruating for the first time, and who then rationalizes this act with the traditional words: "That your cheeks may remain rosy!" or an old Sudanese tribal woman who infibulates the young girls' genitals and only occasionally opens them by force, the cultural shadings are of secondary importance when the psychological meaning becomes evident. The mother's (or mother substitute's) rivalry with the younger girl cannot be denied. By the same token, the college student's anxiety before finals differs little in essence from the anxiety of a young journeyman anticipating the often cruel initiation into the guild.[11] The determinants remain the same: In his vital attempt to identify with the parental counterpart and eventually succeed him, the adolescent's behavior is a result of his psychosomatic upheaval, the urgency of his bodily needs, and the pressures of conflicts, which, governed by unconscious forces, are, in turn, molded by the world around him.

References

1. BEACH, F. A. *Hormones and Behavior.* New York, Paul B. Hoeber, Inc., 1948.
2. BONAPARTE, M. Ueber die Symbolik der Kopftrophäen. *Imago. 14:* 100, 1928.
3. BRYK, F. *Neger-Eros, Ethnologische Studien ueber das Sexualleben bei Negern.* Berlin, A. Marcus & E. Weber's Verlag, 1928, pp. 66–72.
4. CHABOT, H. T. *Verwantschap, Stand en Sexe in Zuid-Celebes.* Groningen-Djakarta, T. B. Wolters Uitg. Mij., 1950, pp. 140 f.
5. DEACON, A. B. *Malekula,* ed. by Wedgwood, Camilla H. London, Routledge, 1934, pp. 260–269.
6. FENICHEL, O. Ueber Trophäe und Triumph. *Internat. Ztschr. Psychoanal. und Imago. 24:* 258, 1939.
7. FINSCH after PLOSS, H. and BARTELS, M. *Das Weib,* 9th ed. Leipzig, Grieben's Verlag, 1908, vol. II, pp. 259 f.
8. FORD, C. S., and BEACH, F. A. *Patterns of Sexual Behavior.* New York, Harper & Brothers, 1951, pp. 171–197.
9. HONIGMAN, J. J. *Culture and Ethos of Kaska Society.* New Haven, Yale University Press, 1949, pp. 189–191.
10. HOOTON, E. A. *Up from the Ape,* 2nd ed. New York, The Macmillan Company, 1947, pp. 243–266.
10a. HOSE, C. and McDOUGALL, W. The *Pagan Tribes of Borneo.* London, The Macmillan Company, 1912, pp. 185–187, vol. 1.
11. KREBS, W. "Alte Handwerksbräuche," in *Schriften der Schweizerischen Gesellschaft fuer Volkskunde.* Basel, 1933, vol. 23.
12. LANDTMAN, G. *The Kiwai Papuans of British New Guinea.* London, The Macmillan Company, 1927, pp. 344 f.
13. LEVINE, R. A. Gusii Sex Offenses: A Study in Social Control. *Am. Anthropologist. 61:* 965, 1959.
14. LYND, R. S., and LYND, H. M. *Middletown, A Study in Contemporary American Culture.* New York, Harcourt, Brace and Company, 1929, pp. 135, 140.
15. MAYER, P. Gusii initiation ceremonies. *J. Roy. Anthropological Inst. 83:* 9, 1953.
16. MUENSTERBERGER, W. "Oral Trauma and Taboo," in *Psychoanalysis and the Social Sciences.* New York, International Universities Press, Inc., 1950, vol. 2, p. 161.
17. MUENSTERBERGER, W. "Perversion, Cultural Norm and Normality," in Lorand, Sandor, and Balint, Michael, *Perversions, Psychodynamics and Therapy.* New York, Random House, Inc., 1956, pp. 55–67.
18. MURDOCK, G. P. "The Common Denominator of Cultures," in Linton, Ralph, *The Science of Man in the World Crisis.* New York, Columbia University Press, 1945, pp. 123–142.
19. NASH, M. *Machine Age Maya, The Industrialization of a Guatemalan Community. Am. Anthrop.,* Memoir No. 87, 1958, pp. 46 f.

20. Nunberg, H. Circumcision and Problems of Bisexuality. *Internat. J. Psycho-Analysis.* 27: 145, 1947.
21. Parkinson, R. *Dreissig Jahre in der Südsee.* Stuttgart, Kohlhammer Verlag, 1907, pp. 440 f.
22. Salinger, J. D. *The Catcher in the Rye.* New York, Little, Brown & Co., 1945, p. 95.
23. Speiser, F. "Ueber Initiationen in der Suedsee," in *Verhandlungen der Naturforschenden Gesellschaft.* Basel, Benno Schwabe & Co., 1929, p. 246.
24. Thurnwald, R. *Die Gemeinde der Banaro: Ehe, Verwandtschaft und Gesellschaftsbau eines Stammes im Innern von Neu-Guinea.* Stuttgart, Ferdinand Enke Verlag, 1921, pp. 21–23.
25. Wagner, G. *The Bantu of North Kavirondo.* London, Oxford University Press, 1949, vol. 1, pp. 364 f.
26. Whiting, J. W. M. *Becoming a Kwoma.* New Haven, Yale University Press, 1941, pp. 63–105.

Index